Exploring ODEs

Exploring ODEs

Lloyd N. Trefethen
University of Oxford

Ásgeir Birkisson
Squarepoint Capital

Tobin A. Driscoll
University of Delaware

Society for Industrial and Applied Mathematics
Philadelphia

The cover image shows an arctic tern on the Snæfellsnes peninsula of Iceland. Photo
by Jón Emil Guðmundsson.

Publications Director	Kivmars H. Bowling
Executive Editor	Elizabeth Greenspan
Developmental Editor	Gina Rinelli Harris
Managing Editor	Kelly Thomas
Production Editor	Louis R. Primus
Copy Editor	Matthew Bernard
Production Manager	Donna Witzleben
Production Coordinator	Cally A. Shrader
Graphic Designer	Lois Sellers

Library of Congress Cataloging-in-Publication Data
Names: Trefethen, Lloyd N. (Lloyd Nicholas), author. | Birkisson, Ásgeir,
    author. | Driscoll, Tobin A. (Tobin Allen), 1969- author.
Title: Exploring ODEs / Lloyd N. Trefethen (University of Oxford), Ásgeir
    Birkisson (Squarepoint Capital), Tobin A. Driscoll (University of
    Delaware).
Other titles: Exploring ordinary differential equations
Description: Philadelphia : Society for Industrial and Applied Mathematics,
    [2018] | Series: Other titles in applied mathematics ; 157 | Includes
    bibliographical references and index.
Identifiers: LCCN 2017046980 | ISBN 9781611975154
Subjects: LCSH: Differential equations.
Classification: LCC QA371 .T67 2018 | DDC 515/.352--dc23 LC record available at
    https://lccn.loc.gov/2017046980

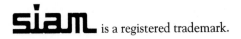

To Kate, Sigrún, and Jen

Contents

1. Introduction

What if all you had to do to solve an ODE were just to write it down?[1] That is the line we will follow in this book. Our emphasis is not just on the mathematics of ODEs, but on how the solutions behave. Do they blow up, decay, oscillate? Are there rapid transitions where they flip from one state to another? Does the behavior change if a coefficient is perturbed or a new term is added? And how can such variety be deployed to explain the world around us? We shall not just talk about these matters but explore them in action.

ODEs are among the core topics of mathematics, with applications so ubiquitous that listing examples almost seems inappropriate. (Heat conduction, chemical reactions, chaos, population dynamics, deformations of a beam, radioactivity, bifurcation theory, stability theory, differential geometry, quantum mechanics, economics, finance, infectious diseases, nerve signals, vibrations, optics, waves, dynamics of networks, special functions, ballistics, planetary dynamics, ...) ODEs are everywhere.

To solve ODEs by writing them down, we will use Chebfun, an open-source MATLAB package that is freely available at `www.chebfun.org`. In MATLAB, you type `x = A\b` to solve the system of equations $\mathbf{Ax} = \mathbf{b}$, where $\mathbf{A}$ is a matrix and $\mathbf{x}$ and $\mathbf{b}$ are vectors. In Chebfun, analogously, you type `y = L\f` to solve the ODE $Ly = f$, where L is a linear or nonlinear differential operator with initial or boundary conditions and y and f are functions. We will obtain solutions this way on nearly every page, presenting them with hundreds of computer-generated plots without discussing the algorithms Chebfun uses to make this

---

[1]ODE stands for *ordinary differential equation*, as the reader presumably knows already.

possible.[2] This is not a book about numerical analysis or computer science. It is a book about ODEs.

Many textbooks on ODEs concentrate on linear problems, because nonlinear ones are rarely analytically solvable. Here, with analytical solutions playing a lesser role, we will be able to give a more balanced treatment and fully appreciate the remarkable effects that come with nonlinearity.

Let's get started with the most basic **initial-value problem (IVP)**,[3]

$$y' + y = 0, \quad t \in [0,3], \quad y(0) = 1. \tag{1.1}$$

We have written this in the standard notation of this book, with t as the independent variable, y the dependent variable, and $y' = dy/dt$.[4] Note that although y and y' are functions of t, we usually do not write them out fully as $y(t)$ and $y'(t)$. You can quickly check that a solution to (1.1) is the function $y(t) = \exp(-t)$, and moreover, it is easily proved that this solution is unique (see Chapter 2). To calculate it with Chebfun, we make a "chebop" that encodes the differential operator of (1.1), which we call L. First we prescribe the interval.

```
L = chebop(0,3);
```

Next we prescribe the differential operator $y \mapsto y' + y$, which is written in the form of a MATLAB anonymous function of t and y, with `diff` denoting differentiation with respect to t.

```
L.op = @(t,y) diff(y) + y;
```

Finally we set the *initial condition* with `L.lbc`, which stands for "left boundary condition."

```
L.lbc = 1;
```

(A boundary condition at the right would be specified with `L.rbc`.) We can now solve (1.1).

```
y = L\0;
```

As expected, the solution is e^{-t}.[5]

---

[2]To learn about Chebfun and its ODE algorithms, see Appendix A and www.chebfun.org.

[3]Throughout this book, some terms are set in italics, while other particularly important ones are set in boldface. To review a chapter, a good way to start is to read the items in italics and boldface and also the chapter summary at the end. Almost all emphasized terms can be found in the index.

[4]For boundary-value problems, which are usually associated with space instead of time, we will change t to x. Some books also make a distinction between y' for a space derivative and $\dot{y}$ for a time derivative, but we shall not do this.

[5]Throughout this book, the Chebfun code segments listed are sufficient to reproduce the mathematical essence of each figure, but MATLAB formatting commands like `title`, `axis`, and `'linewidth'` have been removed. Users wanting to see formatting details can download the M-files for each chapter of the book from www.chebfun.org.

`plot(y)`

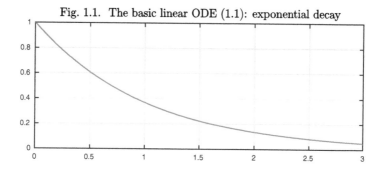

Fig. 1.1. The basic linear ODE (1.1): exponential decay

The problem we have just solved can be classified by the following properties.

F **First-order** (the highest-order derivative is y')
L **Linear** (there are no terms like y^2, $\exp(y)$, or yy')
A **Autonomous** (the equation, though not the solution, is independent of t)
S **Scalar** (there is just one dependent variable y rather than $u, v, w, \ldots$)
H **Homogeneous** (the right-hand side is zero[6])
I **Initial-value problem** (not a boundary-value or eigenvalue problem)

Note that these letters spell the easily remembered word FLASHI. In this book, we will use this word occasionally to encode some of the properties of a problem. If we state that a problem is, say, of type FlaShi, that means that it is a first-order scalar problem, since the letters F and S are capitalized. On the other hand since l, a, h, and i are in lowercase, the problem is nonlinear, nonautonomous, inhomogeneous, and a boundary-value or eigenvalue problem rather than an IVP. In the chapters ahead, we will vary all of these properties and explore in the process a great variety of phenomena. The FLASHI classification will help add structure to the discussion. Sometimes one considers an ODE without specifying initial or boundary conditions, and in this case the I drops away to give just FLASH.

Here is a FLASH classification of the theorems in this book.

Linear, first-order, scalar
FLASH: Thm. 2.1 (separation of variables)
FLASh: Thm. 2.4 (integrating factor)
FLaSH: Thm. 2.2 (separation of variables)
FLaSh: Thm. 2.3 (integrating factor), Thm. 19.1 (periodic)

Nonlinear, first-order, scalar
FlASH: Thm. 3.2 (separation of variables)

---

[6]When we say "the right-hand side is zero," we really mean that the equation contains no nonzero terms that do not involve y. Of course it doesn't matter mathematically whether a term appears on the left or the right of an equation. For nonlinear ODEs, the property of homogeneity does not always have much meaning.

FlaSH: Thm. 3.1 (separation of variables)
FlaSh: Thms. 11.1 and 11.3 (Picard iteration)

Linear, first-order, system
FLAsH: Thm. 14.1 (matrix exponential)
FLAsh: Thm. 14.2 (matrix exponential), Thm. 14.3 (variation of parameters)
FLash: Thm. 19.2 (periodic)

Nonlinear, first-order, system
FlAsH: Thm. 14.4 (linearization), Thm. 15.1 (stability)
Flash: Thms. 11.2 and 11.3 (Picard iteration)

Second-order
fLASH: Thm. 4.1 (solution formula)
fLaSH: Thm. 7.1 (eigenproblems), Thm. 19.3 (Hill's eq.)
flASH: Thm. 14.5 (linearization)

As an illustration of a nonlinear ODE, here is an example of type flASHl, the second-order equation known as the *van der Pol equation*:

$$0.3y'' - (1 - y^2)y' + y = 0, \quad t \in [0, 20], \quad y(0) = 1, \ y'(0) = 0. \qquad (1.2)$$

(The coefficient 0.3 is included to make the solution more interesting.) Because y'' is present, the equation is of second rather than first order (hence f not F), and it is nonlinear because of the coefficient $1 - y^2$ multiplying y' (hence l not L). Here are the interval and the operator, which we name N instead of L as a reminder that it is nonlinear.

```
N = chebop(0,20);
N.op = @(t,y) 0.3*diff(y,2) - (1-y^2)*diff(y) + y;
```

Problem (1.1) had just a single boundary condition, but in (1.2), since it is a second-order equation, there are two. For a simple scalar problem like this, Chebfun permits one to prescribe y and y' at a point by supplying a vector of two numbers.

```
N.lbc = [1;0];
```

Here is the solution.[7]

```
y = N\0; plot(y)
```

---

[7]Readers viewing these pages in color will note that solutions to linear IVPs are usually plotted in green and solutions to nonlinear ones in dark green. Starting in Chapter 5, we will likewise plot solutions to linear BVPs in blue and solutions to nonlinear ones in dark blue. The distinctions between linear and nonlinear equations and between IVPs and BVPs are important, and the colors will serve as a quiet reminder.

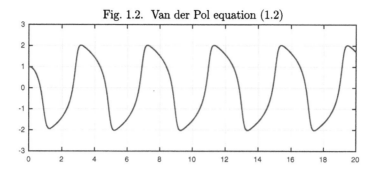
Fig. 1.2. Van der Pol equation (1.2)

Chebfun gives us ready access to the properties of a computed solution y (which is represented as a "chebfun," with a lowercase c since this is a function rather than the name of the software system). For example, here are the positions of the local maxima of y.

```
[mval,mpos] = max(y,'local'); mpos'

ans =
         0     3.1651     7.2375    11.3101    15.3826    19.4552
```

By taking differences of successive maxima, we see that this van der Pol oscillation is settling down to a periodic function with period 4.0725,

```
diff(mpos)'

ans =
    3.1651     4.0725     4.0725     4.0725     4.0725
```

This book is aimed at everyone who is interested in ODEs. If you are an undergraduate taking a course from one of the big texts like Boyce and DiPrima or Edwards and Penney, this is your lightweight companion. (The hard copy from SIAM is inexpensive, and the online version is free.) If you are a graduate student working in any of the mathematical sciences, this may be just the book to take your understanding to the next level. Whoever you are, we aim to increase your appreciation of this fundamental subject.

What does it mean to "solve" an ODE? One kind of solution would be an exact explicit formula, also known as an *analytical solution*. Advantages of analytical solutions include perfect accuracy, generality, explicit dependence on parameters, theoretical insight, and the absence of restriction to a particular range of values of t. The trouble is, most ODE problems, including almost all nonlinear ones, can't be solved analytically. Another kind of solution is a numerical one obtained on a computer. The great advantage of numerical solutions is that they can be obtained for virtually any ODE. That's not the only advantage, however. Another is that numbers are a compact and universal currency, so that by examining results obtained numerically, one can apply one's analysis to a problem at hand or check how one ODE solution compares to another. It is not always obvious how to compare two exact formulas, but we always know how to compare two numbers, whether explicitly as numbers or visually in a plot.

Among the huge variety of interesting ODEs, there are five that keep reappearing over and over in this book:

Second-order linear oscillator. Simple harmonic motion, or with damping.
Van der Pol equation. Nonlinear oscillator, with solutions on a limit cycle.
Nonlinear pendulum. Large-amplitude, with a periodic phase space.
Lorenz equations. Archetypal chaotic system, with three coupled variables.
Linear system. $\mathbf{y}' = \mathbf{A}\mathbf{y}$, with solutions $\exp(t\mathbf{A})\mathbf{y_0}$.

Many other equations will also be mentioned, including the Airy, Belousov–Zhabotinsky, Bernoulli, Bessel, Blasius, Bratu, Brusselator, Carrier, Duffing, Hénon–Heiles, Hill, logistic, Lotka–Volterra, Mathieu, n-body, Oregonator, Painlevé, and Rössler equations.

Easy computer exploration brings new perspectives on ODEs, and we believe we have found distinctive treatments of most of the topics presented in this book, which we hope will blend clarity for beginners with unexpected insights for experts. Here are some items worthy of note in each chapter.

1. *Introduction.* The "FLASHI" classification.
2. *First-order scalar linear ODEs.* Fig. 2.3: smooth vs. bang-bang forcing.
3. *First-order scalar nonlinear ODEs.* Scalarization by complex arithmetic.
4. *Second-order ODEs and damping.* Ex. 4.1: elliptical/nonelliptical orbits.
5. *Boundary-value problems.* Fig. 5.9: side conditions.
6. *Eigenvalues of linear BVPs.* Fig. 6.2: eigenvalues via response curve.
7. *Variable coefficients and adjoints.* Automated computation of adjoints.
8. *Resonance.* Periodic forcing gives periodic solutions, *if* there is damping.
9. *Second-order equations in the phase plane.* BVPs as well as IVPs.
10. *Systems of equations.* SIR epidemiology models in 6 lines of code.
11. *The fundamental existence theorem.* Picard iteration on the computer.
12. *Random functions and random ODEs.* Stochastics via smooth functions.
13. *Chaos.* Transient chaos in the 3-body problem.
14. *Linearization.* Figures showing that, locally, any ODE behaves linearly.
15. *Stable and unstable fixed points.* Application to transition to turbulence.
16. *Multiple solutions of nonlinear BVPs.* Shooting to find multiple solutions.
17. *Bifurcation.* Fig. 17.18: tracking hysteresis as a parameter varies.
18. *Continuation and path-following.* Fig. 18.13: numerical bifurcation.
19. *Periodic ODEs.* Application showing the origin of band gaps.
20. *Boundary and interior layers.* Plots showing asymptotics in action.
21. *Into the complex plane.* Analytic continuation of real solutions.
22. *Time-dependent PDEs.* How ODEs arise from PDEs as $t \to \infty$.

Readers will also find many phenomena explored in the exercises that do not appear in other textbooks.

Any book on ODEs faces the question of how much space to give to applications. As a structure that we hope will prove appealing, we follow the pattern that each chapter ends with a 2–4 page item designated as an Application. This is followed in turn by a few sentences about history, a mention of our favorite reference, and the exercises for that chapter.

With the help of Chebfun, can we really solve any ODE just by writing it down? No, of course not. Examples can readily be devised that defeat this method for reasons including singularities, scaling, stiffness, positivity constraints, or sheer computational scale, and a page about such challenges can be found at the end of Appendix A. Nevertheless, we have been gratified in writing this book to find how easy it has been to explore almost any topic.

APPLICATIONS IN THIS BOOK

Chapter 2. Elimination of caffeine from the bloodstream.
Chapter 3. Classic pursuit problems.
Chapter 4. Skydiver.
Chapter 5. Beam theory and the strength of spaghetti.
Chapter 6. Eigenstates of the Schrödinger equation.
Chapter 7. Adjoints and optimization.
Chapter 8. Moon, sun, and tides.
Chapter 9. Nonlinear pendulum.
Chapter 10. SIR model for epidemics.
Chapter 11. Designer nonuniqueness.
Chapter 12. Metastability, radioactivity, and tunneling.
Chapter 13. Chaos in a food web.
Chapter 14. Linearized Lorenz trajectories.
Chapter 15. Transition to turbulence in a pipe.
Chapter 16. Sending a spacecraft to a destination.
Chapter 17. FitzHugh–Nagumo equations of neural signals.
Chapter 18. Arrhenius chemical reaction.
Chapter 19. Band gaps and forbidden frequencies.
Chapter 20. Why is New York hotter than San Francisco?
Chapter 21. Jacobi sine function.
Chapter 22. Solitons and the KdV equation.

HISTORY. Many of the great mathematicians of the past were involved in establishing the subject of ODEs, starting around 1670, including Newton, Leibniz, Johann and Jacob Bernoulli, Riccati, Clairaut, Euler, d'Alembert, Lagrange, Gauss, and Cauchy. Stepping forward to 100 or so years ago, some other key figures were Poincaré, Picard, Lyapunov, Painlevé, and Goursat.

OUR FAVORITE REFERENCE. For a charismatic tour of the whole subject of ODEs with a historical emphasis, see Chapter I of Hairer, Nørsett, and Wanner, *Solving Ordinary Differential Equations I,* Second Revised Edition, Springer-Verlag, 1993.

ACKNOWLEDGMENTS. Many people have helped us in preparing this book, and we can acknowledge just a few: David Allwright, Patrick Farrell, Abdul-

Lateef Haji-Ali, Nick Hale, Des Higham, Hrothgar, Aurya Javeed, and Tadashi Tokieda. Michael Rawson was a lively participant in a course at NYU that class-tested the book in autumn 2016. We are particularly grateful to Abinand Gopal, Matt Meyers, Niels Møller, and Adam Stinchcombe for reading the entire manuscript at a late stage and offering many helpful suggestions.

> SUMMARY OF CHAPTER 1. *ODEs can rarely be solved analytically, but they can always be solved numerically, and Chebfun provides a convenient tool for doing this. This book explores all kinds of ODE problems, from the elementary to the advanced, both initial-value problems (IVPs) and boundary-value problems (BVPs). ODE problems can be classified by a schema with mnemonic* FLASHI: *F = first-order,* L = *linear,* A = *autonomous,* S = *scalar,* H = *homogeneous,* I = *IVP.*

A note on exercises. The exercises in this book mix the theoretical and the computational, and the labels of computational exercises are <u>underlined</u>. If you are asked, say, to "find a value" of a solution, a computational result is usually expected unless it is explicitly stated that it should be analytical. As a rule, give computed results to 6 digits of accuracy. For theoretical problems, though your final solution should be analytical, you may sometimes find computational explorations helpful along the way.

Exercise 1.1. Local extrema of van der Pol oscillation. In the van der Pol example (1.2), you can find the local maxima with `max(y,'local')`, and similarly for minima with `min`; you can find both minima and maxima at once with `minandmax`. How close is the first local minimum value (at $t \approx 1.2$) to its asymptotic value for $t \to \infty$? Likewise for the first local maximum (at $t \approx 3.2$)?

Exercise 1.2. Classification of ODE problems. Classify the following ODE problems according to the FLASHI scheme.

(a) $y' = \sin(t) - y$, $t \in [0, 100]$, $y(0) = 1$.

(b) $y' = \sin(t) - y^3$, $t \in [0, 100]$, $y(0) = 1$.

(c) (Nonlinear pendulum equation) $y'' = -\sin(y)$, $t \in [0, 10]$, $y(0) = y(10) = 2$.

(d) (Advection-diffusion equation) $0.02y'' + y' + y = 0$, $t \in [0, 1]$, $y(0) = 0$, $y(1) = 1$.

(e) (Airy equation) $0.02y'' - ty = 0$, $t \in [-5, 5]$, $y(-5) = 1$, $y(5) = 0$.

(f) (Harmonic oscillator) $u' = v$, $v' = -u$, $t \in [0, 100]$, $u(0) = 1$, $v(0) = 0$.

(g) $u' = u^2 v$, $v' = -uv^2$, $t \in [0, 2]$, $u(0) = 1$, $v(0) = 0$.

(h) (Bessel equation) $t^2 y'' + ty' + (t^2 - 4)y = 0$, $t \in [0, 8]$, $y(0) = 0$, $y(8) = 1$.

(i) $0.1y'' + yy' = y$, $t \in [-1, 1]$, $y(-1) = -2$, $y(1) = 1$.

(j) (Lotka–Volterra equations) $u' = u(1-v)$, $v' = v(u-1)$, $t \in [0, 10]$, $u(0) = v(0) = 1$.

(k) (Blasius equation) $y''' + 0.5yy'' = 0$, $t \in [0, 10]$, $y(0) = y'(0) = 0$, $y'(10) = 1$.

Exercise 1.3. Airy equation. Plot the solution y of the problem of Exercise 1.2*(e)* and report its maximum value. Letting k denote the coefficient 0.02, do the same with $k = 0.002$. Now make a plot of $\max(y)$ as a function of k for the values $k = 0.001, 0.002, \ldots, 0.039, 0.040$. (We shall explore such effects in Chapter 6.)

Exercise 1.4. Solution with rapid transient. Plot the solution y of the problem of Exercise 1.2*(i)*, and give its maximum slope $s = \max_{t \in [-1,1]} y'(t)$. Do the same with the coefficient 0.1 reduced to 1/20, 1/40, and 1/80.

Exercise 1.5. *Reduction to first-order system.* *(a)* Show how the IVP of Exercise 1.2*(f)* can be rewritten as a second-order scalar IVP involving just the dependent variable u. What are the initial conditions for this IVP? *(b)* Conversely, show how the third-order IVP of Exercise 1.2*(k)* can be rewritten as a first-order system involving three variables u, v, and w. Any higher-order ODE problem can be rewritten as a first-order problem like this, and numerical software for IVPs often requires the problem to be expressed in first-order form.

Exercise 1.6. *How Chebfun represents functions.* Chebfun normally represents solutions $y(t)$ to ODEs by polynomial approximations, typically with an accuracy of about 10 digits, whose degree n may be quite high. The polynomials can be interpreted as interpolants through a sufficiently large number $n + 1$ of samples at *Chebyshev points* defined by $t_j = \cos(\pi j/n)$, $0 \le j \le n$ for $t \in [-1, 1]$, or linearly transplanted to a different interval $[a, b]$. *(a)* Let y be the computed solution of the problem (1.1). Execute `length(y)` to find the number $n + 1$ for this function, and `plot(y,'.-')` to see the associated Chebyshev points. *(b)* Do the same for the computed solution of the van der Pol problem (1.2). Approximately speaking (say, to within 10%), how many interpolation points are there on average per wavelength?

Exercise 1.7. *How Chebfun represents periodic functions.* Chebfun also has a representation for periodic functions that takes advantage of the periodicity, based on trigonometric polynomials (i.e., Fourier series) rather than ordinary algebraic polynomials. Periodic solutions arise naturally in ODEs with periodic coefficients (see Chapter 19). *(a)* Construct an ordinary chebfun for $f(t) = (1.1 - \cos(\pi t))^{-1}$, $t \in [-1, 1]$ with the command `chebfun('1/(1.1-cos(pi*x))')`. What is its length? *(b)* How does the length change if you use `chebfun('1/(1.1-cos(pi*x))','trig')`? (In an appropriate limit, the ratio of the two lengths approaches $\pi/2$.)

2. First-order scalar linear ODEs

Problem (1.1) of the last chapter could be regarded as the prototype of all ODEs. Slightly generalized, it takes the form

$$y' - ay = 0, \quad y(0) = y_0,$$

where a and y_0 are constants. This problem has the solution

$$y(t) = y_0 e^{at},$$

which is as good an argument as any for why the number $e = 2.71828\ldots$ is important. Let us make it a theorem (the proof is in the paragraphs following).

Theorem 2.1. Solution of first-order linear autonomous scalar homogeneous IVP (FLASHI). *The problem*

$$y' - ay = 0, \quad y(0) = y_0, \tag{2.1}$$

where a and y_0 are constants, has the unique solution

$$y(t) = y_0 e^{at}. \tag{2.2}$$

Here are images for eleven values of a from -10 to 10, showing exponential growth for $a > 0$, exponential decay for $a < 0$, and a constant solution for $a = 0$.

```
L = chebop(0,1); L.lbc = 1;
for a = -10:2:10
  L.op = @(t,y) diff(y) - a*y;
  y = L\0; plot(y), hold on
end
```

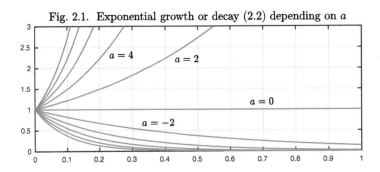

Fig. 2.1. Exponential growth or decay (2.2) depending on a

We can derive (2.2) by writing (2.1) as

$$\frac{dy}{dt} = ay,$$

or equivalently if $y \neq 0$

$$\frac{dy}{y} = a\,dt.$$

(If $y(t) = 0$ for some t then $y(t) = 0$ for all t, a case readily handled separately.) Note that the last step has separated the y and t terms onto the two sides of the equation: we say that (2.1) is **separable**, and this technique is called **separation of variables**. We now integrate both sides of the equation to get

$$\log|y| = at + c$$

for some constant c, or, after exponentiating both sides,

$$y(t) = Ce^{at}$$

with $C = e^c$ if $y > 0$ and $C = -e^c$ if $y < 0$ (a similar adjustment works if y is complex). Taking $C = y_0$ gives (2.2). Moreover, the solution is unique, since any solution $y(t)$ must be of the form Ce^{at} by the reasoning just given, and only $C = y_0$ will match the initial condition.

If $a > 0$, then $y(t)$ increases exponentially with t, whereas if $a < 0$ it decreases exponentially. This simple distinction between exponential growth and decay of solutions to (2.1) is the starting point of the theory of stability of dynamical systems, a recurring theme in the second half of this book.[8]

Equation (2.1) is autonomous (coefficients independent of t) and homogeneous (zero right-hand side). Nothing much changes if we make the problem nonautonomous: we still obtain a solution via the method of separation of variables. What this means is that, instead of a constant coefficient a, we allow a variable coefficient function $a(t)$:

$$y' - a(t)y = 0, \quad y(0) = y_0. \tag{2.3}$$

---

[8]If a is a complex number $\alpha + i\beta$, which makes perfectly good sense mathematically and changes none of the formulas, then since $e^{at} = e^{\alpha t}(\cos \beta t + i \sin \beta t)$, we have exponential increase for $\alpha > 0$ and exponential decrease for $\alpha < 0$. In both cases the solution oscillates as well as growing or decaying.

We separate variables as before to get

$$\frac{dy}{y} = a(t)dt,$$

which implies

$$\log|y(t)| = \int_0^t a(s)ds + c,$$

or equivalently

$$y(t) = C\exp\left(\int_0^t a(s)ds\right) \tag{2.4}$$

for constants c and $C = \pm e^c$. Since the integral takes the value 0 for $t = 0$, the right constant is $C = y_0$.

In the derivation just made we have tacitly assumed a is continuous. However, the integrals in (2.4) and the equation above it make sense more generally, for example, if a is just *piecewise continuous*. We use this term in its standard sense to refer to a function that is continuous apart from at most a finite set of finite jump discontinuities. With this in mind, the following theorem and Theorem 2.3 are stated for piecewise continuous functions, on the understanding that a solution to a piecewise continuous ODE is defined to be a continuous function that is differentiable and satisfies the ODE everywhere except at the points of discontinuity.

Theorem 2.2. Solution of first-order linear scalar homogeneous IVP (FLaSHI). *The problem*

$$y' - a(t)y = 0, \quad y(0) = y_0, \tag{2.5}$$

where y_0 is a constant and $a(t)$ is a continuous or piecewise continuous function, has the unique solution

$$y(t) = y_0\exp\left(\int_0^t a(s)ds\right). \tag{2.6}$$

As an example, consider

$$y' = \sin(t^2)y, \quad t \in [0,8], \quad y(0) = 1. \tag{2.7}$$

A numerical solution gives an elegant oscillatory curve.

```
L = chebop(0,8); L.op = @(t,y) diff(y) - sin(t^2)*y; L.lbc = 1;
y = L\0; plot(y)
```

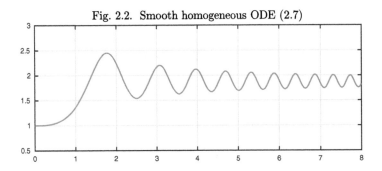

Fig. 2.2. Smooth homogeneous ODE (2.7)

For an example with a coefficient that is only piecewise continuous, suppose we replace $\sin(t^2)$ by $\text{sign}(\sin(t^2))$:

$$y' = \text{sign}(\sin(t^2))y, \quad t \in [0,8], \quad y(0) = 1. \tag{2.8}$$

This corresponds to a "bang-bang" situation in which the system is pushed one way and then the other, always with amplitude 1. Here is the solution.

```
L.op = @(t,y) diff(y) - sign(sin(t^2))*y;
y = L\0; plot(y)
```

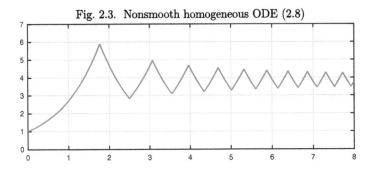

Fig. 2.3. Nonsmooth homogeneous ODE (2.8)

It is striking how this curve resembles the earlier one in form, though the vertical scale has changed considerably. Actually, this second example is mathematically simpler than the first, since it consists of nothing but an alternation of segments of exponential growth Ce^t and exponential decay Ce^{-t}.

Our problem is still homogeneous. We are about to take the next step and introduce a nonzero right-hand side. Before doing this, however, let us examine the significance of homogeneity from an abstract point of view. Suppose we consider the ODE (2.5) *without* a boundary condition,

$$y' - a(t)y = 0, \quad t \in [0,d]. \tag{2.9}$$

By the reasoning above, the solutions of this equation consist precisely of all functions of the form $C\exp(\int_0^t a(s)ds)$ for any constant C. In other words, the set of solutions of (2.9) is a *vector space of dimension* 1 spanned by the basis function $\exp(\int_0^t a(s)ds)$.[9] This conclusion applies to any first-order linear, scalar, homogeneous ODE. The boundary condition of an IVP selects one function out of the vector space. Later we shall see that a second-order linear, scalar, homogeneous ODE has a vector space of solutions of dimension 2, third-order gives dimension 3, and so on.

Now let us modify (2.9) to make the ODE inhomogeneous,

$$y' - a(t)y = g(t), \quad t \in [0, d], \qquad (2.10)$$

for some function $g(t)$. Suppose that somehow or other we find a function $y_{\mathrm{p}}(t)$ that satisfies (2.10). The subscript p stands for "particular": a solution to a linear inhomogeneous ODE is called a **particular solution**. Now let y_{h}, with h standing for "homogeneous," be any nonzero solution to the homogeneous ODE (2.9), such as $\exp(\int_0^t a(s)ds)$ from Theorem 2.2. Then for any constant C, the function

$$y_{\mathrm{p}} + C y_{\mathrm{h}} \qquad (2.11)$$

is another solution to (2.10). This is called the **general solution** to (2.10). In the language of vector spaces, we can say that the set of solutions to the inhomogeneous ODE (2.10) is an *affine space*, which means a vector space shifted by the addition of a constant vector (namely y_{p}).

We have just presented the general framework for solving a first-order linear scalar inhomogeneous IVP: find a particular solution y_{p}, then apply Theorem 2.2 to find a nonzero solution y_{h} to the homogeneous problem. The solutions to the inhomogeneous problem are then all the functions of the form $y_{\mathrm{p}} + C y_{\mathrm{h}}$ for any constant C, and we pick C to match the initial condition. Beginning in Chapter 4 we shall extend the same idea to higher-order ODEs and systems of linear ODEs.

How do we find a particular solution y_{p}? There is a mechanical procedure that in principle achieves this: multiplication by a function known as an **integrating factor**. (We shall see two pages along that, in practice, this approach may be more cumbersome than necessary; the easier alternative is called the method of undetermined coefficients.) Define

$$h(t) = \int_0^t a(s)ds.$$

Then the product rule for differentiation gives

$$[e^{-h(t)}y(t)]' = e^{-h(t)}[y'(t) - y(t)h'(t)],$$

and since $h'(t) = a(t)$, (2.10) reduces this to

$$[e^{-h(t)}y(t)]' = e^{-h(t)}g(t).$$

---

[9]We are using the idea of a vector space in its standard abstract sense. A vector in this space is a function $y(t)$.

The function $e^{-h(t)}$ is the integrating factor. We can integrate both sides to get

$$e^{-h(t)}y(t) - y(0) = \int_0^t e^{-h(s)}g(s)ds,$$

that is,

$$y(t) = e^{h(t)}y(0) + e^{h(t)}\int_0^t e^{-h(s)}g(s)ds.$$

Let us formulate this conclusion as a theorem. The derivation above can be regarded as a proof, at least apart from the statement of uniqueness. Alternatively, one could substitute (2.13) into (2.12) and verify that it is a solution.

Theorem 2.3. Solution of first-order linear scalar inhomogeneous IVP (FLaShI). *The problem*

$$y' - a(t)y = g(t), \quad y(0) = y_0, \tag{2.12}$$

where y_0 is a constant and $a(t)$ and $g(t)$ are continuous or piecewise continuous functions, has the unique solution

$$y(t) = y_0 \exp\left(\int_0^t a(s)ds\right) + \int_0^t g(s)\exp\left(\int_s^t a(r)dr\right)ds. \tag{2.13}$$

Equation (2.13) has an intuitive interpretation. We know from Theorem 2.2 that the influence of an initial condition in the homogeneous equation (2.5) is $y_0\exp(\int_0^t a(s)ds)$. The idea behind (2.13) is that, at each time s, the right-hand side $g(s)$, as it were, "injects a small amount of initial condition" at that point. Each such injection produces a contribution for $t > s$, and the second integral in (2.13) adds up those contributions. So inhomogeneous problems are like homogeneous ones, but with lots of little initial conditions — a continuum of initial conditions — along the way.[10] This way of thinking leads to the method known as *variation of constants* or *variation of parameters,* which can be used to give a different proof of Theorem 2.3 and also applies to ODEs of higher order.

To illustrate these developments, let us consider an IVP that looks a bit like the first nontrivial example of this chapter, (2.7). Instead of taking $\sin(t^2)$ as an oscillating coefficient on the y term, we put it as an inhomogeneous forcing function on the right-hand side:

$$y' + y = \sin(t^2), \quad t \in [0,8], \quad y(0) = 0. \tag{2.14}$$

Here is the solution, a curve that decays toward zero while being forced alternately up and down.

---

[10]This idea can be made precise by the use of the Dirac delta function, though we shall not do that in this book. Engineers call the influence of a signal injected at a point the *impulse response.*

```
L = chebop(0,8); L.op = @(t,y) diff(y) + y; L.lbc = 0;
t = chebfun('t',[0 8]); g = sin(t^2);
y = L\g; plot(y)
```

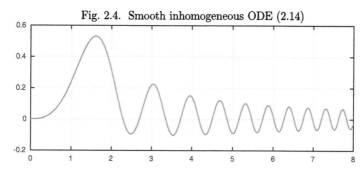

Fig. 2.4. Smooth inhomogeneous ODE (2.14)

As with the transition from (2.7) to (2.8), we can see the same effect more cleanly if we replace $\sin(t^2)$ by $\text{sign}(\sin(t^2))$:

$$y' + y = \text{sign}(\sin(t^2)), \quad t \in [0,8], \quad y(0) = 0. \tag{2.15}$$

```
L.op = @(t,y) diff(y) + y; g = sign(sin(t^2));
y = L\g; plot(y)
```

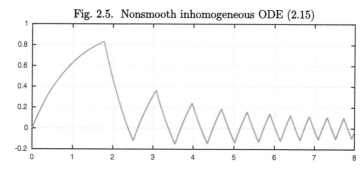

Fig. 2.5. Nonsmooth inhomogeneous ODE (2.15)

Everywhere on this "Sydney Opera House" there is exponential decay towards 0, though after the first few time units, the amplitude is small enough that the curve is dominated by the right-hand side, not the decay.

Here is another example. If $g(t) = 0$, the IVP

$$y' - \cos(t) = -10(y - \sin(t)) + g(t), \quad t \in [0,15], \quad y(0) = 0 \tag{2.16}$$

has solution $y(t) = \sin(t)$, as can be directly verified. Suppose now we introduce a forcing function g that consists of a train of upward impulses located where t is close to an odd integer. Sydney Opera House turns into Batman.

```
L = chebop(0,16); L.op = @(t,y) diff(y) - cos(t) + 10*(y-sin(t));
L.lbc = 0; t = chebfun('t',[0 16]);
g = 10*(abs((t+1)/2-round((t+1)/2))<.05);
y = L\g; plot(y)
```

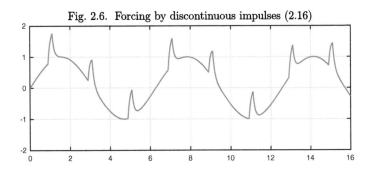

Fig. 2.6. Forcing by discontinuous impulses (2.16)

We mentioned before Theorem 2.3 that although the method of integrating factors provides a general formula for finding a particular solution of a first-order linear scalar inhomogeneous IVP, in many cases a simpler method is available. This is the **method of undetermined coefficients**, and it consists of guessing the form of the solution, then substituting to find coefficients.[11] Often this idea works easily when the right-hand side contains exponentials, because exponentials are preserved under differentiation. Sines, cosines, and polynomials in the right-hand side are also often treatable in this way. (The method is not restricted to first-order equations.)

For example, suppose we have the problem

$$y' + y = \exp(3t). \tag{2.17}$$

Knowing that differentiation preserves a term involving $\exp(3t)$, we consider the trial solution

$$y(t) = A \exp(3t).$$

Inserting this in (2.17) gives

$$(3A + A) \exp(3t) = \exp(3t),$$

from which we see that a particular solution of (2.17) is

$$y_\mathrm{p}(t) = \tfrac{1}{4} \exp(3t).$$

The general solution of (2.17) is accordingly

$$y(t) = \tfrac{1}{4} \exp(3t) + C \exp(-t). \tag{2.18}$$

As another example, consider the equation

$$y' + ty = t \exp(t^2). \tag{2.19}$$

The experienced eye will note that differentiating $w(t) = a \exp(t^2)$ gives $w' = 2tw$, so w will satisfy (2.19) if $2tw + tw = (t/a)w$, that is, $a = 1/3$. Thus $\exp(t^2)/3$ is a particular solution, and the general solution is

$$y(t) = \frac{1}{3} e^{t^2} + C e^{-t^2/2}. \tag{2.20}$$

---

[11] Some textbooks call it the *method of judicious guessing*.

Further examples of the method of undetermined coefficients are explored in Exercise 2.2.

For equations like these that are simple enough to solve exactly, an alternative method may be to do it in an automated way on the computer. If you type certain problems into WolframAlpha, the solution appears quickly. Such an approach might succeed for many of the exercises to be found in elementary ODE textbooks, though it will be less successful for the higher-order, nonlinear, and behavioral investigations that are the bigger part of this field — let alone for conceptual understanding.

Theorem 2.2 concerns the special case of Theorem 2.3 in which the problem is homogeneous, i.e., the right-hand side is zero. Another important special case occurs when the problem is autonomous, with no explicit dependence on t. Here is a theorem recording the solution in that case.

Theorem 2.4. Solution of first-order linear scalar autonomous IVP (FLAShI). *The problem*

$$y' - ay = g, \quad y(0) = y_0, \tag{2.21}$$

where y_0, a, and g are constants, has the unique solution

$$y(t) = y_0 e^{at} + \frac{g}{a} \left[e^{at} - 1 \right], \tag{2.22}$$

or $y(t) = y_0 + gt$ if $a = 0$.

APPLICATION: ELIMINATION OF CAFFEINE FROM THE BLOODSTREAM

If you drink a cup of coffee or a glass of wine, the body absorbs a dose of caffeine or alcohol that takes some time to clear away. The details of how this happens involve a complicated interplay of many organs and processes, but a differential equation model may capture the overall behavior. Here is a model of the elimination of caffeine adapted from R. Newton et al., "Plasma and salivary pharmacokinetics of caffeine in man," *European Journal of Clinical Pharmacology* 21 (1981), pp. 45–52. It falls in the category of models known as *first-order pharmacokinetics*.

The essential point is that to a reasonable approximation, when you're not drinking more coffee, the caffeine level $c(t)$ in your blood is governed by the equation

$$c' = -kc,$$

where k is a positive rate constant. This means that $c(t)$ will decay exponentially, and the decay rate is often expressed as a half-life $t_{1/2}$, defined by

$$e^{-k t_{1/2}} = \frac{1}{2}, \qquad t_{1/2} = \frac{\log(2)}{k}.$$

Experiments show that a 300 mg oral dose of caffeine, such as might be found in a large mug of drip-brewed coffee, creates a concentration of about 8 μg/mL in the blood plasma. This boost is followed by first-order kinetics with a half-life $t_{1/2}$ of about 6 hours, although the rate can vary a great deal from person to person. Here we compute the rate constant k from the half-life $t_{1/2}$ and then define an ODE accordingly, with t representing time in hours over a 24-hour period:

```
t12 = 6; k = log(2)/t12; L = chebop(@(t,c) diff(c)+k*c,[-2,24]);
```

We will assume that 300 mg of caffeine will be ingested over half an hour, increasing the caffeine concentration at a rate of 16 (μg/mL)/hr. Suppose coffee is consumed at 7:00, 10:00, and 15:00. Here is the intake schedule with time measured from the first cup.

```
t = chebfun('t',[-2,24]);
coffee = @(t0) 16*(t > t0)*(t < t0+0.5);
intake = coffee(0) + coffee(3) + coffee(8); plot(intake)
```

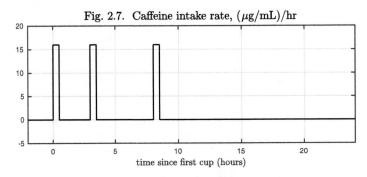

Fig. 2.7. Caffeine intake rate, (μg/mL)/hr

Here is the caffeine level during the 24-hour period.

```
L.lbc = 0; c = L\intake; hold on, plot(c)
```

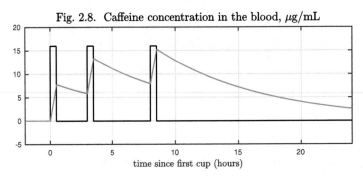

Fig. 2.8. Caffeine concentration in the blood, μg/mL

As you can see, 24 hours is not long enough to clear the caffeine from the bloodstream. For the case of three cups per day repeated periodically, see Exercise 19.7.

HISTORY. Separation of variables goes back to Leibniz and Johann Bernoulli in the 1690s. Integrating factors were introduced a few years later by Euler and Lagrange.

OUR FAVORITE REFERENCE. It is hard to find much to say about first-order scalar linear ODEs. Noting, however, that a theme in this subject is time scales of growth and decay processes, we draw attention to the fascinating *Time in Powers of Ten: Natural Phenomena and their Timescales* by 't Hooft and Vandoren, World Scientific, 2014.

SUMMARY OF CHAPTER 2. *A first-order linear scalar ODE has a one-dimensional affine space of solutions of the form $y_p + Cy_h$, and if an initial condition is specified, it has the unique solution given by Theorem 2.3, which can be derived by multiplying by an integrating factor. In the special case where the problem is homogeneous, we have $y_p = 0$, and the solution to the IVP is given by Theorem 2.2, which can be derived by separation of variables.*

Exercise 2.1. Separation of variables. Use separation of variables to find general solutions to *(a)* $y' = e^{y+t}$, *(b)* $y' = ty + y + t + 1$, *(c)* $y' = (t^2 + 2)/y$. Confirm your answers with WolframAlpha or some other computational tool. Which of these equations are linear?

Exercise 2.2. Method of undetermined coefficients. Use the method of undetermined coefficients to find general solutions to *(a)* $y' = y + e^t$ (try $y = ate^t$), *(b)* $y' = y + t\sin(t)$ (try $y = a\sin(t) + bt\sin(t) + c\cos(t) + dt\cos(t)$), *(c)* $y' = 2y + e^t + 1$, *(d)* $y' = 1 - 2ty$ *(Dawson's integral)*. Confirm your answers with WolframAlpha or some other computational tool.

Exercise 2.3. Interchanging variables to make a problem linear. *(a)* Although the differential equation $y' = y/(t + y)$ is nonlinear, show that it becomes linear if it is rewritten as an equation for dt/dy rather than dy/dt. Solve this linear equation analytically by determining an appropriate integrating factor, and thereby also solve the original nonlinear equation. *(b)* If $y(0) = 1$, what is $y(1)$? Find the solution numerically or analytically. (An analytical solution involves a special function known as the Lambert W-function.)

Exercise 2.4. Choosing a coefficient. Suppose $y_0 = 1$ in (2.5). Give a function $a(t)$ such that the solution $y(t)$ has $y(1) = 2$.

Exercise 2.5. No changes of sign. Consider an IVP (2.5) for which y_0 and $a(t)$ are real (i.e., not complex). Show that the solution $y(t)$ is positive for all t, negative for all t, or zero for all t. What's the strongest analogous result you can state in the case where $a(t)$ is permitted to be complex?

Exercise 2.6. Local extrema of an oscillation. Let t_{50} denote the point where the solution of $y' = -\cos(10/(1 - t))$, $y(0) = 1$, achieves its 50th local maximum (in Chebfun, `[a,b] = max(y,'local')`). *(a)* Determine t_{50} and $y(t_{50})$ numerically, and plot $y(t)$ for $0 \le t \le t_{50}$. *(b)* Confirm the exact value of t_{50} analytically.

Exercise 2.7. Adjusting Batman's ears. *(a)* Use `max(y{6,8})` to calculate the maximum value of $y(t)$ in the interval $[6, 8]$ for the problem of Figure 2.6. *(b)* What happens to the plot, and to this maximum value, if the impulse is made 3 times as wide with 1/3 the amplitude? *(c)* What if it is 1/3 as wide with 3 times the amplitude?

Exercise 2.8. *Temperature of a dead body.* It was observed in 1894 that a human body after death cools at a rate that is "nearly proportional to the difference between the body and the surroundings." (This heat transfer principle is known as Newton's law of cooling. The quote comes from de Saram, Webster, and Kathirgamatamby, "Post-mortem temperature and the time of death," *Journal of Criminal Law, Criminology, and Police Science* 64 (1955), pp. 562–577.) Let's assume that the cooling rate is $-\beta\theta(t)$, where $\theta(t)$ is the difference between body and surrounding temperature, and β is an empirical constant. De Saram et al. measured the temperatures of 41 executed prisoners to test this model. In one case the body temperature was 97.8°F at 11 AM and 96.2°F at 1 PM. The room temperature was held at 86.4°F. *(a)* Use the temperature readings to find a numerical value for β. *(b)* By assuming that at the time of death the body temperature was 98.6°F, determine an approximate time of death.

Exercise 2.9. *Heaviside function.* Many of the examples of this chapter involve ODEs forced by discontinuous right-hand sides. Another way to formulate such problems is with the *step function* or **Heaviside function** $H(t)$, which takes the value 0 for $t < 0$ and 1 for $t > 0$; the value at $t = 0$ is 0.5. Execute the instructions L = chebop(0,2), L.op = @(t,y) diff(y)+y, L.lbc = 1, t = chebfun('t',[0,2]), f = heaviside(t-1), y = L\f. Write down the IVP that is being solved here, plot the solution y just computed, and derive an exact formula for this function. How accurate is the computed value $y(2)$?

Exercise 2.10. *An ODE from Newton (1671) and Taylor series approximations.* One of the first IVPs ever considered was the equation $y' = 1 - 3t + y + t^2 + ty$ with initial condition $y(0) = 0$, presented by Isaac Newton in 1671. Newton solved this by using what we now call a Taylor series, obtaining the representation $y(t) = t - t^2 + t^3/3 - t^4/6 + t^5/30 - t^6/45 + \cdots$. What is the maximum difference between this 6-term approximation and the true solution on the intervals *(a)* $[0, 0.5]$, *(b)* $[0, 1]$, *(c)* $[0, 2]$, and *(d)* $[0, 4]$? Give the numbers and also plot the absolute value of the error as a function of t on a log-log scale. Comment on the plot.

Exercise 2.11. *Equation with sensitive solutions.* Consider the equation $y' + ty = f(t)$ for $t \in [-4, 4]$ with $y(-4) = 0$. *(a)* What is $\max_{t \in [-4,4]} y(t)$ if $f(t) = \sin(t)$? What does this change to if $f(t) = \sin(0.85t)$? *(b)* What term in the formulas of Theorem 2.3 makes it possible for these numbers to vary so greatly?

Exercise 2.12. *Thiele's equation for life insurance.* Simple life insurance is purchased for a length of time T and costs the insured party a fixed premium P per year. If the insured dies during the term of the policy, the insurer must pay a benefit of S. Otherwise, the insured receives nothing. The insurer is required to keep money in reserve for this policy in order to be able to pay out all the claims likely to result from a pooled group of individuals. This is done via the *Thiele differential equation,* first derived in 1875 and published in 1910. Let $V(t)$ for $0 \leq t \leq T$ be the amount of reserve needed for a policy purchased at time $t = 0$. Thiele's equation is $V' = P + \delta V(t) - \mu(t)(S - V(t))$, where δ is the *force of interest* (the interest rate) and $\mu(t)$ is the *force of mortality* (the probability of a person dying per unit time). When the policy expires, no reserve is needed, so $V(T) = 0$.[12] *(a)* Plot the solution $V(t)$ for $\mu(t) = 0.007(t+5)$, $\delta = 0.03$, $P = 800$, $S = 1e6$, and $T = 25$. *(b)* What is the maximal

---

[12]The property of a time-dependent equation being governed by a *final condition* rather than an initial condition arises commonly in financial modeling. The famous example involving a PDE is the Black–Scholes equation.

value of $V(t)$? Is it less than or equal to S? Interpret this inequality financially. *(c)* Assuming $\delta \geq 0$, prove that any solution of the ODE problem will satisfy this inequality.

Exercise 2.13. Without the method of undetermined coefficients. Solve (2.17) using Theorem 2.3.

3. First-order scalar nonlinear ODEs

The first thing to do with nonlinear problems is enjoy them. The chances are you can't solve a particular nonlinear ODE analytically, but there is a wonderful variety of effects to explore. Incidentally, a change of notation applies here: mathematicians usually write a linear differential operator without parentheses, $y \mapsto Ly$, but a nonlinear one with parentheses, $y \mapsto N(y)$. The change of letters from L to N is also a reminder of nonlinearity.

For example, here is a basic linear IVP, really just an integral since y appears only in the term y':

$$y' = 3\cos(t), \quad y(0) = 0. \tag{3.1}$$

Its solution is the sine wave $y(t) = 3\sin(t)$.

```
N = chebop(0,20); N.lbc = 0; N.op = @(t,y) diff(y);
rhs = chebfun('3*cos(t)',[0,20]);
y = N\rhs; plot(y)
```

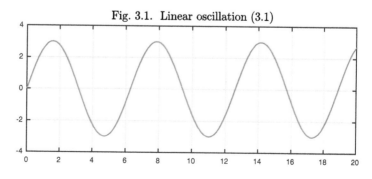

Fig. 3.1. Linear oscillation (3.1)

What happens if we add a nonlinear function of y to the operator? For example, let us construct an ODE that behaves like (3.1) when y has a small amplitude but "shuts off" as $|y|$ increases. An example of such an equation is

$$y' + |y|^2 y = 3\cos(t), \quad y(0) = 0. \tag{3.2}$$

(We write $|y|^2 y$ instead of y^3 to suggest the idea of an amplitude-dependent coefficient $|y|^2$ multiplying the usual y term.) The next plot shows the new solution superimposed on the previous one. Note that the curves are about the same at first, but diverge as the amplitudes grow larger.

```
N.op = @(t,y) diff(y) + y^3;
y2 = N\rhs; plot([y y2])
```

Fig. 3.2. Oscillation with nonlinear damping (3.2)

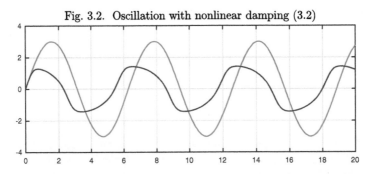

Here is a variant of the same nonlinear idea. Suppose that instead of a "penalty" for large values of $|y|$ we impose a "barrier," preventing $|y|$ from reaching the value 1. Here is an equation with a logarithmic barrier:

$$y' - \frac{1}{2}\log(1 - |y|)y = 3\cos(t). \tag{3.3}$$

The solution is smooth, though it doesn't look it (see Exercise 3.1), and confined to values $-1 < y < 1$.

```
N.op = @(t,y) diff(y) - 0.5*log(1-abs(y))*y;
y3 = N\rhs; plot([y y3])
```

Fig. 3.3. Nonlinear damping by a logarithmic barrier (3.3)

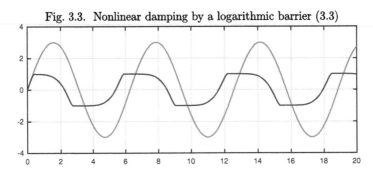

Examples like these, scalar problems of first order, are rather limited. The variety will grow in later chapters when we come to problems of higher order or with multiple variables.

Both (3.2) and (3.3) are written with nonlinearities of the form $g(y)y$ for some function g (equal to $|y|^2$ and $-0.5\log(1-|y|)$, respectively). This form suggests the idea that, locally, a nonlinear ODE should behave approximately linearly. Near any time $t \approx t_0$, it should be possible to approximate the solution by the solution of a linear equation derived, say, by series expansion. This is indeed the case, at least if the coefficients are continuous, and the idea will be made precise in Chapter 14.

For a few special classes of first-order nonlinear ODEs, analytical solutions are available. The most important category of such problems are the **separable equations**. In the last chapter we solved $y' = a(t)y$ by writing it as

$$\frac{dy}{y} = a(t)dt.$$

If we generalize y^{-1} to a continuous function $b(y)$ that does not change sign, we get the equation

$$b(y)dy = a(t)dt,$$

and the two sides can be integrated as before to get a solution at least locally. We record the result as a theorem.

Theorem 3.1. Solution of first-order separable scalar homogeneous IVP (FlaSHI). *Let $a(t)$ be a continuous function of t and let $b(y)$ be a continuous nonzero function of y. A solution $y(t)$ of the problem*

$$b(y)dy = a(t)dt, \quad y(0) = y_0 \tag{3.4}$$

satisfies the equation

$$\int_{y_0}^{y} b(x)dx = \int_{0}^{t} a(s)ds. \tag{3.5}$$

Equation (3.4) has the form $y' = f(t,y)$ (of type FlaSH), but not every equation $y' = f(t,y)$ can be separated in this way. However, another case where separation is possible is if f is independent of t.

Theorem 3.2. Solution of first-order autonomous separable scalar homogeneous IVP (FlASHI). *Let $b(y)$ be a continuous nonzero function of y. A solution $y(t)$ of the problem*

$$b(y)dy = dt, \quad y(0) = y_0 \tag{3.6}$$

satisfies the equation

$$\int_{y_0}^{y} b(x)dx = t.$$

Similarly $y' = f(t,y)$ is separable if f is independent of y — it is just an integral.

A prototypical example of a problem of the form (3.6) is the ODE

$$y' = y^\alpha, \tag{3.7}$$

where α is a constant. Dividing by y^α gives $dy/y^\alpha = dt$ and hence

$$\frac{y^{1-\alpha}}{1-\alpha} = t - t_\mathrm{b}$$

for some constant t_b (the letter b stands for "blowup"). This simplifies to

$$y = \left[(1-\alpha)(t-t_\mathrm{b})\right]^{1/(1-\alpha)}. \tag{3.8}$$

For $\alpha > 1$, this solution exhibits a phenomenon of mathematical and physical interest, *blowup in finite time*. For a specific illustration, consider the IVP

$$y' = y^2, \quad y(0) = 1. \tag{3.9}$$

From (3.8) with $\alpha = 2$, we see that the solution is

$$y = \frac{1}{1-t}, \tag{3.10}$$

which diverges to ∞ at $t_\mathrm{b} = 1$. Here is a plot of the solution up to the point where it reaches the value 100.

```
N = chebop(0,1); N.op = @(t,y) diff(y) - y^2;
N.lbc = 1; N.maxnorm = 100;
y = N\0; plot(y)
hold on, plot([1 1],[0 120],'--')
```

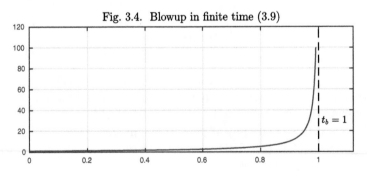

Fig. 3.4. Blowup in finite time (3.9)

Behaviorally, (3.9) and (3.10) are rich in potential applications and interpretations. The ODE (3.9) describes a process where y increases not just in proportion to its current amplitude, but faster. For example, one can imagine that $y(t)$ represents the temperature at time t of a smoldering haystack that smolders faster as it gets hotter. The singularity at $t = 1$ corresponds to the hay catching fire — spontaneous combustion or "thermal runaway." (This simple idea is refined in the Application of Chapter 18.)

Now let us vary the problem slightly and replace (3.9) by

$$y' = y + y^2, \quad y(0) = 1. \tag{3.11}$$

Since the values of y' are now bigger, we expect that blowup will occur again and it will happen sooner. Again a solution can be obtained by separation of variables. We write

$$\frac{dy}{y + y^2} = dt,$$

and integration gives

$$\log\left(\frac{y}{1+y}\right) = t - t_{\mathrm{b}},$$

that is,

$$\frac{y}{1+y} = e^{t - t_{\mathrm{b}}},$$

or equivalently

$$y = \frac{1}{e^{t_{\mathrm{b}} - t} - 1}. \tag{3.12}$$

With the initial condition $y(0) = 1$, we have $t_{\mathrm{b}} = \log 2$, confirming that, as predicted, the blowup is earlier than in (3.10).

```
N.op = @(t,y) diff(y) - y - y^2;
y = N\0; plot(y)
hold on, plot(log(2)*[1 1],[0 120],'--')
```

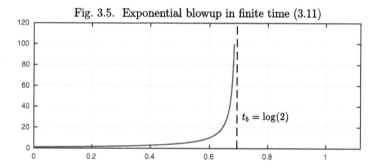

Fig. 3.5. Exponential blowup in finite time (3.11)

We solved (3.11) by separation of variables. As it happens, this is a special case of a more general class of ODEs that can also be solved analytically. A **Bernoulli equation**[13] is an ODE of the form

$$y' = a(t)y + b(t)y^p, \tag{3.13}$$

where p is a constant and $a(t)$ and $b(t)$ are given functions of t. (If $p = 0$, the problem is linear, and if $p = 1$ it is linear and homogeneous. We assume p is not 0 or 1.) If a or b is nonconstant, then separation of variables will not work

---

[13] Named after Jacob Bernoulli, the brother of Johann and uncle of Daniel.

for (3.13), but there is a different approach that still succeeds. Let us multiply by y^{-p} to get

$$y'y^{-p} = a(t)y^{1-p} + b(t).$$

If we now make the substitution

$$u = y^{1-p}, \quad u' = (1-p)y^{-p}y',$$

the equation becomes $(1-p)^{-1}u' = a(t)u + b(t)$, that is,

$$u' = (1-p)a(t)u + (1-p)b(t).$$

This is a linear ODE, which can accordingly be solved by an integrating factor as described in Theorem 2.3, or by the method of undetermined coefficients.

For example, let us generalize the blowup problems (3.9) and (3.11) a little further. Consider the ODE

$$y' = y + ty^2, \quad y(0) = y_0. \tag{3.14}$$

Comparing with (3.11), we see that for $y_0 = 1$ the amplification will be weaker here for $t \in [0,1)$, so we can expect blowup at a time $t_b > \log 2$. Dividing by y^2 converts the equation to

$$\frac{y'}{y^2} = \frac{1}{y} + t, \quad y(0) = y_0,$$

and the change of variables $u = y^{-1}$ converts this to

$$u' + u = -t, \quad u(0) = u_0 = \frac{1}{y_0}.$$

Applying Theorem 2.3 or the method of undetermined coefficients, we find that the solution of this IVP is

$$u(t) = 1 - t + e^{-t}(u_0 - 1),$$

that is,

$$y(t) = \frac{1}{1 - t + e^{-t}(y_0^{-1} - 1)}. \tag{3.15}$$

Examining (3.15), we see that $y_0 = 1$, as in (3.9) and (3.11), is a special case in which the exponential term does not appear. For $y_0 = 1$, therefore, the blowup occurs at exactly the same time $t_b = 1$ as in (3.10). Larger y_0 brings blowup sooner, and smaller y_0 defers it to later. Here are solutions up to $t = 1$ or $y = 100$, whichever comes first, for initial values $y_0 = 0.90, 0.91, \ldots, 1.00$.

```
N.op = @(t,y) diff(y) - y - t*y^2;
for y0 = 0.90:.01:1
  N.lbc = y0; y = N\0; plot(y), hold on
end
```

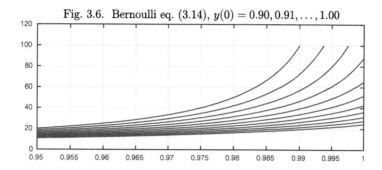

Fig. 3.6. Bernoulli eq. (3.14), $y(0) = 0.90, 0.91, \ldots, 1.00$

We have explored at some length the phenomenon of blowup of solutions to an ODE. Physically, blowup in finite time corresponds to an explosion or another feedback process running out of control. Mathematically, it illustrates the phenomenon of **nonexistence** of solutions to certain nonlinear ODE problems. Because of the blowup at $t_b = 1$, for example, there exists no solution to the problem (3.9) on the interval $[0, 2]$.[14] There is a well-established general theory of existence and uniqueness of solutions to ODE IVPs, presented in Chapter 11. The fundamental result of this theory asserts that the IVP

$$y' = f(t, y), \quad t \in [0, \infty), \quad y(0) = y_0$$

is guaranteed to have a unique solution if f is continuous with respect to t and Lipschitz continuous with respect to y.[15]

From the ODE (3.7) with $\alpha < 1$, we can develop an example of **nonuniqueness** that has a beautiful physical interpretation. Consider (3.7) with $\alpha = 1/2$,

$$y' = y^{1/2}, \quad y(0) = 0. \tag{3.16}$$

From (3.8) we obtain the solution

$$y(t) = \frac{1}{4} t^2.$$

An equally valid solution, however, is $y(t) = 0$, and this is the one that Chebfun will compute. Alternatively, a solution to (3.16) might "get going" at any time $t_0 \geq 0$:

$$y(t) = \begin{cases} 0, & t \leq t_0, \\ \frac{1}{4}(t - t_0)^2, & t \geq t_0. \end{cases}$$

Thus there are not just two possible solutions but an infinite family. Here is a plot of four of them.

---

[14] In Chebfun, if the computed solution hits the limit `N.maxnorm`, then all further values are set to `NaN` — not-a-number.

[15] This means that there exists a constant C such that, for all t and y_1, y_2 in the range of interest, $|f(t, y_2) - f(t, y_1)| \leq C|y_2 - y_1|$. Note that (3.9) loses Lipschitz continuity as $|y| \to \infty$, implying that existence of solutions to this problem can fail only if $|y|$ diverges.

```
t = chebfun('t',[0 6]);
for t0 = 0:3
  t = chebfun('t',[0, t0+2.6]);
  y = 0.25*(t-t0)^2*(t>t0); plot(y), hold on
end
```

Fig. 3.7. Four solutions to (3.16)

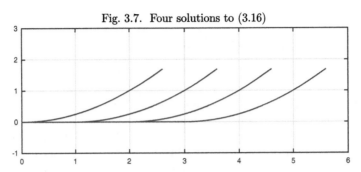

If $y \geq y_0$ for some constant $y_0 > 0$, then the right-hand side of (3.16) is Lipschitz continuous with respect to y. This implies that uniqueness can fail for this problem only at points with $y = 0$, though for any value of t. In Chapter 11 we shall see examples where uniqueness fails at isolated points such as $y = t = 0$.

We mentioned a physical interpretation, and this involves the *leaky bucket problem*. Suppose a bucket of water has a hole in the bottom, so the water flows out. After a certain time, all the water will be gone, and then the bucket remains empty for all time. Here is the nonuniqueness effect in the words of Corless and Jankowski:[16]

> Given an empty bucket, there's no way to tell when it was full — if it ever was.

The connection with (3.16) is provided by *Torricelli's Law* of 1643 (Exercise 3.12). If $y > 0$ is the height of water in a leaky bucket, then y decreases at a rate governed by the equation

$$y' = -Cy^{1/2}$$

for an appropriate constant C. This means that if we take t to be time measured *backward* from the present, the equation is

$$y' = Cy^{1/2},$$

which is essentially (3.16). So Figure 3.7, with time reversed, can be interpreted as a picture of the leaky bucket.

The last chapter was linear and this one is nonlinear, but both have been restricted to scalar problems of first order. Before turning to higher-order problems and systems of equations, we want to illustrate an invaluable trick for

---

[16]See "Variations on a theme of Euler," *SIAM Review* 58 (2016), pp. 775–792. Nonuniqueness for the leaky bucket is also discussed, among other places, in volume 1 of Hubbard and West, *Differential Equations: A Dynamical Systems Approach*.

simplifying computations involving particles in a plane: the use of complex arithmetic. A particle moving in the x-y plane has two coordinates, $x(t)$ and $y(t)$. This suggests an ODE with two dependent variables, but if we define $z(t) = x(t) + iy(t)$, we have just a single, scalar complex variable $z(t)$. This can be remarkably convenient. One reason is that many particle interactions depend on distances between points in the plane, and a distance in the x-y plane can be regarded as the absolute value of a complex number.

Our Application illustrates this use of a complex variable.

Application: classic pursuit problems

Suppose an antelope runs with speed 1 along the vertical line $x = 1$, starting at $(1, 0)$ and going in the positive y-direction. A lioness starts at $(0, 0)$ and pursues the antelope, always moving directly toward the antelope at a fixed speed C.[17] What path does the lioness follow, and when and where does she catch the antelope?

The antelope's path is given as the function $a(t) = 1 + it$; the unknown in this problem is the path of the lioness. In complex arithmetic, we can regard this as a function $z(t)$ given by the IVP

$$z' = C \frac{a(t) - z(t)}{|a(t) - z(t)|}, \quad z(0) = 0. \tag{3.17}$$

Here is a plot showing the lioness's track up to time $t = 4$ for $C = 0.5$, 1, and 1.1.

```
tmax = 4; a = chebfun('1+1i*t',[0 tmax]);
N = chebop(0,tmax); N.lbc = 0; CC = [.5 1 1.1];
for j = 1:3
  C = CC(j); N.op = @(t,z) diff(z) - C*(a(t)-z)/abs(a(t)-z);
  subplot(1,3,j), plot(a,':'), hold on, plot(a(end),'.')
  z = N\0; arrowplot(z)
end
```

Fig. 3.8. The lion chases the antelope

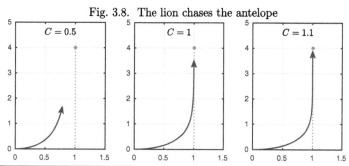

---

[17] The cast of characters is variable, as described in P. J. Nahin, *Chases and Escapes: The Mathematics of Pursuit and Evasion,* Princeton, 2006. One may have a dog chasing a rabbit, a hawk chasing a sparrow, or, in the original treatment by Pierre Bouguer in 1732, a pirate ship chasing a merchant ship.

With $C = 0.5$, the lioness will obviously never catch the antelope, which soon sprints out of reach. With $C = 1$, she still never quite makes the catch. The separation distance is 0.50000015 at $t = 4$, converging exponentially to $1/2$ as $t \to \infty$. For any $C > 1$, on the other hand, the catch will take place. We have stopped this experiment before that point since there is a singularity involved.

Of course, the antelope may zig-zag. Here is another run with $C = 0.5$ and 1 in which she makes a 90° right turn at $t = 2$. As $t \to \infty$ in the latter case, the separation distance approaches $0.2653 \ldots$.

```
a = chebfun({'1+1i*t','-1+2i+t'},[0 2 4]);
N = chebop(0,tmax); N.lbc = 0; CC = [.5 1];
for j = 1:2
  C = CC(j); N.op = @(t,z) diff(z) - C*(a(t)-z)/abs(a(t)-z);
  subplot(1,2,j), plot(a,':'), hold on, plot(a(end),'.')
  z = N\0; arrowplot(z)
end
```

Fig. 3.9. The antelope takes evasive action

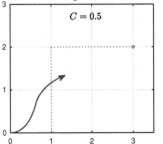
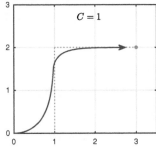

This pursuit problem has only a single unknown trajectory, making it a scalar problem in complex arithmetic and thus fitting the theme of this chapter. The main use of complex arithmetic, however, is for tracking systems of multiple particles in the plane, and we shall use this method to compute planar orbits of planets in Chapter 13 and electrons in Exercises 13.5 and 19.4, as well as looking at a multiparticle pursuit problem in Exercise 10.1.

HISTORY. Nonlinear equations have been part of the study of ODEs from the beginning. For the first thirty years or so, until about 1700, the equations were of first order. Then higher-order equations joined the discussion.

OUR FAVORITE REFERENCE. Even if you don't read German, the book *Differentialgleichungen: Lösungsmethoden und Lösungen* by Erich Kamke (Springer Fachmedien Wiesbaden, 1977) is extraordinary. This book, which appeared in many editions starting in 1942, features a collection of 1600 numbered examples of ODEs with their solutions — the first 576 of them, filling 103 pages, corresponding to first-order equations. It is a monument to the knowledge of ODEs accumulated during their first 300 years and a poignant indication of how different the world was before computers.

SUMMARY OF CHAPTER 3. *Some first-order nonlinear ODEs can be solved by separation of variables, and Bernoulli equations, of the form $y' = a(t)y + b(t)y^p$, can be solved by the change of variables $u = y^{1-p}$. Most other first-order nonlinear problems cannot be solved analytically. The ODE $y' = f(t, y)$ has a unique solution for all t if f is continuous with respect to t and Lipschitz continuous with respect to y. If these conditions do not hold, existence and/or uniqueness may fail.*

Exercise 3.1. Smoothness of the solution to the barrier problem. Despite appearances in Figure 3.3, the solution $y(t)$ of (3.3) is smooth. Confirm this by plotting y, y', and y''. What are the minimum and maximum values of these three functions over the interval $[1, 20]$ (to exclude initial transients)? (You can use a command like y{1,20} to restrict a chebfun to a subinterval.)

Exercise 3.2. Analytical solutions via clever substitutions. One method used by experts in analytical solution of ODEs is to change variables. Find the general solutions of the following problems analytically using the substitutions indicated: *(a)* $y' = e^{t-y} - e^t$ $(u = e^y)$, *(b)* $ty' = y(\log(ty) - 1)$ $(u = ty)$, *(c)* $2tyy' = y^2 - t$ $(u = y^2)$.

Exercise 3.3. A solution with compact support. Consider the IVP $y' = -ty/|y|^{1/2}$, $y(0) = 1$, where $|y|^{1/2}$ represents the positive branch of the square root. *(a)* Find analytically the (unique) solution for $t \in [0, 1]$. *(b)* Find analytically the (unique) solution for $t \in [0, \infty)$.

Exercise 3.4. Spherical flame in microgravity. (Adapted from section 7.9 of C. B. Moler, *Numerical Computing with MATLAB*, SIAM, 2008. A video of a growing flame sphere in microgravity can be found at https://goo.gl/nQ5Vxd.) In the absence of gravity, a flame takes a nearly spherical shape. Oxygen, which fuels the flame, enters the sphere at a rate proportional to its surface area. Combustion consumes the oxygen at a rate proportional to the volume. In appropriate units the radius $r(t)$ is approximately governed by the ODE $dr/dt = r^2 - r^3$. We assume that $r(0) = r_0$. *(a)* Show that the solution satisfies the implicit equation $\log(r/(1-r)) - 1/r = t + C$, and give a formula for C in terms of the initial condition. *(b)* Show that the time t_h at which r takes the value $1/2$ is approximately $1/r_0$ as $r_0 \to 0$. (Note: $1/x$ dominates $\log x$ as $x \to 0$.) *(c)* On one graph, plot numerically obtained solutions for $0 \le t \le 1500$ and $r_0 = 10^{-1}, 10^{-2}, 10^{-3}$. As in Exercise 3.1, plot a zoom of the figure for $r_0 = 10^{-3}$ to confirm that, despite appearances, this solution is smooth.

Exercise 3.5. Multiple routes to the same solution. Consider the ODE $y' + \sin(y) = 0$. *(a)* Find the general solution analytically using separation of variables. *(b)* Find it again by interchanging the independent and dependent variables as in Exercise 2.3.

Exercise 3.6. Some nonlinear problems. Suppose $y(0) = 1$. Determine $y(1)$ analytically if *(a)* $y' = y^{3/2}e^t$, *(b)* $(t+1)y' + 3y = 0$, *(c)* $yy' = t$.

Exercise 3.7. Fixed points and stability. A number y_* is a **fixed point** of an autonomous ODE $y' = f(y)$ if $f(y_*) = 0$; it is **stable** if $f'(y_*) < 0$ and **unstable** if $f'(y_*) > 0$. Find all fixed points and determine their stability or instability for *(a)* $y' = y + y^2$ (eq. (3.11)), *(b)* $y' = y^2 - 1$, *(c)* $y' = y - y^2$ (the logistic equation; see also Exercises 3.15 and 3.16), and *(d)* $y' = \sin(y)$.

Exercise 3.8. Stable and unstable fixed points. *(a)* Now explore equation *(c)* of the last exercise on the computer by making a plot of the trajectories emanating from $y(0) = -1, -0.8, \ldots, 1.8, 2$ on the interval $t \in [0, 4]$. You will need to use the N.maxnorm feature since otherwise some curves will blow up. *(b)* Similarly, explore equation *(d)* of the last exercise with a plot of the trajectories emanating from $y(0) = -15, -14, \ldots, 15$ on the interval $t \in [0, 4]$.

Exercise 3.9. Ghost of a fixed point. Plot the solution of $y' = 1 - a\sin(y)$, $y(0) = 0$ for $t \in [0, 200]$ with $a = 0.9$, 0.99, and 0.999. In each case use `roots(y-2*pi)` to determine the value of t for which $y(t) = 2\pi$.

Exercise 3.10. The Lambert W function. (a) The *Lambert W function* is a function $W(t)$ defined by the functional equation $W(te^t) = t$. It satisfies the differential equation $W'(t) = W(t)/(t + tW(t))$ and takes the value $W(e) = 1$, where $e = 2.718\ldots$. Use this information to solve an ODE to compute the value $W(1)$. *(b)* The number just computed probably matches the exact value of $W(1)$ (readily found on the Web) to about 10 digits of accuracy, because that is Chebfun's default accuracy for ODE solutions. To get more digits, execute `cheboppref.setDefaults('ivpAbsTol',1e-14)` before making the calculation (try `chebfunpref` and `cheboppref` and see Chapter 8 of the *Chebfun Guide* for more information). How accurate is the new value? Afterwards, return to the usual defaults by executing `cheboppref.setDefaults('factory')`.

Exercise 3.11. Antelope on a circle or square. As in Figs. 3.8 and 3.9, suppose a lion begins at $z = 0$ at $t = 0$ and chases the antelope with equal speeds, i.e., $C = 1$ in (3.17). *(a)* Suppose the antelope runs around the unit circle with position $a(t) = e^{it}$. Plot the lion's trajectory over the interval $t \in [0, 2\pi]$. Plot the distance between the two animals as a function of t. At roughly what time t will the distance fall below 0.01? *(b)* Suppose the antelope runs around the unit square, which you can construct with `a = 1 + cumsum(round(exp(pi*.25i*(t+2))/sqrt(2)))` if t is a chebfun for t defined over the time interval of interest. Plot the lion's trajectory over the interval $t \in [0, 8]$. Again plot the distance as a function of t and estimate when this will fall below 0.01.

Exercise 3.12. The leaky bucket problem — Torricelli's law (1643). A cylindrical tank has a hole at the bottom. Water flows out, making the height $y(t)$ of the water decrease from its initial value y_0 to 0 after a certain time. Derive the ODE for this process by considering energy, as follows. The water in the tank has a certain *potential energy* determined by $y(t)$ and hence decreasing at a rate determined by y and y'. As water leaves the hole, this is converted to an equal amount of *kinetic energy* determined by y' and hence increasing at a rate determined by y'. By balancing these two, explain why the ODE has the form $y' = -Cy^{1/2}$. Solve the equation analytically and show that $y(t) = 0$ is reached at a finite time t. If t_0 is doubled, what effect will this have on the drainage time?

Exercise 3.13. Blowup equation with a complex coefficient. Consider equation (3.9) except with a complex coefficient: $y' = Cy^2$, $y(0) = 1$, where C is a constant with a nonzero imaginary part. *(a)* Write down the analytical solution, valid for all t. *(b)* Plot the solutions corresponding to $C = 1 + 1i$ and $C = 1 + 0.1i$.

Exercise 3.14. Complex nonlinear oscillator. The equation $y' = iy + 0.1(1 - |y|^2)y$ might be regarded as a kind of complex, first-order analogue of the van der Pol equation. *(a)* Compute and plot the solution for $y(0) = 0.1$ and $t \in [0, 100]$. *(b)* Use `roots(real(y))` to determine the period of the oscillation, and explain why this is the value that appears.

Exercise 3.15. Logistic equation. Positive solutions of $y' = y$ grow exponentially, but positive solutions of $y' = (1 - y/Y)y$, where $Y > 0$ is a constant known as the *carrying capacity*, asymptote to $y = Y$ as $t \to \infty$. *(a)* Solve the equation analytically for

$y(0) = y_0$. *(b)* Solve it numerically with $Y = 5$ for $t \in [0, 5]$ and make a plot of trajectories with $y_0 = -5, -4, \ldots, 10$. (This equation was derived by Pierre-François Verhulst in the 1830s as a model of population growth after he read Malthus's *Essay on the Principle of Population.*)

Exercise 3.16. Logistic equation with harvesting. Suppose a population is naturally governed by logistic growth but is regularly harvested, obeying $y' = y(1 - y/Y) - H$ for positive constants Y and H. *(a)* Show theoretically that the existence of a steady real solution satisfying $y' = 0$ requires $H < Y/4$. *(b)* Using Chebfun, plot solutions over $[0, 11]$ for $y_0 = 5$, $Y = 5$, and $H = 0.75, 1, 1.25, 1.5$. How do you interpret the solution with $H = 1.5$?

Exercise 3.17. Blowup equation with a t-dependent correction. Positive solutions of $y' = y^2$ blow up to ∞ in finite time, but $y' = y^2 - t^2$ has different behavior. Plot solutions for $t \in [-2, 2]$ with $y(-2) = y_0 = -2, -1.9, -1.8, \ldots, 2$. (Use N.maxnorm = 3.) Describe in words what trajectories appear to look like as $t \to \infty$ as a function of $y_0 \in [-2, 2]$. Approximately what is the critical value of y_0 in this interval?

4. Second-order ODEs and damped oscillations

The most famous of all ODEs is of order two — *Newton's second law of motion*, force equals mass times acceleration:

$$F = ma.$$

What makes this a second-order equation is that acceleration is the second derivative of position with respect to time. Following the standard notation of this book, we can rename a as y'' and solve for it to get

$$y'' = \frac{F(t, y)}{m}. \tag{4.1}$$

This particular form of Newton's law describes a mass m moving along a line with position $y(t)$ at time t and subject to a force F that may depend on t and/or $y(t)$.

Staying with 17th century England for a moment, a famous choice of F is *Hooke's law*,

$$F(t, y) = -by, \tag{4.2}$$

where b is a positive constant. This applies for example to a spring stretched a distance y beyond its rest position. Combining (4.1) and (4.2) gives the ODE

$$y'' = -\frac{by}{m}.$$

We shall write this in a standard form that will also be useful in later chapters by defining

$$\omega = \sqrt{\frac{b}{m}}.$$

The equation becomes

$$y'' + \omega^2 y = 0. \tag{4.3}$$

This is the most basic of all second-order ODEs, the second-order analogue of (1.1), and it governs *simple harmonic motion*. As a second-order equation, it has a two-dimensional space of solutions spanned by the functions

$$\sin(\omega t), \quad \cos(\omega t).$$

Note that these functions are *periodic*, with period T given by the formula

$$T = \frac{2\pi}{\omega}. \tag{4.4}$$

The number ω is the *frequency*.[18] The general solution of (4.3) can be written[19]

$$A\sin(\omega t) + B\cos(\omega t). \tag{4.5}$$

Other representations of this space of solutions are also useful, such as

$$A\sin(\omega t + \phi), \tag{4.6}$$

where ϕ is an phase shift, or the complex exponentials expression[20]

$$Ae^{i\omega t} + Be^{-i\omega t}, \tag{4.7}$$

where A and B may also be complex. This form is particularly useful when one wishes to consider the generalization to situations in which ω is complex, corresponding to a constant ω^2 in (4.2) that is negative or complex. From (4.7) it can be seen that in this case solutions to (4.1) contain components that grow and decay exponentially with t.

Here for example is a solution of (4.3) with $\omega = 1$ and initial conditions $y(0) = 1$, $y'(0) = 0$. We know this solution exactly: it is $y(t) = \cos(t)$. The number displayed in the figure title confirms that the period is 2π.

```
L = chebop(0,60); L.op = @(t,y) diff(y,2) + y; L.lbc = [1;0];
y = L\0; plot(y)
[~,maxima] = max(y,'local'); T = maxima(3) - maxima(2);
```

---

[18]One must be careful to distinguish this *angular frequency*, representing radians per unit time, from the quantity $1/T$, also called frequency, which represents cycles per unit time. The musical note A above middle C corresponds to 440 Hz, which is an angular frequency of ≈ 2765 radians per second.

[19]When the independent variable is x rather than t, ω is replaced by k, known as the *wave number*. In this case $\sin(\omega t)$ and $\cos(\omega t)$ become $\sin(kx)$ and $\cos(kx)$.

[20]Mathematicians generally prefer the complex exponentials representation for linear problems, where sines and cosines can be obtained by appropriate superpositions. For nonlinear problems, superposition is not available, and it is generally necessary to stay with real variables.

Fig. 4.1. Simple harmonic motion (4.3): $T = 6.2832$

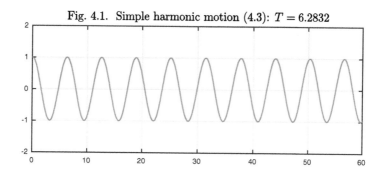

In this book we are always free to experiment. For example, what if we make the problem nonlinear by replacing y by y^5? The equation becomes

$$y'' + y^5 = 0. \tag{4.8}$$

A figure shows that the solution is again a periodic oscillation of amplitude 1, but the period is 34% longer:

```
L.op = @(t,y) diff(y,2) + y^5;
y = L\0; plot(y)
[~,maxima] = max(y,'local'); T = maxima(3) - maxima(2);
```

Fig. 4.2. Nonlinear spring law (4.8): $T = 8.4131$

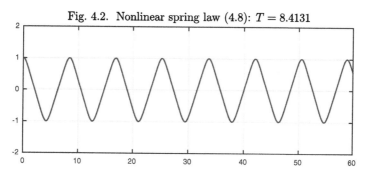

The reason the period has increased is easy to see: $|y^5|$ is smaller than $|y|$ for $|y| < 1$, so this nonlinear spring has a weaker restoring force than the linear one and oscillates more slowly. The shape of the oscillation has also changed, coming closer to a sawtoothed alternation of straight segments. We are closer to a "bang-bang" situation, with most of the acceleration, hence most of the curvature, appearing for $y \approx \pm 1$.

As another experiment, let us return to the original linear problem (4.3) but add a small term involving the first derivative, giving an equation associated with *damped oscillation*,[21]

$$y'' + 0.1y' + \omega^2 y = 0. \tag{4.9}$$

---

[21] In the van der Pol equation (1.2), we saw a similar oscillator except with nonlinear damping: positive damping for $|y| > 1$, negative for $|y| < 1$.

Physically, this corresponds to an additional applied force that is proportional to velocity and in the opposite direction, slowing motions down. Here is the result, again with $\omega = 1$ and $y(0) = 1$, $y'(0) = 0$.

```
L.op = @(t,y) diff(y,2) + 0.1*diff(y) + y;
y = L\0; plot(y)
[~,maxima] = max(y,'local'); T = maxima(3) - maxima(2);
```

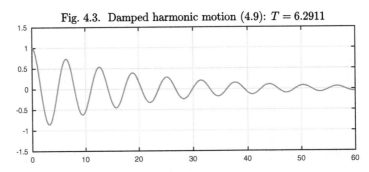

Fig. 4.3. Damped harmonic motion (4.9): $T = 6.2911$

Note from the number displayed in the figure title that the "period" is greater than 2π, but only about 1% greater; we shall explain this in a moment. Strictly speaking, this solution is not periodic, but the maxima are still separated by fixed intervals. We shall see in (4.13) that y is equal to a periodic function times a decaying exponential.

Few subjects are more vital to practical engineering than the damping of oscillations.[22] In cars and aircraft, vibrations with frequencies on the order of hundreds or thousands of hertz must be damped to keep sound levels tolerable. In bridges and buildings, vibrations with frequencies closer to 1–5 hertz must be damped to avoid catastrophic failures in storms and earthquakes. The mathematics of this kind of engineering is well advanced, relying heavily on finite-element simulations on large computers. One of the world's most famous damping devices must be the 660-ton steel pendulum suspended from the 92nd to the 87th floor of the skyscraper Taipei 101 in Taiwan. This damper has become a tourist attraction and even has its own mascot, known as the Damper Baby.

It is interesting to consider the implications of linearity and nonlinearity in the three problems we have examined so far. The shape of the first solution, for the linear problem (4.3), is scale independent: if the initial condition is doubled, the solution will double too. The second solution, for the nonlinear problem (4.8), is scale dependent: if the initial condition is doubled, the solution will change shape as well as amplitude, developing even sharper sawtooths. The third solution, for the linear damped oscillator (4.9), is the most interesting from this point of view. Again, linearity implies scale independence, so that doubling the data will double the solution. What is new is that, since the

---

[22]Standard texts on the analysis of vibration include L. Meirovitch, *Elements of Vibration Analysis*, and S. S. Rao, *Mechanical Vibrations*.

wave is decaying as a function of t, the scale independence has a substantive implication: as t varies, the amplitude can change but not the shape. Thus it follows from linearity that the crests of the wave solution to (4.9) must be separated by fixed intervals, and hence that the decay must be exponential.

Let us consider now the mathematics of a general problem of this form, a *second-order constant-coefficient scalar linear homogeneous differential equation*,

$$y'' + \varepsilon y' + \omega^2 y = 0, \tag{4.10}$$

where ε and ω are constants. (Since no initial or boundary conditions have been specified, the classification of (4.10) is fLASH.) As mentioned in the introduction, this is one of the five most important equations of this book, and it will keep reappearing in various contexts. In applications ε will usually be nonnegative, although mathematically $\varepsilon < 0$ and $\varepsilon > 0$ are really the same story — for negating ε is equivalent to negating t, that is, time reversal. None of the formulas or theorems care whether ε is positive or negative.

Motivated by (4.7), let us look for a solution to (4.10) of the form

$$y(t) = e^{rt}$$

for a constant r. Inserting this trial solution in (4.10) gives the condition

$$r^2 + \varepsilon r + \omega^2 = 0,$$

which is a quadratic equation with roots

$$r = -\frac{\varepsilon}{2} \pm \sqrt{\frac{\varepsilon^2}{4} - \omega^2}. \tag{4.11}$$

We call these the **characteristic roots** of (4.10). Equivalently, we could write

$$r = -\frac{\varepsilon}{2} \pm i\sqrt{\omega^2 - \frac{\varepsilon^2}{4}}. \tag{4.12}$$

The product of r_- and r_+ is always ω^2, independently of the value of ε.

For simplicity, let us suppose that ε and ω are real. Then the formula (4.12) is the more useful one if $\varepsilon^2/4 < \omega^2$, i.e., $\varepsilon < 2\omega$, which we call the *underdamped* or *subcritically damped* case. The factor i reveals that solutions are oscillatory. In particular, if $\varepsilon = 0$, (4.12) reproduces the solutions $y = \exp(\pm i\omega t)$ of (4.7). For $\varepsilon > 0$, we get exponentially decaying solutions of the form

$$y(t) = e^{-\varepsilon t/2} \exp\left(\pm it\sqrt{\omega^2 - \frac{\varepsilon^2}{4}}\right). \tag{4.13}$$

This formula explains the decaying wave seen in the solution to (4.9). With $\varepsilon = 0.1$, the decay rate is $e^{-t/20}$, as we can confirm by adding dashed lines to the figure.

```
ep = 0.1; envelope = chebfun(@(t) exp(-ep*t/2),[0 60]);
hold on, plot([envelope, -envelope],'--')
```

Fig. 4.4. Showing the exponential envelope from (4.13)

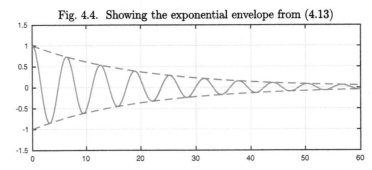

Formula (4.13) also explains the slight increase of the period T above 2π we have noted. Adapting (4.4), we see that the period of the decaying wave (or more precisely of its oscillatory factor) is now

$$T = 2\pi \left/ \sqrt{\omega^2 - \frac{\varepsilon^2}{4}} \right. . \tag{4.14}$$

Thus damping slows down the frequency of oscillation. It is the squaring of ε in this formula that explains why the modification to T in our experiment has been so slight. To leading order, the addition of linear damping does not change the frequency of an oscillating system; the change of frequency is at the second order.[23] An evaluation of (4.14) confirms the value of T reported in the caption of Figure 4.3:

```
om = 1; T = 2*pi/sqrt(om^2 - ep^2/4)
```

```
T = 6.2911
```

Continuing with the assumption that ε and ω^2 in (4.10) are real, suppose on the other hand $\varepsilon^2/4 > \omega^2$, i.e., $\varepsilon > 2\omega$, the *overdamped* or *supercritically damped* case. Now (4.11) becomes more useful than (4.12), and we see that the solutions to (4.10) do not oscillate but grow or decay exponentially. If $\varepsilon > 0$ and $\omega^2 > 0$, they both decay, though at different rates.

Equation (4.10) is a second-order linear equation, and that is why it has two linearly independent solutions and requires two initial conditions to determine a unique solution.[24] If the two values r_+ and r_- of (4.11) or (4.12) are distinct, then the general solution to (4.10) is

$$y(t) = Ae^{r_+t} + Be^{r_-t}. \tag{4.15}$$

---

[23] For this reason engineers often begin an analysis of frequency of vibrations of machines and structures by ignoring damping. The same insensitivity of frequency to damping benefited watchmakers in the days of watches with balance springs, a design method going back to Hooke himself.

[24] Recall that in any vector space, two vectors $\mathbf{v}$ and $\mathbf{w}$ are linearly independent if $A\mathbf{v}+B\mathbf{w} = \mathbf{0}$ holds only with $A = B = 0$. Here, our vectors are functions $y(t)$.

If $\omega^2 = \varepsilon^2/4$, however, or $\varepsilon = 2\omega$, then r_+ and r_- are the same. This is the *critically damped* case, and we have to look elsewhere to find a second linearly independent solution of the ODE. A suitable choice is $y(t) = te^{rt}$, as can be verified by substituting this function directly in (4.10). In this case we accordingly get the general solution

$$y(t) = (A + Bt)e^{rt}. \tag{4.16}$$

Here is a theorem to summarize these observations.

Theorem 4.1. Solution of second-order linear scalar constant-coefficient ODE (fLASH). *The equation*

$$y'' + \varepsilon y' + \omega^2 y = 0 \tag{4.17}$$

has a two-dimensional vector space of solutions. For $\varepsilon < 2\omega$ (subcritical damping) the general solution is

$$y(t) = e^{-\varepsilon t/2}\Big[A\sin\big(t\sqrt{\omega^2 - \varepsilon^2/4}\big) + B\cos\big(t\sqrt{\omega^2 - \varepsilon^2/4}\big)\Big], \tag{4.18}$$

for $\varepsilon > 2\omega$ (supercritical damping) it is

$$y(t) = A\exp\big(-\varepsilon t/2 + t\sqrt{\varepsilon^2/4 - \omega^2}\big) + B\exp\big(-\varepsilon t/2 - t\sqrt{\varepsilon^2/4 - \omega^2}\big), \tag{4.19}$$

and for $\varepsilon = 2\omega$ (critical damping) it is

$$y(t) = (A + Bt)\exp\big(-\varepsilon t/2\big). \tag{4.20}$$

Proof. The solutions described are certainly linearly independent, so all that must be proved is that the dimension of the space of solutions is not greater than 2. This can be derived from the uniqueness statement of Theorem 11.2 if the second-order scalar problem (4.17) is written as a first-order problem in two variables. ∎

Here are three images showing solutions of (4.17) with subcritical, critical, and supercritical damping. Critical damping is plainly the fastest.

```
L = chebop(0,20); L.lbc = [1;0]; om = 1; epep = [0.1 2 10];
for j = 1:3
  subplot(1,3,j); ep = epep(j);
  L.op = @(t,y) diff(y,2) + ep*diff(y) + om^2*y;
  y = L\0; plot(y)
  r1 = -ep/2 + sqrt(ep^2/4-om^2); r2 = -ep/2 - sqrt(ep^2/4-om^2);
end
```

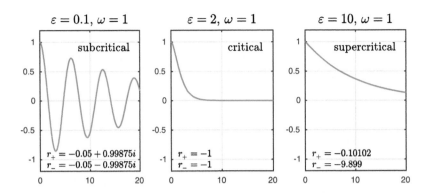

One of the most important and interesting aspects of oscillatory systems is their response to external inputs — the inhomogeneous variant of (4.17). This will be the subject of Chapter 8.

APPLICATION: SKYDIVER

Here is an example adapted from D. B. Meade, "ODE models for the parachute problem," *SIAM Review* 40 (1998), pp. 327–332.

If there were no air resistance, a falling skydiver would experience only the force of gravity: $h''(t) = -g$, where h is height above the earth and $g = 9.8$. (We use MKS units, i.e., meters-kilograms-seconds.) The speed of fall would increase linearly and the height would decrease quadratically.

However, the air resistance quickly becomes significant as the skydiver's speed increases. The atmosphere creates a force called *drag* that opposes gravity. For reasons of fluid mechanics that we will not go into, this force can be reasonably modeled as $F_D = kv^2$, where $v = h'$ is the velocity and k (in units kg/m) depends on properties of the air and the skydiver.[25] The gravity and drag forces are in balance when they have equal magnitudes, giving the condition $mg = kv^2$, where m is the mass of the skydiver. Since there is no net force on the skydiver under this condition, the velocity will not change, and this value $v_T = -\sqrt{mg/k}$ is known as the *terminal velocity*.

If we express Newton's law for the skydiver in terms of the velocity, we have

$$v' = \frac{kv^2}{m} - g = g\left(\frac{v^2}{v_T^2} - 1\right),$$

which is separable. Integration leads to

$$v(t) = -v_T \tanh\left(\frac{gt}{v_T} + C\right)$$

---

[25]Thus the drag force here is different from that of (4.17), which depends just linearly on the velocity. As a rule one sees linear drag for bodies moving slowly through a fluid (laminar flow) and quadratic drag at higher speeds (turbulent flow).

for an arbitrary constant C. Since this is an explicit function of t, v can be integrated again to get $h(t)$, but we will omit that result here and move to numerical solutions for simplicity. A reasonable approximation is $v_T \approx 55$ m/s for the standard "belly-down" position in free fall. This enables us to calculate height and velocity for a dive starting at 4 km altitude.

```
g = 9.8; vT = 55; h0 = 4000;
L = chebop(@(t,h) diff(h,2)-g*(diff(h)^2/vT^2 - 1),[0 75]);
L.lbc = [h0;0]; hfree = L\0; plot(diff(hfree))
```

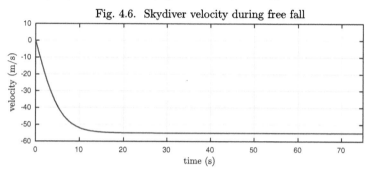

Fig. 4.6. Skydiver velocity during free fall

Terminal velocity is reached in about 15 seconds.

The reason skydivers need parachutes is that, without them, their terminal velocities would be terminal! The function of a parachute is to greatly increase the drag and thereby induce a much smaller terminal velocity, which we may take to be, say, 10 m/s. A typical altitude at which to open the parachute is $h = 800$ m, which occurs for our model at the time

```
tp = roots(hfree-800)
tp = 62.0719
```

So our skydiver can enjoy a whole minute of free fall. Then, with the parachute open, the second phase of her dive is given by

```
vT = 10; h0 = 800;
L = chebop(@(t,h) diff(h,2)-g*(diff(h)^2/vT^2 - 1),tp+[0 90]);
L.lbc = [hfree(tp);deriv(hfree,tp)];
hchute = L\0; plot(diff(hchute))
```

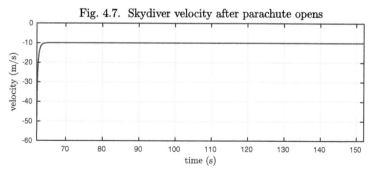

Fig. 4.7. Skydiver velocity after parachute opens

The dive ends with $h = 0$, at time

```
t0 = roots(hchute)
```

```
t0 = 140.8692
```

We can plot the entire course of the dive by concatenating the two phases.

```
h = join(hfree{0,tp},hchute); plot(h)
```

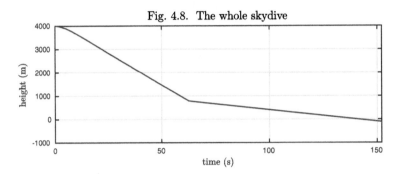

Fig. 4.8. The whole skydive

Taking the derivative gives the velocity as a function of time.

```
plot(diff(h))
```

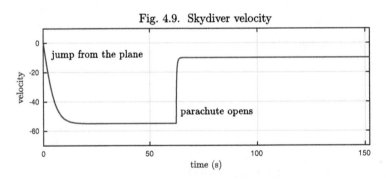

Fig. 4.9. Skydiver velocity

HISTORY. Much of this chapter goes back to the brilliant 17th century rivals Robert Hooke, Christiaan Huygens, and Isaac Newton. The names of Hooke and Newton are associated with the two most famous force laws for F in the equation $F(y) = my''$. Hooke's law puts $F(y)$ proportional to y, leading to simple harmonic motion and elasticity. Huygens studied such oscillations too and was the inventor of the pendulum clock. Newton's law for gravity puts $F(y)$ proportional to y^{-2}, leading to elliptical orbits and cosmology. When y is effectively constant, as with gravity at the surface of the earth, so is the force F — the situation experienced by our skydiver and also by an apple falling from Newton's tree.

OUR FAVORITE REFERENCE. For a salutary view of how ODEs meet reality, see J. C. Dixon, *The Shock Absorber Handbook,* 2nd ed., Wiley, 2007. Chapter 2, on vibration theory, presents the material we have discussed in the vivid context of behavior of motor vehicles. To optimize comfort, passenger cars are usually designed in the underdamped regime, whereas to optimize handling, race cars are closer to critically damped.

SUMMARY OF CHAPTER 4. *The scalar, linear, autonomous second-order ODE $y'' + \varepsilon y' + \omega^2 y = 0$ has a two-dimensional vector space of solutions. If ω is real and $\varepsilon > 0$, all solutions decay exponentially. For $\varepsilon < 2\omega$ (subcritical damping), the solution is an oscillatory function times an exponential envelope, and for $\varepsilon > 2\omega$ (supercritical damping) it is a superposition of two exponentials with different time constants.*

Exercise 4.1. Hooke and Newton elliptical orbits. Taking $y(t)$ to be complex as usual for tracking orbits in a plane, we can write $y'' = -y|y|^{p-1}$ for the classic problem of a point orbiting in a central field. Produce seven plots showing the orbits over $t \in [0, 40]$ emanating from the initial conditions $y(0) = 1$, $y'(0) = 0.5i$ for $p = -2, -1.5, -1, \ldots, 1$; in each case use `axis([-1 1 -1 1])`, `axis square`. The case $p = 1$ corresponds to Hooke's law, and the orbit is an ellipse with center $y = 0$. The case $p = -2$ corresponds to Newton's law of gravitation, and the orbit is an ellipse with one focus at $y = 0$. (V. I. Arnol'd uses the terms *Hooke ellipse* and *Newton ellipse*. If the ellipses are viewed as sets in the complex plane, then the square of a Hooke ellipse is a Newton ellipse.)

Exercise 4.2. Kepler's equal-area law. For a particle in an elliptical orbit in an inverse-square field, the area swept out per unit time is constant. *(a)* If $y(t)$ is an orbit computed as in Exercise 4.1, show mathematically why the command `A = cumsum(imag(diff(y)*conj(y)))` computes a chebfun representing the area $A(t)$ swept out as a function of time t (`cumsum` is Chebfun's indefinite integral operator). *(b)* Perform this calculation and plot the result (with $p = -2$ for the inverse-square force). What is $A(40)$?

Exercise 4.3. Exact equations. Sometimes an ODE is a derivative of an equation of lower order. For example, the equation $y'' + ty' + y = 0$ can be written $(y' + ty)' = 0$. Use this observation to find the analytical solution to this ODE *(a)* in general, and *(b)* with $y(0) = 1$, $y'(0) = 1$.

Exercise 4.4. Falling to earth. Suppose Earth is a uniform sphere of mass M and radius R, and a small body of mass $m \ll M$ is initially motionless at a height $h(0) = h_0$ above the surface and attracted downward by the gravitational force $F = GmM/(R+h)^2$, where G is the universal gravitational constant. *(a)* Write down an ODE IVP whose solution gives $h(t)$ as a function of t. *(b)* Solve it analytically to get a formula for t_c, the time at which the body hits the surface. *(c)* Rewrite this formula in terms of explicit numbers using the approximate values $M = 6 \times 10^{24}$ kg, $R = 6 \times 10^6$ m, and $G = 6 \times 10^{-11}\mathrm{m^3kg^{-1}s^{-2}}$. *(d)* What height h_0 leads to $t_c = 1$ minute?

Exercise 4.5. Second solution for critical damping. Confirm analytically that $y(t) = te^{rt}$ is a solution of (4.10) in the critically damped case $\varepsilon = 2\omega$.

Exercise 4.6. Critical damping example. (a) What value $\omega = \omega_c$ in (4.9) gives critical damping? *(b)* Fix ω at this critical value and compute solutions with the ε parameter

0.1 of (4.9) taking values 0.09, 0.1, and 0.11. Superimpose semilogy plots of $|y(t)|$ against t for these three choices. Comment on why one of the three curves has a shape different from the others, and on why two of them have nearly the same slope.

Exercise 4.7. A weak nonlinear spring. Suppose a particle with rest position $y = 0$ is subject to an asymmetric restoring force $y'' = -y \exp(-y)$. *(a)* Plot $y(t)$ for $t \in [0, 200]$ for initial conditions $y(0) = 0$ and $y'(0) = 0.5$, 1, and 1.5. *(b)* Define the idea of an "escape velocity" for this system for trajectories beginning at $y = 0$. Based on the experiments of *(a)*, and other experiments if you wish, what can you say about its numerical value? *(c)* By thinking in terms of kinetic and potential energy, determine the escape velocity analytically. (The potential energy can be defined as the work required to bring the particle in from ∞, where work is defined as an integral of force times distance.)

Exercise 4.8. Acceleration of the skydiver. Repeat the calculation for the skydiver application and plot the acceleration as a function of time. What is the maximum acceleration in MKS units, and as a multiple of the gravitational acceleration g? This number is unrealistically large, and would probably kill the skydiver. Explain in a general way what kind of effects you think have been omitted from the model that in practice would make the acceleration not so extreme.

Exercise 4.9. Hard nonlinearity. Most springs get stiffer at high displacements. To see the effect on the period T, compute and plot T for the equation $y'' + y + y^3 = 0$ for solutions with initial velocity $y'(0) = 0$ and initial amplitudes $y(0) = 0.0, 0.1, \ldots, 5$. Explain why the period changes as $y(0)$ increases.

Exercise 4.10. Friction and sliding of a penny. A penny of mass 1 sits at position $y(t)$, starting motionless at $y(0) = 0$, on a wooden board inclined at angle θ from the horizontal. The board is slowly tilted up according to $\theta = 0.1t$ for $t \in [0, 10]$. The gravitational force downward on the penny can be resolved into $f_t = \sin(\theta)$ in the y direction along the board and $f_n = \cos(\theta)$ normal to the board. Meanwhile there is a frictional force $f_f = -\mu_k f_n$ on the penny, where $\mu_k = 0.5$ is a coefficient of kinetic friction, so long as the penny is sliding. On the other hand if $f_t \leq \mu_s f_n$, where $\mu_s = 1$ is a coefficient of static friction, then the penny is stationary, with $f_f = -f_t$. *(a)* Formulate this problem as an IVP in Chebfun and compute and plot the solution $y(t)$. Where is the penny at $t = 10$? How many times continuously differentiable is the trajectory $y(t)$? *(b)* Repeat both parts of *(a)* under the assumption $\mu_s = \mu_k = 0.5$.

Exercise 4.11. Nondimensionalization. Show how, by introducing a variable u equal to a suitable multiple of y, the equation $y'' + ay' + by = 0$ can be reduced to $u'' + \varepsilon u' + u = 0$. What is ε in terms of a and b?

5. Boundary-value problems

Now it is time to open the big door that will double the richness of our study of ODEs. With second- and higher-order equations, since they need more than one boundary condition, we have the prospect of not just IVPs but also **BVPs**, that is, **boundary-value problems**.

Boundary-value problems are everywhere in the sciences. Broadly speaking, ODEs whose independent variables represent time are usually IVPs modeling *dynamics*. ODEs whose independent variables represent space are usually BVPs modeling *equilibria*.[26] These differences are fundamental, and in this book we will usually change the independent variable from t to x when working with a BVP. In particular, y' and y'' will now denote dy/dx and d^2y/dx^2 instead of dy/dt and d^2y/dt^2. As mentioned in a footnote in Chapter 1, we will also plot solutions of BVPs in blue instead of green.

As our first example of a BVP, here is the solution of

$$y'' = -y, \quad x \in [0, 60], \ y(0) = 1, \ y(60) = 0. \tag{5.1}$$

The value of y at $x = 0$ is specified, but not its derivative. A solution is found to match the value of y specified at the other end of the interval.

```
L = chebop(0,60); L.op = @(x,y) diff(y,2) + y;
L.lbc = 1; L.rbc = 0;
y = L\0; plot(y)
```

---

[26]Of course, there are exceptions. A notable area where BVPs arise with a time variable is *control theory*, in which the engineer seeks to make a system attain certain function values at certain times. The Application of Chapter 16 is in this category.

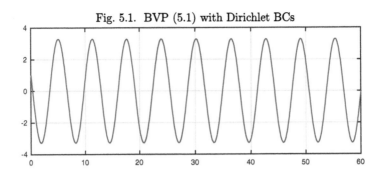

Fig. 5.1. BVP (5.1) with Dirichlet BCs

Here is the solution to another BVP, in which the condition at the right involves the derivative y' rather than the value of y itself,

$$y'' = -y, \quad x \in [0, 60], \ y(0) = 1, \ y'(60) = 0. \tag{5.2}$$

A condition involving y is called a **Dirichlet** condition, and a condition involving y' is called a **Neumann** condition. A condition that mixes both y and y' is called a **Robin** condition. (To specify a Robin condition in Chebfun, such as $y'(60) - y(60) = 1$, for example, we could write `L.rbc = @(y) diff(y)-y-1`.)

```
L.rbc = 'neumann';
y = L\0; plot(y)
```

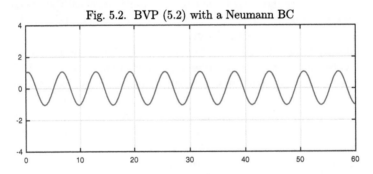

Fig. 5.2. BVP (5.2) with a Neumann BC

The significance of boundary conditions becomes more striking if we look at equation (4.10) with $\omega^2 < 0$, where one solution exponentially grows and the other exponentially decays. To illustrate, we revert to the Dirichlet condition of (5.1) and take $\varepsilon = 0$, $\omega^2 = -1$ in (4.10),

$$y'' = y, \quad x \in [0, 60], \ y(0) = y(60) = 1. \tag{5.3}$$

Note that the solution shown below is close to zero except near the endpoints, where it is far from zero in two regions known as **boundary layers**. Here we begin to see strongly the difference between IVPs and BVPs. This curve in principle might have been the solution of an IVP if the initial data had been chosen just right, but such a solution would hardly be likely to arise in practice.

On the contrary, from the curve it is clear that this solution is probably being driven by conditions imposed at the two ends. We shall consider boundary layers in detail in Chapter 20.

```
L.op = @(x,y) diff(y,2) - y;
L.lbc = 1; L.rbc = 1;
y = L\0; plot(y)
```

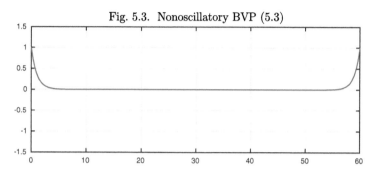

Fig. 5.3. Nonoscillatory BVP (5.3)

For the problem above, the characteristic roots (4.11)–(4.12) are $r_{\pm} = \pm 1$. The solution we have plotted can be approximated very closely as

$$y(x) \approx e^{-x} + e^{x-60}. \qquad (5.4)$$

See Exercise 5.1.

Suppose we are given a second-order constant-coefficient scalar linear homogeneous ODE BVP of the form (4.10). To solve it, following Theorem 4.1, we would look for a function in the vector space spanned by $e^{r_+ x}$ and $e^{r_- x}$, or e^{rx} and xe^{rx} in the critically damped case, that satisfies the boundary conditions. Just as in the last chapter, a small variation of this approach applies to an inhomogeneous problem of the form

$$y'' + \varepsilon y' + \omega^2 y = f(x), \qquad (5.5)$$

where f is a given forcing function. If we can find a particular solution y_p to (5.5), then the general solution is obtained by adding elements from this two-dimensional vector space. When f is simple, a particular solution can often be obtained by inspection or the method of undetermined coefficients.

Here is an example. Suppose we put the linear function $f(x) = (x - 20)/20$ on the right-hand side of (5.3),

$$y'' = y + (x - 20)/20, \quad x \in [0, 60], \ y(0) = y(60) = 0. \qquad (5.6)$$

A particular solution to this equation is $y_p(x) = -(x - 20)/20$, and from here one can readily obtain a formula for the solution plotted below (Exercise 5.2).

```
L.op = @(x,y) diff(y,2) - y; L.lbc = 0; L.rbc = 0;
rhs = chebfun('(x-20)/20',[0 60]);
y = L\rhs; plot(y)
```

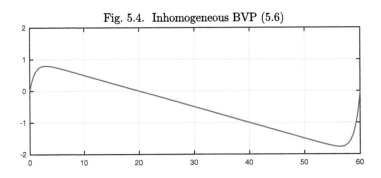

Fig. 5.4. Inhomogeneous BVP (5.6)

For a nonlinear variation, let us change the term y in (5.6) to y^3,

$$y'' = y^3 + (x - 20)/20, \quad x \in [0, 60], \ y(0) = y(60) = 0. \tag{5.7}$$

The resulting curve is an interesting variation on Figure 5.4. The zero of $y(x)$ near $x = 20$, incidentally, is not exactly at $x = 20$, more like 19.99999999985.

```
L.op = @(x,y) diff(y,2) - y^3;
y = L\rhs; plot(y)
```

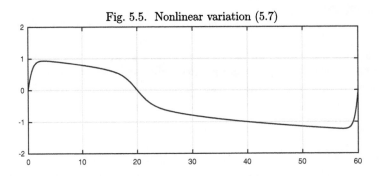

Fig. 5.5. Nonlinear variation (5.7)

Returning to linear problems, let us explore some of the variety of boundary conditions that may arise. Here is an *advection-diffusion* equation:

$$0.02y'' + y' + y = 0, \quad x \in [0, 1]. \tag{5.8}$$

First let us solve it with two Dirichlet boundary conditions $y(0) = 0$, $y(1) = 1$.

```
L = chebop(0,1); L.op = @(x,y) 0.02*diff(y,2) + diff(y) + y;
L.lbc = 0; L.rbc = 1;
y = L\0; plot(y)
```

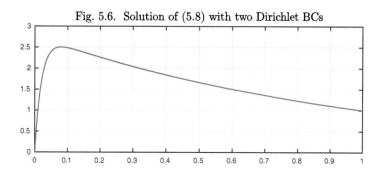

Fig. 5.6. Solution of (5.8) with two Dirichlet BCs

Next we change the right boundary condition to Neumann form, $y'(1) = 1$.

```
L.rbc = @(u) diff(u)-1;
y = L\0; plot(y)
```

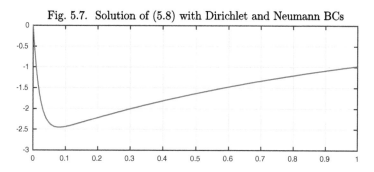

Fig. 5.7. Solution of (5.8) with Dirichlet and Neumann BCs

Here we couple the two endpoints with the conditions $y(0) = 1$, $y'(1) = -y'(0)$.

```
L.lbc = 1; L.rbc = []; L.bc = @(x,y) deriv(y,1) + deriv(y,0);
y = L\0; plot(y)
```

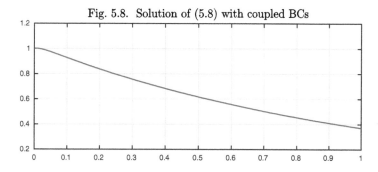

Fig. 5.8. Solution of (5.8) with coupled BCs

Not all "boundary" conditions must be based at the boundaries. For example, we might seek a solution with $y(0) = 1$ and $\int_0^1 y(x)dx = 0$, so that y has mean zero. A nonstandard condition like this is sometimes called a *side condition*.

```
L.bc = @(x,y) sum(y);
y = L\0; plot(y)
```

Fig. 5.9. Solution of (5.8) with an integral condition

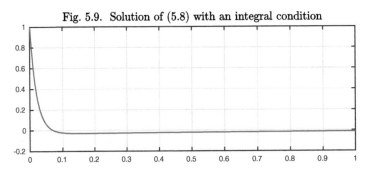

So far we have considered second-order equations. With equations of third order or higher, there is the possibility of mixing boundary and interior conditions. For example, here is the solution to a third-order problem with boundary conditions at three distinct points, marked by dots in the plot for emphasis.

$$y''' + y = 1, \quad x \in [0,2], \ y(0) = 0, \ y(1) = y(2) = 1. \tag{5.9}$$

```
L = chebop(0,2); L.op = @(x,y) diff(y,3) + y;
L.lbc = 0; L.rbc = 1; L.bc = @(x,y) y(1)-1;
y = L\1; plot(y), hold on, plot(0:2,y(0:2),'.')
```

Fig. 5.10. Solution of 3rd-order eq. (5.9) with interior condition

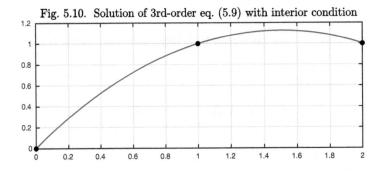

Throughout this discussion we have avoided mentioning existence and uniqueness. This is because these matters are not straightforward for BVPs, even linear ones, because of the possible presence of *eigenvalues*. This will be the subject of the next chapter. For nonlinear BVPs there are further nonuniqueness possibilities that are both interesting and scientifically important, as we will explore in Chapters 16–18. As an example of nonuniqueness in a nonlinear BVP, consider the solution that Chebfun finds to the nonlinear equation

$$\frac{1}{2}y'' + y^2 = 1, \quad x \in [-1,1], \ y(-1) = y(1) = 0. \tag{5.10}$$

```
N = chebop(-1,1); N.op = @(x,y) .5*diff(y,2) + y^2;
N.lbc = 0; N.rbc = 0;
y = N\1; plot(y)
```

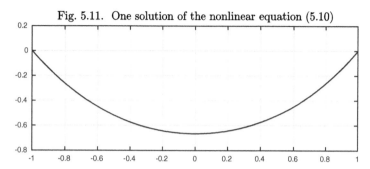

Fig. 5.11. One solution of the nonlinear equation (5.10)

If we ask Chebfun to look for a solution starting from the initial guess $y(x) = \cos(\pi x/2)$ rather than its default initial guess $y(x) = 0$, however, a different and equally valid solution is found, which we superimpose on the same plot.

```
N.init = chebfun('cos(pi*x/2)');
y = N\1; hold on, plot(y)
```

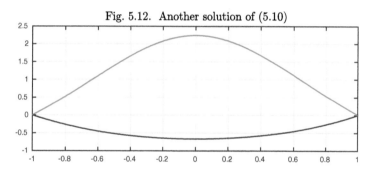

Fig. 5.12. Another solution of (5.10)

Does (5.10) have exactly these two solutions, or are there more? There is no general theorem that gives an answer to such questions, but we shall make some progress on them in Chapter 16.

APPLICATION: BEAM THEORY AND THE STRENGTH OF SPAGHETTI

In physics and engineering an idealized *string* can sustain a tension but has no stiffness — no resistance to bending — and this leads to second-order ODEs. This is where we would start, say, in studying the sounds produced by a guitar. An idealized *beam*, on the other hand, has stiffness and resists bending, even though we still model it as a one-dimensional object. This leads to fourth-order ODEs, and the same equations apply to the girders of the Eiffel tower as to a piece of dried spaghetti.

In the simplest setting, omitting dimensional constants and assuming infinitesimal deflections, the equation takes the form

$$y''''(x) = f(x), \tag{5.11}$$

where $f(x)$ is the vertical force applied at position x along a beam and $y(x)$ is the vertical deflection at that point. The derivatives of y can be interpreted as follows:

$y(x)$ and $y'(x)$: position and slope,

$y''(x)$: bending moment, whose square is energy density,

$y'''(x)$: vertical force,

$y''''(x)$: force density.

In a time-dependent problem, a nonzero value of $y''''(x)$ would be associated with vertical acceleration $-y''''(x)$, but we are considering here the static problem. Equation (5.11) represents the condition that the force caused by the bending of the beam is balanced by an external force $f(x)$, so there is no acceleration.

For example, suppose a beam of length 2 and weight density 1 is clamped at $x = \pm 1$,

$$y'''' = -1, \quad y(-1) = y'(-1) = y(1) = y'(1) = 0. \tag{5.12}$$

An image shows that the beam sags a little in the middle (the deflection is $1/24$). We plot y with a thicker line to suggest stiffness. This and the next few calculations, incidentally, can be done on paper (Exercise 5.4), though that would change if complications were introduced such as variable coefficients.

```
L = chebop(-1,1); L.op = @(x,y) diff(y,4);
L.lbc = [0;0]; L.rbc = [0;0];
y = L\-1; d1 = norm(y,inf); plot(y)
```

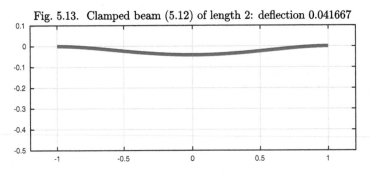

Fig. 5.13. Clamped beam (5.12) of length 2: deflection 0.041667

Next, instead of clamping the beam at $x = 1$, let us fix the position there but not the slope. In such a case one has what is called a *natural boundary condition*, $y''(1) = 0$. The deflection of the beam at the midpoint doubles, and the maximum deflection, which is now located to the right of the midpoint, increases by a factor of about 2.079. (The exact maximal deflection is $(39 + 55\sqrt{33})/4096$.)

```
L.rbc = @(y) [y; diff(y,2)];
y = L\-1; d2 = norm(y,inf); plot(y)
```

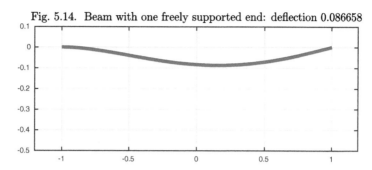

Fig. 5.14. Beam with one freely supported end: deflection 0.086658

Alternatively, we can let both ends be free. Symmetry is restored, and the maximum deflection is in the middle again, with value 5/24.

```
L.lbc = @(y) [y; diff(y,2)];
y = L\-1; d3 = norm(y,inf); plot(y)
```

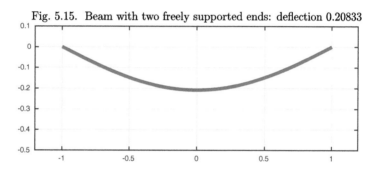

Fig. 5.15. Beam with two freely supported ends: deflection 0.20833

This brings us to the spaghetti problem. Here in Oxford, we bought a pack of spaghetti at a local newsagent. We taped some pennies[27] to the end of a piece, making a cantilever that can be modeled as a massless beam clamped at $x = 0$ with a weight w applied at $x = d$:

$$y'''' = 0, \quad y(0) = y'(0) = y''(d) = 0, \ y'''(d) = w. \tag{5.13}$$

```
d = 2; L = chebop(0,d); L.op = @(x,y) diff(y,4);
L.lbc = [0; 0]; L.rbc = @(y) [diff(y,2); diff(y,3)-0.1];
y = L\0; d4 = norm(y,inf); plot(y)
penny = d+1i*(y(end)-.01)+.08*(chebfun('exp(1i*t)',[0, 2*pi])-1i);
hold on, fill(real(penny),imag(penny))
```

---

[27]Conveniently for our experiment, the British 2p coin weighs exactly the same as two pennies.

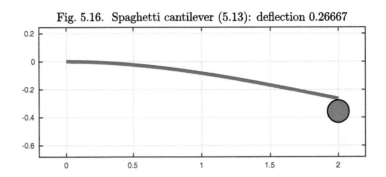

Fig. 5.16. Spaghetti cantilever (5.13): deflection 0.26667

We could have measured these deflections for various cantilever lengths d and numbers of pennies, but it seemed more fun to investigate, for a given number of pennies, what is the length of cantilever at which the spaghetti breaks? With up to four pennies no breaking occurs — at 26 cm, the piece of spaghetti is too short. But for $5, 6, \ldots, 16$ pennies we found these breaking lengths in cm:

```
d = [17.1 14.6 12.9 8.8 9.0 7.5 6.7 6.6 5.2 5.3 4.7 4.4];
```

Here is a plot of the data, showing how the breaking weight decreases as the length d increases.

```
xx = linspace(4.7,17.5); plot(xx,80./xx), hold on
plot(d,5:16,'.')
```

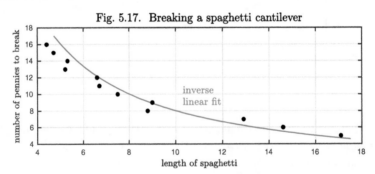

Fig. 5.17. Breaking a spaghetti cantilever

As the red line shows, the relationship appears to be inverse linear, and we explain this as follows. A piece of spaghetti breaks when its curvature $|y''(x)|$ exceeds a critical value for some x. From calculation or analysis of (5.13), one finds that, as a function of d, y scales as wd^3, where w again is the weight. This means that y' scales as wd^2, and y'' scales as wd. If wd is to remain bounded as $d \to \infty$, we must have $w = O(d^{-1})$.

Returning from spaghetti to mathematics for a moment, it is interesting to note that the solutions of $u'''' = 0$ are precisely the polynomials of degree ≤ 3. Thus the study of idealized beams with no body forces $f(x)$ is equivalent to the study of cubic polynomials that satisfy various boundary conditions. This connection is famous in numerical analysis, where the classic wooden flexible rulers used for designing shapes in the aircraft and shipbuilding industries evolved into the mathematical *splines* used all across computational science and engineering.

HISTORY. Beam theory goes back to Euler and Jacob Bernoulli in the mid-18th century. It was later that the explicit study of boundary-value problems became a field of mathematics in its own right with the investigations of *Sturm–Liouville problems* in the 1830s by Charles Sturm and Joseph Liouville. French mathematics had a period of extraordinary productivity following the French Revolution and Napoleonic wars, with leading figures including Fourier (born 1768), Poisson (1781), Cauchy (1789), Sturm (1803), and Liouville (1809).

OUR FAVORITE REFERENCE. A standard work among numerical analysts is Ascher, Mattheij, and Russell, *Numerical Solution of Boundary Value Problems for Ordinary Differential Equations,* SIAM, 1995 (first published in 1988). Its appealing concrete style is well established by Section I.2 on p. 7, which begins, "In this section we have collected 22 instances of BVPs which arise in a variety of application areas."

SUMMARY OF CHAPTER 5. *When an ODE is of order $d \geq 2$, it will normally have a d-dimensional solution space, making it possible for different boundary conditions to be specified at different points. In the simplest case $d = 2$, we get a two-point boundary-value problem. Problems of elasticity and solid mechanics lead to fourth-order equations. Existence and uniqueness of solutions are not as straightforward for BVPs, even linear ones, as for IVPs. Nonlinear BVPs may have multiple solutions.*

Exercise 5.1. BVPs and IVPs.[28]   *(a)* Determine analytically the exact solution to (5.3). How much does it differ from the approximation (5.4)? *(b)* As remarked in the text, though a curve may be "obviously" the solution to a BVP, in principle it could equally have been the solution to an IVP. For this problem (5.3), what initial condition on $y'(0)$ would be needed to achieve the same solution? *(c)* If that initial condition is multiplied by 0.99, is the resulting value $y(60)$ less than or greater than Avogadro's number?

Exercise 5.2. Exact solution to (5.6). *(a)* Derive a formula for the exact solution to (5.6). *(b)* Do the same for the case where the right-hand side is changed to $(x - 20)^2/400$.

Exercise 5.3. Sixth-order BVP. The ODE $y^{(6)} - ay' + y = 0$, $x \in [-4, 4]$, where $a \in [0, 2]$ is a parameter, has boundary conditions $y(-4) = y'(-4) = y''(-4) = 0$, $y(4) = 1$, $y'(4) = y''(4) = 0$. If $y(0) = 0$, what is a?

Exercise 5.4. Exact beam formulas. Find exact formulas for the solutions presented in Figures *(a)* 5.13, *(b)* 5.15, and *(c)* 5.14. The reason for this ordering is that the solutions of Figures 5.13 and 5.15 are simpler because of symmetry.

Exercise 5.5. Exact spaghetti formula. Find an exact formula for the solution plotted in Figure 5.16.

---

[28]This exercise is related to the numerical method for solving ODE BVPs known as *shooting,* and highlights some of the challenges of that method. We shall say more about shooting in Chapter 16.

Exercise 5.6. Cubic and quartic dependence. It is readily confirmed that on an interval of length d, the deflections of Figures 5.13–5.15 scale as $O(d^4)$, whereas in Figure 5.16, as noted in the text, it is $O(d^3)$. Thus for large enough d the clamped beam will sag more than the cantilever. Yet the clamped beam is supported at *both* ends, so surely it should bend less. Resolve this paradox.

Exercise 5.7. Blasius equation. A classic nonlinear BVP due to Blasius is $2y''' + yy'' = 0$, $y(0) = y'(0) = 0$, $y'(\infty) = 1$. Solve this with Chebfun, replacing ∞ by 10. Plot the result and report the values of $y''(0)$ and $y(10) - 10$, both of which are good approximations to what one would get on $[0, \infty)$. (For more information see J. P. Boyd, "The Blasius function in the complex plane," *Experimental Mathematics* 8 (1999), pp. 381–394.)

Exercise 5.8. Eliminating inhomogeneous boundary conditions. Suppose we have a linear inhomogeneous BVP with inhomogeneous boundary data. To be specific, let us say it is a second-order problem $Ly = f$, $y(0) = \alpha$, $y(1) = \beta$. *(a)* Let y_1 and y_2 be two linearly independent solutions to the homogeneous problem and let y_{left}, y_{inner}, and y_{right} be particular solutions with $f = \beta = 0$, $\alpha = \beta = 0$, and $f = \alpha = 0$, respectively. Write expressions for a particular solution of the BVP and for the general solution. *(b)* A different approach is as follows. Let Y be *any* smooth function that satisfies $Y(0) = \alpha$ and $Y(1) = \beta$; Y does not have to satisfy the differential equation. Show how the general solution of the BVP can be derived using Y.

Exercise 5.9. Water droplet. The height of the surface of a water droplet satisfies $y'' = (y - 1)(1 + (y')^2)^{1.5}$ with $y(\pm 1) = 0$. What is the height at the midpoint $x = 0$?

Exercise 5.10. Nonlinear problems and Newton iteration. Chebfun solves linear BVPs by solving linear systems of equations obtained by discretizing in x, as described in Appendix A. For nonlinear BVPs, there is an additional Newton iteration involved, discussed in Appendix A and also briefly in Chapter 16. *(a)* Rerun the problem of equation (5.3) and Figure 5.3 using `tic` and `toc` to measure how long the computation takes. (As with all timing experiments, do this several times to make sure the numbers have settled down.) Plot the solution y on a semilog scale and also report the length of the chebfun as in Exercise 1.6. *(b)* Now do the same calculations again but with the right-hand side of (5.3) changed from y to $y^{1.01}$, and superimpose the new solution curve y on the same plot. How is the computing time affected? How is the length of the chebfun affected? *(c)* Show the outputs that result when L is executed without a semicolon for these two computations. Note the indication that in part *(b)*, Chebfun has determined that the operator is nonlinear and must be treated by different numerical methods.

6. Eigenvalues of linear BVPs

The first BVP of the last chapter, equation (5.1), can be written

$$y'' + by = 0, \quad x \in [0, 60], \ y(0) = 1, \ y(60) = 0 \tag{6.1}$$

with $b = 1$, and the solution had amplitude about 3.3. Look what happens if b is reduced by just 1%, to 0.99.

```
b = 0.99; L = chebop(0,60); L.op = @(x,y) diff(y,2) + b*y;
L.lbc = 1; L.rbc = 0;
y = L\0; plot(y)
```

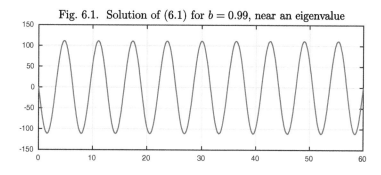

Fig. 6.1. Solution of (6.1) for $b = 0.99$, near an eigenvalue

The amplitude has increased to 111.3! With $b = 0.9897$, it is about 16606, and with $b = (19\pi/60)^2 \approx 0.98970199$, it reaches "infinity": the BVP has no solution.

What is happening is that the solution depends on a division by a number that is close to zero. In this chapter we will explore the mathematics of situations like this. For a simple problem like (6.1), the algebra is elementary, but the implications, including the phenomenon of resonance for time-dependent partial differential equations (see Chapter 22), are far-reaching.

Let's begin with the elementary algebra. From equation (4.5), we know that the general solution of (6.1) is

$$y(x) = A\sin(kx) + B\cos(kx)$$

with $k = \sqrt{b}$. The boundary conditions in (6.1) correspond to the equations

$$B = 1, \quad A\sin(60\sqrt{b}) + B\cos(60\sqrt{b}) = 0.$$

This can be regarded as a 2×2 matrix problem for the unknowns A and B, an especially easy one since the first equation is trivial. The solution is

$$B = 1, \quad A = -\cot(60\sqrt{b}),$$

where $\cot x = \cos x/\sin x$ as always. Here is the value of A for $b = 0.99$.

```
b = 0.99; A = -cot(60*sqrt(b))
```

```
A = -111.2836
```

And here it is for $b = 0.9897$.

```
b = 0.9897; A = -cot(60*sqrt(b))
```

```
A = 1.6606e+04
```

With $b = (19\pi/60)^2$, we get $60\sqrt{b} = 19\pi$, and the cotangent is infinite. Likewise it would be infinite with $b = (j\pi/60)^2$ for any positive integer j.

We are seeing here the phenomenon of eigenvalues of a differential operator with boundary conditions. To frame the matter more generally, let L be the linear operator $L : y \mapsto y''$ on $[0, 60]$ and let us consider the problem

$$Ly = y'' = \lambda y + f, \quad x \in [0, 60], \ y(0) = \alpha, \ y(60) = \beta, \qquad (6.2)$$

where λ is a given number and f is a function of x. It is clear that regardless of the choices of f, α, and β there can be no unique solution of (6.2) if there exists a nonzero function $v(t)$ that satisfies the homogeneous equation

$$Lv = v'' = \lambda v, \quad v(0) = v(60) = 0. \qquad (6.3)$$

The reason is that any multiple of v could be added to y, and the result would still satisfy (6.2). Such a function is called an **eigenfunction** of L, and λ is the corresponding **eigenvalue**. Another way to say it is that an eigenvalue of a linear operator L is a number λ such that the operator $L - \lambda I$, acting on functions satisfying the homogeneous boundary conditions, has a nontrivial nullspace. (Here I denotes the identity operator, mapping a function y to itself.) An eigenfunction v of L is a nonzero function in this nullspace. Note that any nonzero multiple of an eigenfunction is also an eigenfunction for the same λ.

Let's do an experiment to scan systematically for eigenvalues of the operator L of (6.2). Since λ is the negative of b in (6.1), the eigenvalues will be negative numbers, and the smallest will be quite close to zero. Here we arbitrarily pick boundary conditions $y(0) = e$ and $y(60) = \pi$ and the forcing function $f(x) = \exp(-(x - 10)^2)$, and we solve the ODE successively with $\lambda = -0.03000, -0.02998, -0.02996, \ldots, 0$. For each value of λ we plot a dot representing $\max_{x \in [0,60]} |y(x)|$.

```
f = chebfun('exp(-(x-10)^2)',[0 60]); L.lbc = exp(1); L.rbc = pi;
for lambda = -0.03:.0002:0
  L.op = @(x,y) diff(y,2) - lambda*y;
  y = L\f; plot(lambda,norm(y,inf),'.'), hold on
end
```

Fig. 6.2. $\max_x |y(x)|$ for solutions to (6.2) with various values of λ

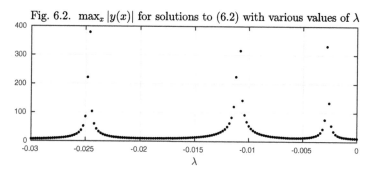

The evidence is clear: there are three eigenvalues of L in this range, lying near -0.003, -0.01, and -0.025. Here are plots of the solutions $y(x)$ for these values of λ.

```
f = chebfun('exp(-(x-10)^2)',[0 60]); llam = [-.003 -.01 -.025];
for j = 1:3
  lambda = llam(j); L.op = @(x,y) diff(y,2) - lambda*y;
  subplot(1,3,j), plot(L\f)
end
```

Fig. 6.3. Three large solutions of (6.2)

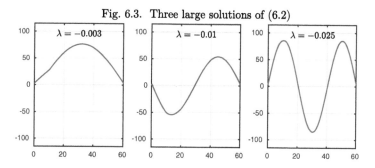

The amplitudes of all three functions are on the order of 100, and we could have made them larger by estimating the eigenvalues more accurately. Just as the three values of λ approximate the first three eigenvalues of L (i.e., the three smallest eigenvalues in absolute value), the three functions approximate multiples of the corresponding eigenfunctions. Note that these curves have 1, 2, and 3 humps, respectively, separated by 0, 1, and 2 interior zeros, called **nodes**. The property that the jth eigenfunction of L has exactly $j - 1$ nodes is typical of eigenfunctions for a wide range of differential operators.[29]

Eigenvalues and eigenfunctions are much too important for us to have to find them by "scanning values of λ"! Chebfun computes these quantities directly with the `eigs` command. We can find the first five eigenvalues of L like this.

```
L.op = @(x,y) diff(y,2); sort(eigs(L,5),'descend')'
ans =
    -0.0027    -0.0110    -0.0247    -0.0439    -0.0685
```

To get eigenfunctions as well as eigenvalues we can type

```
[V,D] = eigs(L,5); llam = diag(D);
[llam,ii] = sort(llam,'descend'); V = V(:,ii);
```

A plot of the first three eigenfunctions shows convincing approximations of multiples of the curves above.[30]

```
for j = 1:3
  subplot(1,3,j), plot(V(:,j))
end
```

Fig. 6.4. First three eigenfunctions of (6.3)

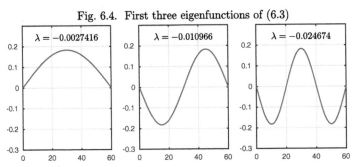

From these images it appears that the jth eigenfunction consists of the sine function scaled so that exactly j lobes, i.e., $j/2$ periods, fit in the interval $[0, 60]$,

$$v_j(t) = \sin(j\pi t/60), \quad j = 1, 2, \ldots . \qquad (6.4)$$

---

[29] In particular this holds for the self-adjoint equation $(p(x)y')' + q(x)y = \lambda y$ on an interval $[a, b]$ with homogeneous Dirichlet, Neumann, or Robin boundary conditions, where p' and q are continuous real functions and $p(x) > 0$. Such problems are the subject of Sturm–Liouville theory.

[30] As mentioned earlier, eigenfunctions are only defined up to multiplicative constants. Those returned by Chebfun are scaled to have square integral equal to 1, a normalization that determines their shape apart from an arbitrary choice of sign.

Substituting this trial solution in (6.3) confirms that it is indeed an eigenfunction. The associated eigenvalue comes out as

$$\lambda_j = -(j\pi/60)^2, \quad j = 1, 2, \ldots, \tag{6.5}$$

and this formula enables us to confirm the five numbers computed above,

```
-((1:5)*pi/60).^2
ans =
   -0.0027   -0.0110   -0.0247   -0.0439   -0.0685
```

The eigenfunctions of L are **orthogonal**, which means that the number

$$a_{ij} = \int_0^{60} v_i(x) v_j(x) dx \tag{6.6}$$

is zero whenever $i \neq j$.[31] To see why, consider two arbitrary functions v_i and v_j satisfying the homogeneous boundary conditions. Using integration by parts, we compute

$$\int_0^{60} (Lv_i(x)) v_j(x) dx = \int_0^{60} v_i''(x) v_j(x) dx = -\int_0^{60} v_i'(x) v_j'(x) dx,$$

where we have discarded boundary terms that are zero because of the boundary conditions on v_j. A second integration by parts exploiting the zero boundary conditions on v_i shows that this is equal to

$$\int_0^{60} v_i(x) v_j''(x) dx = \int_0^{60} v_i(x) (Lv_j(x)) dx.$$

Thus we have

$$\int_0^{60} (Lv_i) v_j dx = \int_0^{60} v_i (Lv_j) dx. \tag{6.7}$$

An operator satisfying this property for arbitrary functions v_i and v_j is said to be **self-adjoint**. Now suppose v_i and v_j are eigenfunctions of a self-adjoint operator L corresponding to eigenvalues λ_i and λ_j with $\lambda_i \neq \lambda_j$. Then (6.7) becomes

$$\lambda_i \int_0^{60} v_i v_j dx = \lambda_j \int_0^{60} v_i v_j dx,$$

and if $\lambda_i \neq \lambda_j$, this implies that v_i and v_j must be orthogonal. We shall repeat this calculation in greater generality for Theorem 7.1 in the next chapter.

Let us verify orthogonality numerically for the operator L of (6.2). The object **V** computed above by `eigs` is a *quasimatrix* of dimensions $\infty \times 5$, whose five "columns" are the functions $v_1, \ldots, v_5$. The object $\mathbf{V}^T\mathbf{V}$ is the product of the $5 \times \infty$ transpose of **V** with **V** itself, that is, the 5×5 matrix of entries a_{ij} defined by (6.6), $1 \leq i, j \leq 5$, known as a *Gram matrix*. Orthogonality of the eigenfunctions is confirmed by the fact that this matrix has zero entries off the diagonal.

---

[31]Eigenvectors of real symmetric matrices are also orthogonal when they correspond to distinct eigenvalues. The proofs are closely related.

```
A = V'*V

A =
    1.0000    0.0000    0.0000    0.0000   -0.0000
    0.0000    1.0000    0.0000   -0.0000   -0.0000
    0.0000    0.0000    1.0000   -0.0000    0.0000
    0.0000   -0.0000   -0.0000    1.0000   -0.0000
   -0.0000   -0.0000    0.0000   -0.0000    1.0000
```

The fact that the entries on the diagonal are equal to 1, making **A** the identity matrix, indicates that the eigenfunctions are not just orthogonal but **orthonormal**, a consequence of the normalization mentioned in footnote 30 (p. 66).

Eigenvalue problems are associated with homogeneous boundary conditions, because they are all about identifying nontrivial solutions of the homogeneous problem. It does not make sense, for example, to specify $v(0) = 1$ for an eigenvalue problem. A variation that does make sense, however, is to change a homogeneous boundary condition from Dirichlet to Neumann form. For example, here is what happens if we change the right-hand boundary condition of (6.3) from $v(60) = 0$ to $v'(60) = 0$.

```
L.rbc = 'neumann'; sort(eigs(L,5),'descend')'

ans =
   -0.0007   -0.0062   -0.0171   -0.0336   -0.0555
```

The eigenfunctions have zero slope at the right boundary.

```
[V,D] = eigs(L,5); llam = diag(D);
[llam,ii] = sort(llam,'descend'); V = V(:,ii);
for j = 1:3
  subplot(1,3,j), plot(V(:,j))
end
```

Fig. 6.5. Eigenfunctions with a Neumann BC

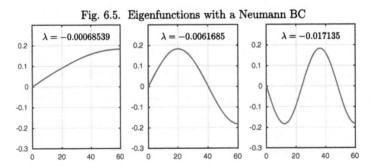

The images reveal $1/2, 3/2, 5/2, \ldots$ lobes of the sine function scaled to $[0, 60]$, suggesting the general formula

$$v_j(x) = \sin((j - \tfrac{1}{2})\pi x/60), \quad j = 1, 2, 3, \ldots. \tag{6.8}$$

As before, substitution confirms that these are eigenfunctions, with eigenvalues

$$\lambda_j = -((j - \tfrac{1}{2})\pi/60)^2, \quad j = 1, 2, \ldots . \tag{6.9}$$

The numbers match properly,

```
-((0.5:4.5)*pi/60).^2
```

```
ans =
    -0.0007   -0.0062   -0.0171   -0.0336   -0.0555
```

Again the eigenfunctions are orthonormal,

```
V = chebfun(V); A = V'*V
```

```
A =
     1.0000    0.0000    0.0000   -0.0000   -0.0000
     0.0000    1.0000    0.0000   -0.0000   -0.0000
     0.0000    0.0000    1.0000   -0.0000   -0.0000
    -0.0000   -0.0000   -0.0000    1.0000   -0.0000
    -0.0000   -0.0000   -0.0000   -0.0000    1.0000
```

Eigenfunctions of differential operators are not always orthogonal. For example, here is an advection-diffusion problem adapted from equation (4.9):

$$Ly = y'' + 0.1y', \quad x \in [0, 60], \ y(0) = 1, \ y'(0) = 0. \tag{6.10}$$

Unlike the other operators of this chapter, this one is not self-adjoint. Here are the first four eigenfunctions. Note that the nonzero boundary value specified in (6.10) is ignored by Chebfun in solving the eigenvalue problem, which is defined in terms of homogeneous boundary conditions as always.

```
L = chebop(0,60);
L.op = @(x,y) diff(y,2) + 0.1*diff(y); L.lbc = 1; L.rbc = 0;
[V,D] = eigs(L,5); llam = diag(D);
[llam,ii] = sort(llam,'descend'); V = V(:,ii);
for j = 1:4
  subplot(2,2,j), plot(V(:,j))
end
```

Fig. 6.6. Eigenfunctions of (6.10)

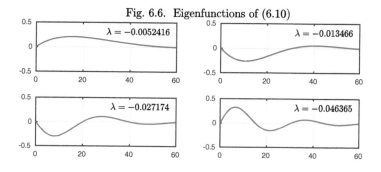

The matrix of inner products confirms that the eigenfunctions are nonorthogonal.

```
V = chebfun(V); A = V'*V
```

```
A =
    1.0000   -0.7644   -0.4227    0.2301    0.1318
   -0.7644    1.0000    0.7684   -0.4386   -0.2484
   -0.4227    0.7684    1.0000   -0.7759   -0.4520
    0.2301   -0.4386   -0.7759    1.0000    0.7802
    0.1318   -0.2484   -0.4520    0.7802    1.0000
```

Here are some higher eigenfunctions, corresponding to eigenvalues λ_8, λ_{16}, λ_{24}, and λ_{32}. The higher the eigenvalue, the more oscillations.

```
[V,D] = eigs(L,32); llam = diag(D);
[llam,ii] = sort(llam,'descend'); V = V(:,ii);
for j = 1:4
  subplot(2,2,j), plot(V(:,8*j))
end
```

Fig. 6.7. Some higher eigenfunctions

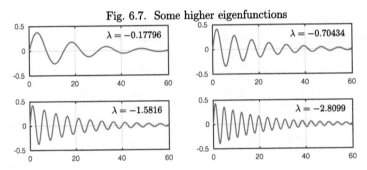

APPLICATION: EIGENSTATES OF THE SCHRÖDINGER EQUATION

One of the biggest scientific discoveries of all time was the Schrödinger equation of quantum mechanics, in 1926, which in principle reduces much of the subject of chemistry to self-adjoint eigenvalue calculations. It is from this date that eigenvalues and eigenfunctions became a universally known tool in the physical sciences.

The steady-state (time-reduced) 1D Schrödinger equation on a finite or infinite interval $[-d, d]$ takes the form

$$-h^2 y'' + V(x)y = \lambda y, \quad x \in [-d, d], \ y(-d) = y(d) = 0, \qquad (6.11)$$

where $V(x)$ is a fixed potential function and h is Planck's constant. Equation (6.11) describes what states a particle may occupy, in the quantum theory, if it is confined to the given interval and subject to an energy potential $V(x)$ there. (More precisely, h^2 in (6.11) should be $h^2/8\pi^2\mu$, where h is the true Planck constant and μ is the mass of the particle.) The eigenvalue λ corresponds to the energy of a particle in that state, and its probability density of being at each point $x \in [-d, d]$ is equal to $|y(x)|^2$, where y is the corresponding normalized eigenfunction.[32]

The simplest choice of $V(x)$ would be a constant; the corresponding eigenfunctions are sines and cosines. Next simplest is a parabola such as $V(x) = x^2$, corresponding to a linear restoring force as in a Hookean spring; this is the *quantum harmonic oscillator.* Here we use Chebfun to compute the first ten eigenstates of this problem with $h = 0.1$, taking $d = 3$ as a good approximation to $d = \infty$. Following a format standard in physics, we show the potential function as a heavy black curve and plot each eigenfunction raised up by an amount corresponding to its eigenvalue. Higher curves correspond to higher energies.

```
x = chebfun('x',[-3 3]); V = x^2; h = 0.1;
L = chebop(-3,3); L.bc = 0; L.op = @(x,y) -h^2*diff(y,2) + V*y;
[W,D] = eigs(L,10); diag(D)'
for k = 1:10, plot(D(k,k)+0.06*W{k}), hold on, end
plot(V)
```

```
ans =
     0.1000    0.3000    0.5000    0.7000    0.9000
     1.1000    1.3000    1.5000    1.7000    1.9000
```

Fig. 6.8. First ten eigenstates of (6.11) for harmonic oscillator

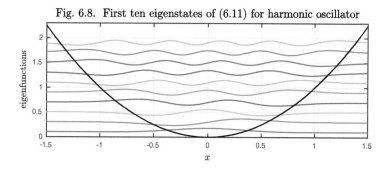

This problem can be solved exactly with Hermite polynomials (for $d = \infty$); the eigenvalues are $1, 3, 5, \ldots$ times h, hence $0.1, 0.3, 0.5, \ldots$ for our choice $h = 0.1$.

The energy levels of systems like this determine the states of atomic and molecular systems and of the photons they emit or absorb. A photon emitted by a radiating system will have a wavelength corresponding to the difference

---

[32]This is an ODE problem because there is just one particle in one dimension. For n particles in three dimensions, it would be a PDE in $3n$ independent variables, far too difficult in most cases to be solved numerically. That is why we say that Schrödinger's equation reduces chemistry to mathematical calculations "in principle." In practice, chemists have developed powerful methods for approximating the equations for multiple-particle systems, including those that led to the Nobel Prize for Kohn and Pople in 1998.

between two energies, and much of what we know about objects outside our solar system, including the expanding universe and the Big Bang, comes from analyzing such wavelengths. Closer to home, the glowing color of a "neon" fabric comes from the phenomenon of fluorescence, in which the fabric absorbs light at ultraviolet wavelengths and radiates it away at a wavelength corresponding to the difference between two quantum energy eigenstates.

Chebfun has a command `quantumstates` for automating such calculations (which sets $h = 0.1$ by default). We illustrate this here with a modified function V by adding a small peak in the middle, a *potential barrier,* making V what is known as a *double-well potential.*

```
V = x^2 + 1.5*exp(-(x/.25)^4);
[U,D] = quantumstates(V), eigenvalues = diag(D)'
```

```
eigenvalues =
      0.4436      0.4459      0.8802      0.8890      1.2743
      1.3061      1.6088      1.7053      1.9174      2.0918
```

Fig. 6.9. Eigenstates of a double-well potential

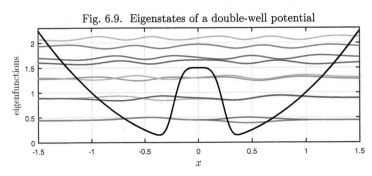

The effect on the lower eigenvalues is dramatic if you look at the numbers printed above: the lower ones now fall in *nearly degenerate pairs.* This is because the potential barrier nearly decouples the left and right halves, so that it is approximately as if we had two identical, uncoupled copies of a single-well eigenvalue problem. The lowest eigenvalue 0.4436 corresponds to an even eigenfunction, whereas the next lowest, only slightly higher at 0.4459, corresponds to an odd eigenfunction that is almost equal to the same function multiplied by sign(x). The third and fourth eigenvalues and eigenfunctions have similar behavior, but not as pronounced; at this energy level the two wells are less perfectly decoupled. This kind of close but inexact agreement of eigenvalues as a result of approximate but imperfect symmetry, known as *line splitting,* is of tremendous importance in physics and led to Nobel Prizes for the Zeeman effect in 1902 (line splitting in a magnetic field) and the Stark effect in 1919 (line splitting in an electric field).

Further remarkable things happen if we change the potential of Figure 6.9 slightly, moving the barrier to the right a distance 0.01. The eigenvalues, still in nearly degenerate pairs, do not change very much. The lower eigenfunctions, however, change completely. Now they are *localized,* with the lowest eigenfunction being concentrated in the bigger well, the next-lowest in the narrower well, and so on. In Figure 6.10 we plot just these two lowest eigenfunctions in the two cases of the symmetric-well potential and the slightly asymmetric one.

```
V2 = x^2 + 1.5*exp(-((x-.01)/.25)^4);
[U2,D] = quantumstates(V2,'noplot'); eigenvalues = diag(D)'
subplot(1,2,1), plot(U(1:2)), subplot(1,2,2), plot(U2(1:2))
```

```
eigenvalues =
     0.4350    0.4546    0.8713    0.8981    1.2691
     1.3114    1.6072    1.7068    1.9171    2.0918
```

Fig. 6.10. Eigenfunction localization

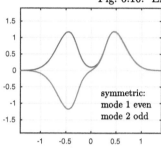
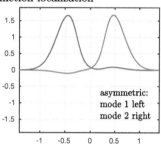

More advanced phenomena of localization are related to transparency of glass, insulating properties of ceramics, and further Nobel Prizes. In fact, it can be argued that eigenvalue problems are related to the Physics Nobel Prizes of 1902 (Zeeman), 1903 (Becquerel, Curie & Curie), 1907 (Michelson), 1911 (Wien), 1917 (Barkla), 1918 (Planck), 1919 (Stark), 1921 (Einstein), 1922 (Bohr), 1923 (Millikan), 1924 (Siegbahn), 1927 (Compton), 1929 (de Broglie), 1930 (Raman), 1932 (Heisenberg), 1933 (Schrödinger & Dirac), 1943 (Stern), 1944 (Rabi), 1945 (Pauli), 1952 (Bloch & Purcell), 1954 (Born), 1955 (Lamb), 1956 (Schockley, Bardeen & Brattain), 1961 (Mössbauer), 1962 (Landau), 1963 (Wigner, Mayer & Jensen), 1964 (Townes, Basov & Prokhorov), 1965 (Tomonago, Schwinger & Feynman), 1966 (Kastler), ...

HISTORY. The starting ideas of eigenvalue analysis go back about 200 years to Fourier, Poisson, Sturm, and Liouville. Sylvester and Cayley were diagonalizing matrices in the 1850s, and by the 1880s the analysis of eigenfunctions for vibrating membranes and the theory of sound was well established. The terms "eigenvalue" and "spectral theory," however, seem to have come later, coined by Hilbert around the turn of the 20th century.

OUR FAVORITE REFERENCE. Although eigenvalues are everywhere in the mathematical sciences, it is hard to find discussions of *why* they matter so much. What is it about the seemingly arbitrary algebraic property $Ly = \lambda y$ that demands our attention? Such a discussion can be found in Chapter 1 of Trefethen and Embree, *Spectra and Pseudospectra: The Behavior of Nonnormal*

Matrices and Operators, Princeton University Press, 2005, where four answers to the question are proposed.

SUMMARY OF CHAPTER 6. *A second-order scalar linear ODE* $Ly = y'' + a(x)y' + b(x)y = f(x)$ *has a two-dimensional affine space of solutions, assuming* a, b, *and* f *are continuous or piecewise continuous. For an IVP* $Ly = f$ *with two initial conditions, it follows that there exists a unique solution. For a BVP with two boundary conditions, however, there exists a unique solution if and only if there is no nonzero solution of the homogeneous problem* $Lv = 0$ *with homogeneous boundary conditions. Such a solution is called an eigenfunction of* L *with eigenvalue 0. More generally, if* λ *is a number and* v *is a nonzero solution of* $Lv = \lambda v$ *with homogeneous boundary conditions, then* v *is an eigenfunction of* L *with eigenvalue* λ.

Exercise 6.1. *Generalized eigenfunctions and an approximate delta function.* Consider the generalized eigenvalue problem $y''(x) + \lambda F_\varepsilon(x)y(x) = 0$ with $y(-1) = y(1) = 0$, where $F_\varepsilon(x)$ is $(2\varepsilon)^{-1}$ for $|x| < \varepsilon$ and 0 otherwise. The first k eigenvalues $D(1,1), \ldots, D(k,k)$ and eigenfunctions $V\{1\}, \ldots, V\{k\}$ can be obtained by executing `[V,D] = eigs(L,M,k)` with `x = chebfun('x')`, `F = (abs(x)<ep)/(2*ep)`, `L = chebop(@(x,y) diff(y,2),[-1 1],0,0)`, `M = chebop(@(x,y) -F(x)*y)`. (*a*) Plot the first eight eigenfunctions with $\varepsilon = 0.5$ and also with $\varepsilon = 0.1$. For plotting consistency, normalize each one by multiplying it by -1 if it is negative at $x = 0.75$. (*b*) Which eigenfunctions are even and which are odd? How many zeros do they have in $(-1, 1)$?

Exercise 6.2. *Even and odd eigenfunctions.* (*a*) Prove that if u is a function on $[-1, 1]$ that is neither even nor odd, then $u(x)$ and $u(-x)$ are linearly independent. (*b*) Let L be an "even" linear operator on $[-1, 1]$ in the sense that if L maps $u(x)$ to $v(x)$, then it maps $u(-x)$ to $v(-x)$. Prove that if $v(x)$ is an eigenfunction of L with eigenvalue λ, then $v(-x)$ is an eigenfunction of L with the same λ. (*c*) Assuming the eigenvalues of L are all of multiplicity one, show that every eigenfunction of L is either even or odd.

Exercise 6.3. *Flute and clarinet.* Let $p(x, t)$ denote the deviation from atmospheric pressure at time t at a distance x along a flute or clarinet of length D that is playing its lowest note with all its keys closed. A not unreasonable approximation is that p satisfies the partial differential equation $\partial^2 p/\partial t^2 = c^2 \partial^2 p/\partial x^2$, where c is the speed of sound. A further not unreasonable approximation is that the note will consist of a superposition of waves $p(x, t) = \sin(\omega_j t)v_j(x)$, where $v_j(x)$ is the jth eigenfunction of the differential operator $Ly = c^2 y''$ and the corresponding eigenvalue is $-\omega_j^2$. (*a*) For a flute, the instrument is open to the atmosphere at both ends and the appropriate boundary conditions are $y(0) = y(D) = 0$. Assuming $c = 340$ m/s and $D = 0.66$ m, what would you expect the first three values $\omega_1, \omega_2, \omega_3$ to be? What frequency in hertz does ω_1 correspond to? What note of the scale is this closest to? (Middle C is 261.6 Hz and the A above it is 440 Hz.) (*b*) For a clarinet, it is the velocity rather than the pressure deviation that is zero at the mouthpiece, and this leads to boundary conditions $y'(0) = y(D) = 0$. Answer the same questions as before, now taking $D = 0.60$ m. (*c*) The flute has an *octave key* that opens a hole about halfway along, which raises certain notes by an octave. Explain in a general way how this works, based on attenuation of certain eigenmodes. (The full details are nonlinear, but do not worry about this.) *(d)* The clarinet has a *register key* that opens a hole about one-third of the way along, which raises certain notes by an interval of a twelfth, i.e., a frequency ratio of approximately 3. Adapt your explanation of part *(a)* to explain why the hole is located where it is and why the frequencies are tripled.

Exercise 6.4. Exponential weight. Consider the exponentially weighted eigenvalue problem $y'' = -\lambda e^x y$ on $[0, 10]$ with $y(0) = y(10) = 0$. Compute the lowest eight eigenvalues and plot the corresponding eigenfunctions, multiplying each one by -1 if necessary to ensure $y'(0) > 0$. (This is actually a generalized eigenvalue problem, as in Exercise 6.1, so you will need to define two chebops and call, e.g., `eigs(L,M,8)`.) Which is the first eigenfunction of this problem that is not positive on $(0, 5]$?

Exercise 6.5. Davies's complex harmonic oscillator. *(a)* Use Chebfun to compute the first four eigenvalues of the problem $-y'' + ix^2 y = \lambda y$ on $(-\infty, \infty)$ with $u(\pm\infty) = 0$. For the computation it will suffice to replace ∞ by 8. *(b)* The eigenvalues of the usual harmonic oscillator, without the factor i, are well known to be $1, 3, 5, 7, \dots$. Use this fact and a suitable change of variables to explain the result of part *(a)* analytically.

Exercise 6.6. Robin boundary condition. *(a)* Use Chebfun to compute the first six eigenvalues of the problem $y'' = -\lambda y$ on $[0, \pi]$ with $y(0) = 0$ and $y(\pi) = y'(\pi)$. Plot the eigenfunctions. *(b)* One of the eigenfunctions is quite different from the others. Explain this by working out the form of the eigenfunctions analytically.

Exercise 6.7. Defective eigenvalue problem. *(a)* Repeat part *(a)* of the last problem with the boundary conditions $y(0) = 0$ and $y'(\pi) = y'(0)$, computing the first seven eigenvalues. Note that the nonzero eigenvalues come in degenerate pairs. (On the computer the pairs will differ at around the eighth digit, a numerical artifact involving the square root of machine precision.) *(b)* In linear algebra we encounter matrices with *defective eigenvalues,* meaning that their geometric multiplicity, the number of linearly independent eigenvectors, is less than their algebraic multiplicity. The simplest example (in MATLAB notation) is the 2×2 matrix `[0 1; 0 0]`. For the ODE of this problem, we have the same situation. (If you check the eigenfunctions you will find that they appear to be slightly distinct, with imaginary components around the eighth digit, but this is again a numerical artifact.) Determine analytically the smallest nonzero eigenvalue λ in absolute value and an associated eigenfunction v. *(c)* Although there is only one linearly independent function v, satisfying $(L - \lambda)v = 0$, there is another linearly independent *principal function* w such that $(L - \lambda)^2 w = 0$. Find such a function w analytically.

7. Variable coefficients and adjoints

In this chapter we focus on second-order problems with variable coefficients. Locally, near a particular value of x, solutions look like what we've seen in Chapters 4–6, featuring oscillation or exponential growth and decay depending on the coefficients. Globally, over a wider interval of x values, these structures can combine in interesting ways.

To begin, let us consider the simplest variable coefficient of all, one that jumps abruptly from one constant to another:

$$y'' - 10\operatorname{sign}(x)y = 0. \tag{7.1}$$

For $x < 0$ the coefficient is 10, and for $x > 0$ it is -10. Thus this is a second-order ODE with piecewise continuous coefficients, generalizing the first-order such problems of Chapter 2, and a solution is defined as a function y with a continuous derivative that satisfies the equation except at the points of discontinuity.[33] Here is the solution on $[-10, 10]$ with boundary conditions $y(-10) = y(10) = 1$.

```
L = chebop(-10,10); L.op = @(x,y) diff(y,2) - 10*sign(x)*y;
L.lbc = 1; L.rbc = 1;
y = L\0; plot(y)
```

---

[33] One way to justify this condition is to think of the discontinuous coefficient ODE as the limit of smooth ODEs with sharper and sharper transitions. The second derivative y'' cannot be continuous at $x = 0$, since it satisfies (7.1).

Fig. 7.1. Equation with a sign change (7.1)

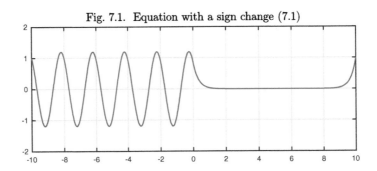

There is no mystery about this picture. On the left, the ODE is $y'' + 10y = 0$, with oscillatory solutions $A\sin(\sqrt{10}x) + B\cos(\sqrt{10}x)$. On the right, it is $y'' - 10y = 0$, with exponentially growing and decaying solutions $C\exp(\sqrt{10}x) + D\exp(-\sqrt{10}x)$. The solution makes a continuously differentiable transition between these behaviors at $x = 0$ and matches the boundary conditions. Note in particular the exponential boundary layers to the right of $x = 0$ and to the left of $x = 10$. It is not hard to work out this solution exactly by solving four equations for the four unknowns A, B, C, D (Exercise 7.1).

Abrupt changes of coefficients arise frequently in applications. Equally important in practice, and mathematically more interesting, are cases where coefficients change continuously, and the prototypical ODE of this kind is the **Airy equation**,

$$y'' - xy = 0. \tag{7.2}$$

Note that $10\,\mathrm{sign}(x)$ has given way to simply x. Again we have one sign for $x < 0$ and another for $x > 0$, but now with a smooth transition. Here is the solution with the same domain and boundary conditions as before.

```
L.op = @(x,y) diff(y,2) - x*y;
y = L\0; plot(y)
```

Fig. 7.2. Airy equation (7.2)

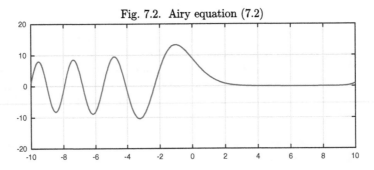

Qualitatively speaking, this image is much like the last one. For $x > 0$, the two solutions of the ODE are exponentially growing and decaying, slowly near $x = 0$ and faster near $x = 10$. For $x < 0$, they are oscillatory, with slow oscillations near $x = 0$ and faster ones near $x = -10$. The point $x = 0$ where the equation changes from one type to another is called a **turning point**. A notable difference from the last image is that the amplitude is ten times larger. This is because, by chance, we are close to an eigenvalue. If the interval had been $[-9.7, 9.7]$ instead of $[-10, 10]$, the roles would have been reversed, with the solution to (7.1) having the high amplitude (Exercise 7.3).

The Airy equation arises in applications in optics, quantum mechanics, and other fields in the analysis of wave effects near interesting edges, including George Airy's original application in 1838 related to the colors of the rainbow.[34]

With almost any ODE, it is generally interesting to reduce the magnitude of the coefficient of the highest derivative term to see what happens, and specifically to sharpen the separation between local and global behavior. (An ODE problem with a small leading coefficient is called a **singular perturbation problem**; see Chapters 18 and 20.) Here we replace y'' by $0.01y''$.

```
L.op = @(x,y) 0.01*diff(y,2) - x*y;
y = L\0; plot(y)
```

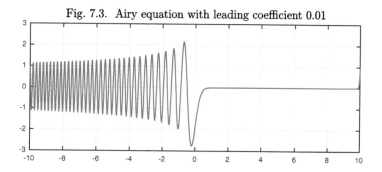

Fig. 7.3. Airy equation with leading coefficient 0.01

On the left, instead of 3 or 4 wavelengths, there are now about 35, as can be verified by Chebfun:

```
length(max(y{-10,0},'local'))

ans = 35
```

This increase is by a factor of about 10, that is, $\sqrt{100}$.

Like any second-order linear homogeneous ODE, the Airy equation has a two-dimensional vector space of solutions. One unique solution in this vector space (up to a constant factor) has the special property of decaying to 0 as $t \to \infty$, and a particular normalization of this solution is called the *Airy function* $\mathrm{Ai}(x)$. The curves we have seen above are almost, but not quite exactly,

---

[34]The Airy equation is also a prototype in the theory of asymptotics, where it illustrates fundamental ideas related to steepest descent contours, asymptotics beyond all orders, and Stokes lines. One can also think of it as a step toward the subject of *multiphysics*, which is concerned with problems and computations coupling physical media of different kinds.

multiples of Ai(x), or Ai($10x$) for the last example. As it happens, there is an integral representation for Ai(x),

$$\mathrm{Ai}(x) = \frac{1}{\pi} \int_0^\infty \cos\left(xs + \frac{s^3}{3}\right) ds. \tag{7.3}$$

It can be shown that at $x = 0$, Ai(x) and its derivative take the values

$$\mathrm{Ai}(0) = \frac{3^{-2/3}}{\Gamma(2/3)}, \quad \mathrm{Ai}'(0) = \frac{-3^{-1/3}}{\Gamma(1/3)}, \tag{7.4}$$

where Γ is the gamma function, and with these two conditions the solution to (7.2) is specified fully. The standard choice of a second linearly independent solution, which goes by the label Bi(x), is the solution of (7.2) satisfying

$$\mathrm{Bi}(0) = \frac{3^{-1/6}}{\Gamma(2/3)}, \quad \mathrm{Bi}'(0) = \frac{3^{1/6}}{\Gamma(1/3)}, \tag{7.5}$$

which has the integral representation

$$\mathrm{Bi}(x) = \frac{1}{\pi} \int_0^\infty \left(e^{xs - s^3/3} + \sin(xs + s^3/3)\right) ds. \tag{7.6}$$

Whereas Ai(x) approaches 0 as $x \to \infty$, Bi(x) approaches ∞. As $x \to -\infty$, Ai and Bi have asymptotically the same amplitude, with a phase difference of $\pi/2$, so that one is approximately zero where the other is approximately extremal. We can plot these two solutions by solving the ODE as a "middle-value problem" (this is not a standard term), with y and y' prescribed by (7.4) and (7.5) at $x = 0$.

```
L = chebop(-10,10); L.op = @(x,y) diff(y,2) - x*y;
g1 = gamma(1/3); g2 = gamma(2/3);
Ai0 = 3^(-2/3)/g2; Aip0 = -3^(-1/3)/g1;
L.bc = @(x,y) [y(0)-Ai0; feval(diff(y)-Aip0,0)];
Ai = L\0; plot(Ai), Bi0 = 3^(-1/6)/g2; Bip0 = 3^(1/6)/g1;
L.bc = @(x,y) [y(0)-Bi0; feval(diff(y)-Bip0,0)];
Bi = L\0; hold on, plot(Bi)
```

Fig. 7.4. Airy functions

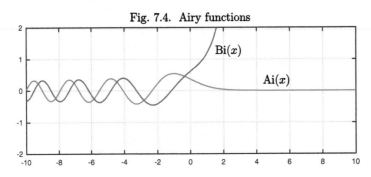

In applications, turning points of ODEs may arise wherever the nature of the "physics" changes. Though the variable coefficient at such a point may not be exactly linear, it will usually be possible to approximate it locally by a linear function. Consequently the Airy function is relevant to many problems with turning points. We can illustrate these effects by changing the variable coefficient of (7.2) to $\sin(x)$. Specifically, consider

$$0.003y'' - \sin(x)y = 1, \quad x \in [-4\pi, 4\pi], \; y(-4\pi) = y(4\pi) = 0. \qquad (7.7)$$

The solution is charming.

```
L = chebop(-4*pi,4*pi); L.op = @(x,y) 0.003*diff(y,2)-sin(x)*y;
L.lbc = 0; L.rbc = 0;
y = L\1; plot(y)
```

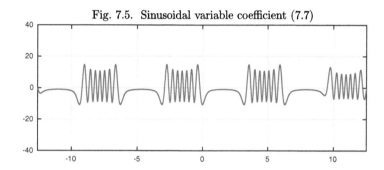

Fig. 7.5. Sinusoidal variable coefficient (7.7)

Though one could hardly expect to find an exact formula for such a function, the essence of the matter is simple enough: oscillation in regions with $\sin(x) < 0$, exponential growth and decay in regions with $\sin(x) > 0$. Locally near each turning point, $y(x)$ is approximately equal to a suitably scaled Airy function, and the approximation would get more precise if the small coefficient 0.003 were reduced further.

Airy-like equations feature transitions between exponential and oscillatory behavior. When a first-order term is introduced in a variable-coefficient equation, new possibilities arise. For example, consider the BVP

$$0.001y'' + xy' + xy = 0, \quad x \in [-2, 2], \; y(-2) = -4, \; y(2) = 2. \qquad (7.8)$$

The solution features an **interior layer** at the turning point $x = 0$, which would grow sharper if the coefficient 0.001 were further reduced.

```
L = chebop(-2,2); L.op = @(x,y) .001*diff(y,2)+x*diff(y)+x*y;
L.lbc = -4; L.rbc = 2;
y = L\0; plot(y)
```

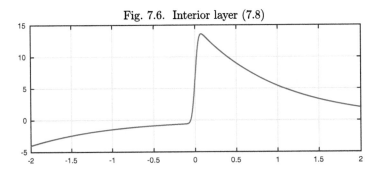

Fig. 7.6. Interior layer (7.8)

We shall look at this and other problems with boundary and interior layers in Chapter 20.

Having explored some ODEs with variable coefficients, we now turn to an area of ODE theory that is of particular interest when the coefficients are variable: the notion of an **adjoint** and the associated property of **self-adjointness**.[35] Many theoretical properties are related to adjoints, including whether eigenvalues are real and whether eigenfunctions are orthogonal. Many practical matters are tied to adjoints too, notably the behavior of solutions with respect to perturbations and the examination of how the outputs of processes governed by ODEs depend on the inputs.

Let L be a second-order linear differential operator acting on functions on $[-1, 1]$. The coefficients may be variable, so L takes the form

$$Ly = a(x)y'' + b(x)y' + c(x)y,$$

which as usual we will write more simply as

$$Ly = ay'' + by' + cy. \tag{7.9}$$

Now we consider the inner product of v and Ly, where v and y are two functions defined on $[-1, 1]$. For full generality, it is necessary in this business to include the possibility of complex functions, because even if an operator has real coefficients, its eigenfunctions and eigenvalues may be complex. Thus the inner product formula includes a bar over v denoting the complex conjugate:

$$\int_{-1}^{1} \bar{v} Ly = \int_{-1}^{1} a\bar{v}y'' + b\bar{v}y' + c\bar{v}y.$$

(We omit the dx factors for simplicity.) If we integrate the first and second terms by parts, this becomes

$$\int_{-1}^{1} \bar{v} Ly = (a\bar{v}y' + b\bar{v}y)\Big|_{-1}^{1} + \int_{-1}^{1} -(a\bar{v})'y' - (b\bar{v})'y + c\bar{v}y,$$

and if we integrate the first term in the integral by parts a second time, we get

$$\int_{-1}^{1} \bar{v} Ly = (a\bar{v}y' - (a\bar{v})'y + b\bar{v}y)\Big|_{-1}^{1} + \int_{-1}^{1} (a\bar{v})''y - (b\bar{v})'y + c\bar{v}y.$$

[35]Not much in the rest of the book depends on this material.

In other words,

$$\int_{-1}^{1} \bar{v}Ly - \overline{L^*v}y = J(\bar{v}, y), \tag{7.10}$$

where L^* is the **formal adjoint** of L, defined by

$$L^*v = (\bar{a}v)'' - (\bar{b}v)' + \bar{c}v, \tag{7.11}$$

and $J(\bar{v}, y)$ is the bilinear **conjunct** or **concomitant** of $\bar{v}$ and y,

$$J(\bar{v}, y) = (a\bar{v}y' - (a\bar{v})'y + b\bar{v}y) \Big|_{-1}^{1}. \tag{7.12}$$

In words, $\int_{-1}^{1} \bar{v}Ly$ *is the same as* $\int_{-1}^{1} \overline{L^*v}y$, *apart from boundary effects.* Equation (7.10) is known as **Green's formula**, and it is a univariate prototype of the multivariate Green's formulas that one finds in the study of partial differential equations.

Comparing (7.9) and (7.11), we see that L^* differs from L in three ways: the functions are conjugated, the sign of the odd-order derivative term is negated, and the parentheses have moved so that a and b are differentiated. We can write out (7.11) fully as

$$L^*v = \bar{a}v'' + (2\overline{a'} - \bar{b})v' + (\overline{a''} - \overline{b'} + \bar{c})v, \tag{7.13}$$

and similarly (7.12) can be expanded as

$$J(\bar{v}, y) = a(\bar{v}y' - y\overline{v'}) + (b - a')\bar{v}y \Big|_{-1}^{1}. \tag{7.14}$$

By taking the adjoint of (7.13), it is readily verified that the formal adjoint of the formal adjoint is the original operator,

$$(L^*)^* = L.$$

An operator is **formally self-adjoint** if $L^* = L$, and from (7.13) it is readily verified that if the coefficient functions are real, then this is the case if and only if $a' = b$.

Thus, for example, if $Ly = y'' + y' + y$, we have $L^*v = v'' - v' + v$ and $J(\bar{v}, y) = (\bar{v}y' - y\overline{v'} + \bar{v}y) \big|_{-1}^{1}$. Clearly L is not formally self-adjoint since L and L^* are different. Taking the arbitrary choices $v(x) = \exp(x)$ and $y(x) = \text{Ai}(x)$, here is the left side of (7.10):

```
L = chebop(-1,1); L.op = @(x,y) diff(y,2) + diff(y) + y;
x = chebfun('x'); v = exp(x); y = airy(x);
v'*(L*y) - y'*(L'*v)
```

```
ans = -0.4289
```

A calculation of $J(\bar{v}, y)$ confirms that the right side of (7.10) is the same:

```
Jfun = @(vb,y) vb.*diff(y) - y.*diff(vb) + vb.*y;
J = @(vb,y) feval(Jfun(vb,y),1) - feval(Jfun(vb,y),-1);
J(conj(v),y)
```

ans = -0.4289

As a similar example with variable coefficients, for the entirely arbitrary operator $Ly = xy'' + J_0(x)y' + \sec(x)y$, we have $L^*v = xv'' + (2 - J_0(x))v' + (\sec(x) - J_0'(x))v$ and $J(\bar{v}, y) = x(\bar{v}y' - y\overline{v'}) + (J_0(x) - 1)\bar{v}y \mid_{-1}^{1}$. Here again is the left side of (7.10),

```
L.op = @(x,y) x*diff(y,2) + besselj(0,x)*diff(y) + sec(x)*y;
v'*(L*y) - (L'*v)'*y
```

ans = -1.0412

and here is the right side,

```
Jfun = @(vb,y) x.*(vb.*diff(y)-y.*diff(vb)) + ...
               (besselj(0,x)-1).*vb.*y;
J = @(vb,y) feval(Jfun(vb,y),1) - feval(Jfun(vb,y),-1);
J(conj(v),y)
```

ans = -1.0412

The word "formally" in the expressions "formal adjoint" and "formally self-adjoint" means: "apart from boundary conditions." To speak of a true adjoint without this qualification, we need to consider not just an operator but a BVP. Let L together with certain homogeneous boundary conditions define a BVP, which we will write with a script letter as $\mathcal{L}$. The **adjoint BVP** $\mathcal{L}^*$ is the BVP in which L is changed to L^* and the boundary conditions are changed to **adjoint boundary conditions**, which are homogeneous boundary conditions on v such that the conjunct (7.14) is always zero. There exists a unique set of adjoint boundary conditions with this property, though we shall not prove this.

For example, suppose a BVP for the operator L of (7.9) has boundary conditions $y(-1) = y(1) = 0$. Then (7.14) reduces to $J(\bar{v}, y) = a(1)\overline{v(1)}y'(1) - a(-1)\overline{v(-1)}y'(-1)$. The values of $y'(1)$ and $y'(-1)$ could be anything, so to ensure $J(\bar{v}, y) = 0$ we must assume two conditions:

$$\overline{v(-1)} = 0, \quad \overline{v(1)} = 0,$$

or equivalently

$$v(-1) = 0, \quad v(1) = 0.$$

These are the adjoint boundary conditions.

For another example, if the boundary conditions are $y(-1) = y'(1) = 0$, (7.14) reduces to $J(\bar{v}, y) = -a(-1)\overline{v(-1)}y'(-1) - a(1)y(1)\overline{v'(1)} + [b(1) - a'(1)]\overline{v(1)}y(1) = 0$, and this will be zero for all y if the following two conditions hold:

$$\overline{v(-1)} = 0, \quad a(1)\overline{v'(1)} + [b(1) - a'(1)]\overline{v(1)} = 0,$$

or equivalently

$$v(-1) = 0, \quad \overline{a(1)}v'(1) + [\overline{b(1)} - \overline{a'(1)}]v(1) = 0.$$

So these are the adjoint boundary conditions. In Chebfun, where each chebop may have boundary conditions attached, the computed adjoint of a chebop is not just the formal adjoint but the adjoint BVP, with adjoint boundary conditions.

Suppose $\mathcal{L}$ is a BVP and $\mathcal{L}^*$ is its adjoint. Then for any functions y and v satisfying the BCs of $\mathcal{L}$ and $\mathcal{L}^*$, respectively, the right-hand side of (7.10) will vanish, giving

$$\int_{-1}^{1} \bar{v}Ly = \int_{-1}^{1} \overline{L^*v}y. \tag{7.15}$$

A BVP is **self-adjoint** if it is the same as its adjoint BVP, i.e.,

$$\int_{-1}^{1} \bar{v}Ly = \int_{-1}^{1} \overline{Lv}y, \tag{7.16}$$

again for any v and y satisfying the appropriate boundary conditions (which are now the same for both v and y). From this identity we can derive the following conclusions.

Theorem 7.1. Self-adjoint eigenproblems (fLaSHi). *Let $\mathcal{L}$ be a self-adjoint linear homogeneous BVP. Then the eigenvalues of $\mathcal{L}$ are real, and the eigenfunctions corresponding to distinct eigenvalues are orthogonal; i.e., if y and v are eigenfunctions with eigenvalues $\lambda \neq \mu$, then $\int_{-1}^{1} \bar{v}y = 0$.*

Proof. Let y be an eigenfunction of $\mathcal{L}$ with eigenvalue λ. Then (7.16) gives

$$\lambda \int_{-1}^{1} \bar{y}y = \int_{-1}^{1} \bar{y}Ly = \int_{-1}^{1} \overline{Ly}y = \bar{\lambda} \int_{-1}^{1} \bar{y}y.$$

Since y is nonzero (part of the definition of an eigenfunction), the integral of $\bar{y}y$ is nonzero, and thus this identity implies $\lambda = \bar{\lambda}$, which establishes the first claim. Now let v be another eigenfunction of $\mathcal{L}$ with eigenvalue $\mu \neq \lambda$. Then another calculation of the same pattern gives

$$\lambda \int_{-1}^{1} \bar{v}y = \int_{-1}^{1} \bar{v}Ly = \int_{-1}^{1} \overline{Lv}y = \mu \int_{-1}^{1} \bar{v}y.$$

Since $\mu \neq \lambda$, this establishes the claim of orthogonality. ∎

If a self-adjoint operator $\mathcal{L}$ has real coefficients, then the eigenfunctions can be taken to be real, so the complex conjugates in the calculations above can be dropped.

APPLICATION: ADJOINTS AND OPTIMIZATION

Whenever something has to be perturbed, optimized, or designed and there is a differential equation involved, there's a good chance there may be a role for the adjoint. Here we'll give just a hint of how this may work. An interesting paper from which to learn more is M. B. Giles and N. A. Pierce, "An introduction to the adjoint approach to design," *Flow, Turbulence and Combustion* 65 (2000), pp. 393–415.

We show the idea with an artificial example. Suppose y is the solution of

$$y'' + \sin(x/10)y' + y = f(x) = \exp(-(x-k)^2), \quad y(0) = y(100) = 0 \quad (7.17)$$

for some integer k between 1 and 100, and we want to know, which choice of k will maximize the integral $I(f) = \int_0^{100} y(x)\,dx$? You can think of this as a prototype of a problem of finding the maximal lift on an airfoil in various flow conditions.

The obvious approach is to simply solve all 100 of these BVPs. However, this will take a while, as we can see by solving just the first 10 of them.

```
L = chebop(@(x,y) diff(y,2) + sin(x/10)*diff(y) + y, [0 100]);
L.lbc = 0; L.rbc = 0; x = chebfun('x',[0 100]); tic
for k = 1:10
  f = exp(-(x-k)^2); y = L\f; disp([k sum(y)])
end
toc
     1.0000    -2.2089
     2.0000    -1.0548
     3.0000     3.2140
     4.0000     7.7218
     5.0000     8.1427
     6.0000     1.6446
     7.0000    -9.7058
     8.0000   -17.0143
     9.0000    -7.1469
    10.0000    27.4458
Elapsed time is 2.323716 seconds.
```

Use of the adjoint enables us to solve one BVP rather than 100 of them. The key observation is that since $I(f)$ is just a single number that depends linearly on f (i.e., I is a linear functional), it must be possible to write I in the form

$$I(f) = \int_0^{100} vf$$

for some function v defined on $[0, 100]$. (This property of linear functionals is called the *Riesz representation theorem*. In this application all the functions are real, so we dispense with complex conjugates.) In fact, if g is the constant function 1 on $[0, 100]$, then v is the solution of the adjoint BVP $\mathcal{L}^*v = g$. To derive this characterization, we note that

$$I(f) = \int_0^{100} gy.$$

Therefore the two equations

$$\mathcal{L}y = f, \quad \mathcal{L}^*v = g \tag{7.18}$$

imply

$$I(f) = \int_0^{100} gy = \int_0^{100} [\mathcal{L}^*v]y = \int_0^{100} v\mathcal{L}y = \int_0^{100} vf. \tag{7.19}$$

By taking advantage of this formula, instead of solving 100 ODE BVPs, we can now evaluate 100 inner products. First we confirm that the first 10 of these give the same numbers as before.

```
tic, v = L'\1;
for k = 1:10
  f = exp(-(x-k)^2); disp([k v'*f])
end
```

```
    1.0000    -2.2089
    2.0000    -1.0548
    3.0000     3.2140
    4.0000     7.7218
    5.0000     8.1427
    6.0000     1.6446
    7.0000    -9.7058
    8.0000   -17.0143
    9.0000    -7.1469
   10.0000    27.4458
```

Next we evaluate all 100 inner products and plot the maximal solution, which turns out to correspond to $k = 32$.

```
tic, v = L'\1; d = [];
for k = 1:100
  f = exp(-(x-k)^2); d(k) = v'*f;
end
[maxint, kmax] = max(d), toc
f = exp(-(x-kmax)^2); y = L\f; plot(y)
```

```
maxint = 7.2869e+04
kmax = 32
Elapsed time is 1.047531 seconds.
```

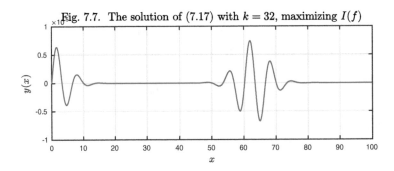

Fig. 7.7. *The solution of (7.17) with $k = 32$, maximizing $I(f)$*

The function v has an interpretation: it quantifies the effect on $I(f)$ of the value of f at each $x \in [0, 100]$. Consequently v is also the *most efficient shape* that f may take, measured in the 2-norm, if our goal is to maximize $I(f)$. That is, suppose we want to find a function f with $\|f\|_2 = 1$ such that $I(f)$ is maximized. Applying the Cauchy–Schwarz inequality to (7.19) gives

$$I(f) \leq \|v\|_2 \|f\|_2,$$

with equality if f is a multiple of v. So the maximal value of $I(f)$ for $\|f\|_2 = 1$ is achieved by the choice $f = v/\|v\|_2$, and the value is equal to $\|v\|_2$,

```
maxval = norm(v)
```

```
maxval = 1.7303e+05
```

A plot of v shows that $I(f)$ is most sensitive to the values of $f(x)$ for $x \approx 32$, as is consistent with Figure 7.7.

```
plot(v)
```

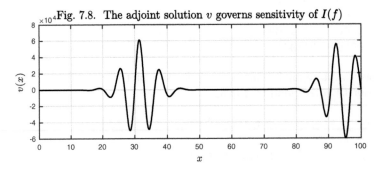

Fig. 7.8. *The adjoint solution v governs sensitivity of $I(f)$*

HISTORY. George Biddell Airy, who used Airy functions in analysis of the colors of the rainbow in 1838, was one of the leading astronomers and mathematical physicists of the 19th century. As Astronomer Royal in Britain during 1835–1881, nearly half a century, he was largely responsible for the adoption of the longitude line through Greenwich as the earth's prime meridian.

OUR FAVORITE REFERENCE. Though there are a hundred functional analysis books that discuss adjoints in the abstract, it is hard to find more down-to-earth discussions of adjoint differential equations in the style of this book. One source we like is Max D. Gunzburger, *Perspectives in Flow Control and Optimization*, SIAM, 2003. As promised in the title, this book gives fascinating perspectives on the meaning of adjoints — even in the opening 8 pages.

SUMMARY OF CHAPTER 7. *Algebraically, second-order linear ODEs with variable coefficients have the same structure as those with constant coefficients: there is a two-dimensional space of solutions, and an IVP can always be solved but a BVP will have a unique solution if and only if it does not correspond to an eigenvalue of the associated homogeneous problem. Locally, solutions approximate solutions of ODEs with constant coefficients, especially when the coefficient of the second derivative term is small. Interesting transitions occur at turning points, where a coefficient changes sign; the prototype is $x = 0$ for the Airy equation $y'' - xy = 0$. A linear ODE BVP $\mathcal{L}$ has an adjoint $\mathcal{L}^*$ consisting of the formal adjoint operator together with adjoint boundary conditions. If $\mathcal{L}$ is self-adjoint, its eigenvalues are real and its eigenfunctions corresponding to distinct eigenvalues are orthogonal.*

Exercise 7.1. Exact solution of the jump problem (7.1). (a) Determine the exact solution of (7.1) with $y(-10) = y(10) = 1$. *(b)* Determine the eigenvalues of the corresponding linear operator with boundary conditions $y(-10) = y(10) = 0$.

Exercise 7.2. An ODE of Euler. Consider the ODE $y'' + (a/t)y' + (b/t^2)y = 0$. Show that it can be reduced to a simpler problem by the substitution $\tau = \log(t)$ and use this method to find the general solution.

Exercise 7.3. Dependence on interval length. (a) What is the value of the ratio of $\max_x |y(x)|$ for (7.2) divided by the same quantity for (7.1)? *(b)* What happens to this ratio if the interval is changed from $[-10, 10]$ to $[-9.7, 9.7]$?

Exercise 7.4. Intersection of Ai(x) and Bi(x). Use Chebfun `roots` to calculate the value x_0 closest to 0 for which $\text{Ai}(x_0) = \text{Bi}(x_0)$. In MATLAB you can calculate $\text{Ai}(x)$ and $\text{Bi}(x)$ with `airy(x)` and `airy(2,x)`, respectively.

Exercise 7.5. Airy functions with many oscillations. Solve the Airy equation on the interval $[-D, 0]$ with boundary conditions $y(-D) = 1$, $y(0) = 0$ for $D = 10, 20, 40, \ldots, 320$. Plot the solution in each case and measure how long it takes Chebfun to solve the differential equation. For comparison, measure how long it takes to construct a chebfun for $\text{Ai}(x)$ on $[-32, 0]$ directly from MATLAB's `airy` command.

Exercise 7.6. Sine oscillations. The solution of (7.7) shows seven maxima in $[-\pi, 0]$ in Figure 7.5. What does the count become if the coefficient 0.003 is reduced by a factor of 16?

Exercise 7.7. Taylor series solution of Airy equation. Exercise 2.10 mentioned a classic analytical solution method for linear ODEs, the use of Taylor series. Suppose $y(t) = \sum_{k=0}^{\infty} a_k t^k$ is a convergent Taylor series solution for (7.2) near $t = 0$. *(a)* Show that $a_2 = a_5 = a_8 = \cdots = 0$. *(b)* Give a formula for $a_3, a_6, a_9, \ldots$ in terms of a_0. *(c)* Give a formula for $a_4, a_7, a_{10}, \ldots$ in terms of a_1. *(d)* Show that the radius of convergence of the series is ∞, implying that Airy functions are analytic throughout the complex t-plane.

Exercise 7.8. *Eigenvalues of the Airy operator.* *(a)* Calculate the roots of $Ai(x)$ in $[-10, 10]$. *(b)* Calculate the first six eigenvalues of the Airy operator $L : y \mapsto y'' - xy$ with homogeneous boundary conditions on $[0, \infty)$. (It suffices to replace ∞ by 15.) *(c)* Explain this coincidence with an analytical verification. To get the idea it may help to plot the eigenfunctions.

Exercise 7.9. *Legendre equation and polynomials.* If n is a nonnegative integer, the solution to the BVP $[(1 - x^2)y']' + n(n + 1)y = 0$, $y(-1) = (-1)^n$, $y(1) = 1$ has a special property: it is a polynomial, known as the *Legendre polynomial* of degree n, for which the standard notation is P_n. *(a)* Compute P_{10} and P_{40} by solving the BVP and plot them. You can confirm that your calculation is successful by comparing these functions with `legpoly(10)` and `legpoly(40)`. *(b)* The Legendre polynomials are orthogonal: $\int_{-1}^{1} P_m(x)P_n(x)\,dx$ is equal to $2/(2n + 1)$ if $m = n$ and 0 otherwise. Confirm this numerically by computing the inner products of P_{10} with itself, P_{10} with P_{40}, and P_{40} with itself. (In Chebfun, the inner product of u and v is u'*v.)

Exercise 7.10. *An oscillatory pulse.* *(a)* Plot the solution of $0.01y'' - 0.01y' - xy = 1$ for $x \in [-10, 10]$ with $y(-10) = y(10) = 0$. Determine (i) the maximum value, (ii) the width of the highest peak measured at half its height, and (iii) the distance over which the oscillations decay by a factor of 10. *(b)* Produce the same plots and numbers in the three alternative cases where the y'' coefficient is reduced to 0.005, or the y' coefficient, or both.

Exercise 7.11. *Condition for self-adjointness.* *(a)* Use (7.13) to verify that if the coefficient functions are real, then the operator L of (7.9) is formally self-adjoint if and only if $a' = b$. *(b)* What is the analogous condition if the coefficients are complex?

Exercise 7.12. *Self-adjoint and nonself-adjoint.* Let $\mathcal{L}$ be the BVP $e^x y'' + e^x y' + xy = 0$ with boundary conditions $y(-1) = y'(1) = 0$. *(a)* Show analytically that $\mathcal{L}$ is self-adjoint. *(b)* Compute the first six eigenvalues and eigenfunctions of $\mathcal{L}$, showing that the eigenvalues are real and the eigenfunctions are numerically orthogonal. *(c)* Show that if the ODE is changed to $e^x y'' + y' + xy = 0$, the eigenvalues remain real but the eigenfunctions are no longer orthogonal, and verify that the eigenvalues of $\mathcal{L}$ are the same as those of $\mathcal{L}^*$. *(d)* On the other hand, it can be shown by an adaptation of the argument of Theorem 7.1 that the jth eigenfunction of $\mathcal{L}^*$ is orthogonal to the kth eigenfunction of $\mathcal{L}$ for $j \neq k$. Verify this numerically.

Exercise 7.13. *Optimizations with the adjoint.* *(a)* Repeat the optimization illustrated in the Application, but maximizing $I(f) = \int_0^{100} xy(x)\,dx$. *(b)* Repeat again, but maximizing $I(f) = \int_{30}^{50} y(x)\,dx$.

Exercise 7.14. *Adjoint of Exercise 6.7.* Exercise 6.7 explored an ODE eigenvalue problem with defective eigenvalues, a situation that can arise only if the operator $\mathcal{L}$ involved is nonself-adjoint. Work out analytically the adjoint $\mathcal{L}^*$ for this problem. In particular, what are the adjoint boundary conditions?

8. Resonance

Certain systems have one or more natural frequencies at which they oscillate. If you force such a system by an input that oscillates at close to a natural frequency, the response may be very large in amplitude. In this chapter we explore this phenomenon.

The basic idea is linear, autonomous, and inhomogeneous. Following (4.3), consider the ODE of simple harmonic motion,

$$y'' + \omega^2 y = f(t), \tag{8.1}$$

where ω is a real constant. One application of this equation is to a linear pendulum, where $y(t)$ represents the (small) angle from the vertical at time t. Here ω^2 takes the value g/L, where g is the earth's gravitational acceleration and L is the length of the pendulum. Let us imagine that the pendulum is a girl on a playground swing. The issue to be examined is the response of the swing to the forcing function f, which we can interpret as the acceleration introduced by the girl's mother, who is pushing.

There is really just one bit of physics in (8.1), and that is that the associated homogeneous equation

$$y'' + \omega^2 y = 0 \tag{8.2}$$

has solutions $\sin(\omega t)$ and $\cos(\omega t)$. This is what we mean when we say that the **natural** or **resonant frequency** of (8.1) is ω.[36] To focus on the simplest possible setting, let us look at solutions $y(t)$ driven by the sinusoidal forcing

---

[36] As in Chapter 4, what we call a frequency could more fully be called an angular frequency.

function $f(t) = \sin(\nu t)$ for some $\nu \neq \omega$,

$$y'' + \omega^2 y = \sin(\nu t). \tag{8.3}$$

As a reminder of this not very standard notation we note

$$\boxed{\omega = \textit{resonant frequency}, \quad \nu = \textit{forcing frequency}.}$$

We can solve (8.3) analytically. Inserting the trial solution $y(t) = A\sin(\nu t)$ gives

$$(-\nu^2 + \omega^2)y = \frac{y}{A},$$

which implies that a particular solution is

$$y_{\mathrm{p}}(t) = \frac{\sin(\nu t)}{\omega^2 - \nu^2}.$$

The general solution is accordingly

$$y(t) = \frac{\sin(\nu t)}{\omega^2 - \nu^2} + B\sin(\omega t) + C\cos(\omega t) \tag{8.4}$$

for constants B and C. Note that this is a superposition of sine/cosine waves of two different frequencies, so in general, $y(t)$ is not periodic.

For example, suppose we take $y(0) = y'(0) = 0$, giving the IVP

$$y'' + \omega^2 y = \sin(\nu t), \quad t \geq 0, \; y(0) = y'(0) = 0. \tag{8.5}$$

Choosing $B = -(\nu/\omega)/(\omega^2 - \nu^2)$ and $C = 0$ in (8.4) to match the initial conditions, we get the solution

$$y(t) = \frac{\sin(\nu t) - (\nu/\omega)\sin(\omega t)}{\omega^2 - \nu^2}. \tag{8.6}$$

Here is a calculation for $t \in [0, 200]$ with $\omega = 1$ and $\nu = 0.7$.

```
L = chebop(0,200); L.lbc = [0;0]; L.op = @(t,y) diff(y,2) + y;
t = chebfun('t',[0 200]);
f = sin(0.7*t); subplot(2,1,1), plot(f)
y = L\f; subplot(2,1,2), plot(y)
```

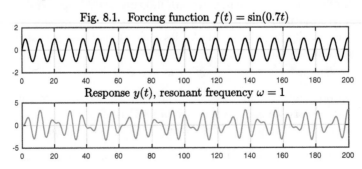

Fig. 8.1. Forcing function $f(t) = \sin(0.7t)$

Response $y(t)$, resonant frequency $\omega = 1$

This solution is an incoherent signal of no great interest. On the other hand, suppose we take $\nu = 0.95$, a value much closer to ω.

```
f = sin(0.95*t); subplot(2,1,1), plot(f)
y = L\f; subplot(2,1,2), plot(y)
```

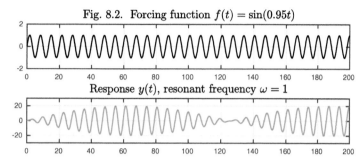

Fig. 8.2. Forcing function $f(t) = \sin(0.95t)$

Now the response shows great regularity and a high amplitude, about 20, which builds up over an interval of 60 time units. This is **resonance**, which we can define as the pumping of energy into or out of a system by a driving function oscillating at close to a natural frequency. The mother is pushing the swing at close to its natural rate. The growth in amplitude occurs so long as her input is in advance of the phase of the growing oscillation. Eventually, however, after around time $t = 60$, the impulses lag behind the phase of the swing and she starts extracting energy. The cycle goes on in the effect known as *beating*, with alternating long stretches of energy injection and energy extraction. (No actual mother, of course, would be so mechanical.)

All of the above is mathematically correct, and an important base case on which to build one's understanding of resonance, but it is physically unrealistic. If an autonomous system is forced by a periodic signal $f(t) = \sin(\nu t)$, then surely we would expect it to have a periodic solution $y(t)$ with the same frequency, at least for large t, after the effect of the initial conditions has died away. Why hasn't this happened? The problem is that (8.3) includes no damping, so the effect of the initial conditions never dies away. We can see this in formulas (8.4) and (8.6), where B and C take values determined by the initial conditions and the associated $\sin(\omega t)$ and $\cos(\omega t)$ terms persist forever.

The picture changes fundamentally if we add a small amount of damping, generalizing (8.3) as in (4.10) to

$$y'' + \varepsilon y' + \omega^2 y = \sin(\nu t) \tag{8.7}$$

for some small $\varepsilon > 0$. Here is the first example again, but now, with two response curves shown: the first for (8.3) without damping, the same as before, and the second for (8.7) with damping coefficient $\varepsilon = 0.04$.

```
L2 = chebop(0,200); L2.lbc = [0;0];
L2.op = @(t,y) diff(y,2) + 0.04*diff(y) + y;
f = sin(0.7*t); subplot(3,1,1), plot(f)
```

```
y = L\f;   subplot(3,1,2), plot(y)
y = L2\f;  subplot(3,1,3), plot(y)
```

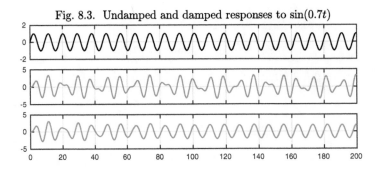

Fig. 8.3. Undamped and damped responses to $\sin(0.7t)$

With damping, it is clear that as $t \to \infty$, the solution approaches a periodic form with frequency ν. By appropriate changes in the earlier formulas, we can work out the details analytically. It is tempting to start with the trial solution $y(t) = A\sin(\nu t)$ again, but this will not work because the y' term will introduce a cosine. We could get around this with a trial solution containing both a sine and a cosine, but it is algebraically simpler to combine the two by introducing complex exponentials. Thus we replace (8.7) by

$$y'' + \varepsilon y' + \omega^2 y = \exp(i\nu t), \qquad (8.8)$$

and the imaginary part of the solution will correspond to the solution (8.6). Inserting $y(t) = A\exp(i\nu t)$ gives

$$(-\nu^2 + i\nu\varepsilon + \omega^2)y = \frac{y}{A},$$

which implies that a particular solution is

$$y_{\mathrm{p}}(t) = \frac{\exp(i\nu t)}{\omega^2 + i\nu\varepsilon - \nu^2}. \qquad (8.9)$$

From equation (4.13) in Chapter 4, it can be deduced that the general solution to (8.8) will be a linear combination of this function $y_{\mathrm{p}}(t)$ with terms decaying exponentially at the rate $\exp(-\varepsilon t/2)$. This confirms that the general solution will be asymptotically periodic as $t \to \infty$.

Now we add damping to the second experiment, with $\nu = 0.95$. Again the response settles down to a periodic form, with somewhat smaller amplitude than before.

```
f = sin(0.95*t); subplot(3,1,1), plot(f)
y = L\f;   subplot(3,1,2), plot(y)
y = L2\f;  subplot(3,1,3), plot(y)
```

Fig. 8.4. Undamped and damped responses to $\sin(0.95t)$

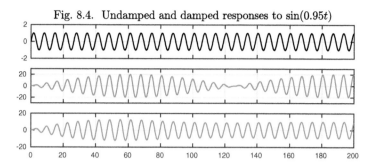

The relationship between forcing and response in resonance has an element of phase as well as amplitude. In the trio of images above, say, take a look at the forcing and response curves at the final time $t = 200$. We see that all three curves have a maximum near this point, reflecting the fact that in (8.4), since $\nu < \omega$, the denominator is positive, and in (8.9) it is nearly positive though slightly complex. Thus the input and the responses are *in phase*. Suppose we now change ν to 1.05, a value equally close to ω but larger rather than smaller. Now the denominators of (8.4) and (8.9) are negative and nearly negative, respectively, and looking near $t = 200$ in the figure below confirms that the forcing and response functions have moved out of phase by an angle of π, that is, 180 degrees. This is a basic difference in the physics of the two kinds of resonance phenomena.

```
f = sin(1.05*t); subplot(3,1,1), plot(f)
y = L\f;  subplot(3,1,2), plot(y)
y = L2\f; subplot(3,1,3), plot(y)
```

Fig. 8.5. Responses to $\sin(1.05t)$, with 180 degree phase shift

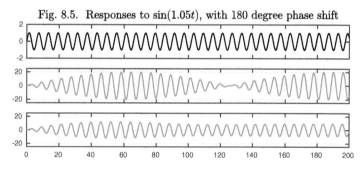

We can summarize the phase lag situation (for sufficiently small damping ε) according to whether the forcing frequency is lower or higher than the resonant frequency:

$$\boxed{\nu < \omega \text{: } \textit{no phase lag}, \quad \nu > \omega \text{: } 180° \textit{ phase lag.}}$$

For more precision, see Exercise 8.7.

As ν gets closer to ω, the maximum amplitude of $y(t)$ for the undamped equation (8.3) increases to ∞, and so does the time scale over which it achieves that maximum. If $\nu = \omega$ exactly, the forcing and the oscillation are synchronized forever. Energy keeps getting pumped into the system, and the amplitude grows without limit. This unbounded growth for undamped oscillation corresponds to a singularity in the formulas (8.4) and (8.6), but not in the IVP itself or its solution, which shows simply a linear increase with t. In the damped cases, the growth asymptotes to a fixed amplitude.

```
f = sin(t); subplot(3,1,1), plot(f)
y = L\f;   subplot(3,1,2), plot(y)
y = L2\f;  subplot(3,1,3), plot(y)
```

Fig. 8.6. Responses to $\sin(t)$, with 90 degree phase shift

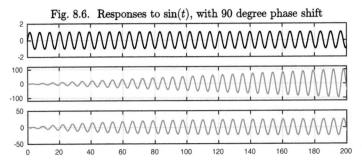

The linearly growing solution to an undamped resonant system forced at the resonant frequency is called a **secular solution**. In this case we can derive that the exact solution of (8.5) is

$$y(t) = \frac{-t\cos(\omega t)}{2\omega^2} + \frac{\sin(\omega t)}{2\omega^3};$$
(8.10)

the term involving $t\cos(\omega t)$ is the secular one. Secular terms arise whenever an ODE has an inhomogeneous forcing function that is itself a solution to the homogeneous problem.

What about the phase lag in this special situation $\nu = \omega$? Looking at the figures near the final time $t = 200$, we see that, as one might guess, the lag is now midway between the two cases we have seen before, namely one quarter of a wavelength, an angle of $\pi/2$ or $90°$. We can confirm this algebraically by noting that in the formula (8.10), although the forcing function is the sine, the secular term of the response involves the negative of the cosine. In a case with damping, the $90°$ lag comes from the i in the denominator of (8.9).

The discussion so far has concerned the response of (8.1) or its damped cousin to a pure sine wave, but of course, not every forcing function will be so simple. More generally, if f is a function that looks approximately like a sine wave for a certain range of values of t, we may expect to see approximately corresponding behavior for a time. Here is an experiment to illustrate. Consider

$$f(t) = \sin((t/100) \cdot t),$$

a function whose frequency starts at $\nu = 0$ for $t = 0$ and then increases linearly to $\nu = 4$ at $t = 200$ since $(t^2/100)' = t/50$. (In Chapter 17 we will do a number of such experiments with parameters slowly varying with t.) The response $y(t)$ shown in Figure 8.7 does nothing very interesting until near $t = 50$, when it grows to a considerable amplitude due to resonance. Soon the forcing drifts out of tune again, after which no further significant transfer of energy from the forcing function takes place. The undamped response curve shows a permanent record of the brief moment of resonance near $t = 50$, and the damped response curve dies away slowly on the time scale $\exp(-\varepsilon t/2)$.

```
f = sin((t/100)*t); subplot(3,1,1), plot(f)
y = L\f;  subplot(3,1,2), plot(y)
y = L2\f; subplot(3,1,3), plot(y)
```

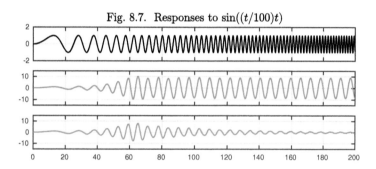

Fig. 8.7. Responses to $\sin((t/100)t)$

This chapter has focused on linear equations, because the basic mechanism of resonance is linear. However, resonance occurs in nonlinear systems too. For example, generalizing (8.7) in the case $\omega = 1$, consider the nonlinear pendulum equation

$$y'' + \varepsilon y' + 45\sin(y/45) = \sin(\nu t), \qquad (8.11)$$

where the constant 45 has been chosen arbitrarily, corresponding to a rather weak nonlinearity. Here are the undamped and damped solutions (with $\varepsilon = 0.04$ as usual) in the same format as before.

```
N = chebop(0,200); N.lbc = [0;0];
N2 = chebop(0,200); N2.lbc = [0;0];
N.op = @(t,y) diff(y,2) + 45*sin(y/45);
N2.op = @(t,y) diff(y,2) + .04*diff(y) + 45*sin(y/45);
f = sin(0.95*t); subplot(3,1,1), plot(f)
y = N\f;  subplot(3,1,2), plot(y)
y = N2\f; subplot(3,1,3), plot(y)
```

Fig. 8.8. Nonlinear responses to $\sin(0.95t)$, eq. (8.11)

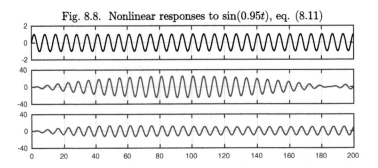

Note that in comparison to Figure 8.4, the amplitude and the time scale have increased. This is because in this example, nonlinearity has weakened the restoring force, decreasing the natural frequency of the system, thereby bringing the forcing frequency closer to resonance.

APPLICATION: MOON, SUN, AND TIDES

Everybody knows that the moon causes the tides, with a further contribution from the sun. But there are some surprises along the way related to the material of this chapter.

The resonant system here consists of the earth's oceans, and the forcing function consists of the gravitational force from the moon, whose direction changes as the earth turns. With respect to a fixed point on Earth, the moon appears to go around about once every 24.8 hours. This means the tidal forcing from the moon has a period of about $T = 12.4$ hours, since, as many books and web pages will tell you, the moon's gravity both pulls on the ocean nearest it more than on the earth below *and* pulls on the earth below more than on the ocean on the far side. So our forcing function, with time measured in hours, has frequency $\nu = 2\pi/T \approx 0.507$. Here's a picture over 672 hours, i.e., four weeks.

```
t = chebfun('t',[0,672]); Tmoon = 12.4;
numoon = 2*pi/Tmoon; f = cos(numoon*t); plot(f)
```

Fig. 8.9. First approximation to tidal forcing

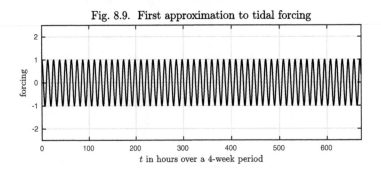

t in hours over a 4-week period

There are two big day-to-day corrections to be added to this picture. The first is the influence of the sun. As it happens, the gravitational force from the sun is about 180 times as big as that from the moon. This big factor doesn't matter, however, since tides depend on gravity being stronger on one side of the earth than the other: what matters is the *gradient* of the gravitational force. This is about twice as great for the moon as for the sun. Moreover, the period associated with the sun's forcing is of course simply 12 hours, not 12.4. The difference in periods causes a slow beating in and out of phase, giving a combined gravitational forcing from the moon and sun like this.

```
Tsun = 12; nusun = 2*pi/Tsun;
f = cos(numoon*t) + 0.46*cos(nusun*t); plot(f)
```

Fig. 8.10. Correction for the sun: bigger forcing every 2 weeks

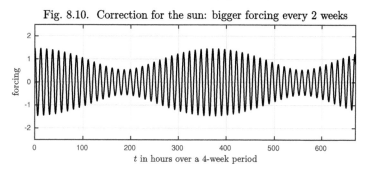

t in hours over a 4-week period

When the moon is new or full, it is aligned with the sun (a configuration called *syzygy*) and we we have big *spring tides*. A week later it is 90° off and we have smaller *neap tides*.

The other big correction is the one that makes tides alternate big-small-big-small. Whereas the moon's orbit is close to the ecliptic (the plane of the solar system), the earth's is tilted by 23%. That means that if you live somewhere between the equator and a pole, as the earth turns during the day, you may alternate between close to the ecliptic at one high of the gravitational forcing function and 90° away at the next. So the forcing function near you looks more like this (the details will depend on latitude and season of the year).

```
f = .8*cos(numoon*t) + .2*cos(numoon*t/2) ...
    + .8*.46*cos(nusun*t) + .2*.46*cos(nusun*t/2); plot(f)
```

Fig. 8.11. Correction for tilting of Earth's axis

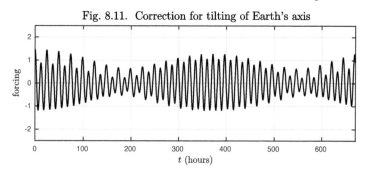

t (hours)

Figure 8.11 sketches half of the tide problem, the gravitational forcing. (We've omitted longer time scale annual effects, as the earth moves around the sun, and also the variation in the moon's distance from the earth since its orbit is not a circle.) The other half concerns the resonant response by the water on Earth. The full details of this are very complicated, for the oceans have complicated boundaries. Nevertheless, we can see a part of the picture by ignoring the continents and imagining that the ocean is a uniform cover of the earth a few miles deep. What is the natural frequency of this system? The answer is determined by how fast waves travel across the ocean — not the little waves one might surf on, but the so-called *shallow-water waves* associated with tsunamis. It turns out that these travel about half as fast as the earth rotates. (It would be different if the ocean were deeper.)

So Earth's tides are in the regime $\nu > \omega$, where *the forcing frequency exceeds the resonant frequency*. This means that we can expect the tides to be about half a period out of phase with the moon. Since the moon's forcing peaks not once but twice per day, this 180° difference in mathematical phase corresponds to a 90° difference in geometric orientation. We can sketch it like this:

```
earth = chebfun('exp(1i*x)',[0 2*pi]);
fill(real(earth),1.2*imag(earth),[.42 .57 .84]), hold on
fill(real(earth),imag(earth),[.8 .8 .8]), moon = 6+.4*earth;
fill(real(moon),imag(moon),[.96 .95 .72])
```

Fig. 8.12. Tides on Earth, out of phase with gravitational input

tidal bulge

Earth

Moon

Many of us have seen figures like this, perhaps even when we were teenagers first learning about the tides. But the pictures usually show the bulges pointing in line with the moon, not at right angles! That's correct in a certain static sense, as it conveys the underlying gravitational force, but it's wrong dynamically.

We hasten to emphasize that the actual behavior of tides on Earth is far more complex than Figure 8.12 and the discussion above recognize. For example, the phase lag is diminished by damping, which is not negligible, and at high latitudes by the smaller distance around the globe, which brings the natural frequency of oscillation close to the frequency of gravitational input. Most importantly, we have ignored the continents completely, whose presence changes the details in a manner that varies from place to place. See for example E. I. Butikov, "A dynamical picture of the oceanic tides," *American Journal of Physics* 70 (2002), pp. 1001–1011. Because of these effects, if you actually look at tide data to see whether reality better fits Figure 8.12 or its opposite, you are likely to find that the data are all over the place. See Exercise 8.4.

History. It was Newton who figured out the fundamental dynamics of Earth's tides, in his *Principia,* as a consequence of the same law of gravity that explains orbits of planets around the sun.

Our favorite reference. For a delightful tour of resonance and many other effects, check out E. J. Heller, *Why You Hear What You Hear: An Experiential Approach to Sound, Music, and Psychoacoustics,* Princeton University Press, 2013. It is hard to read even a single page of Heller's book without learning something interesting.

Summary of Chapter 8. *Resonance is the interaction between a system with a natural frequency of oscillation and external forcing at a nearby frequency. Over a period of oscillations, a great deal of energy can be injected into an oscillating system by this effect. If the damping is small, forcing at the resonant frequency introduces a phase shift of 90 degrees and forcing above the resonant frequency results in a phase shift of 180 degrees. In systems with damping, forcing by a periodic function of frequency ν leads to a solution that approaches periodic form as $t \to \infty$.*

Exercise 8.1. *Exploiting resonance to increase amplitude.* For a given frequency ν, consider the solution to $y'' + y = 1 - \cos(\nu t)$, $y(0) = 1$, $y'(0) = 0$. *(a)* If ν is set equal to the resonant frequency ω for this equation, compute the time t_c at which $y(t)$ first reaches the value 10. *(b)* What is the smallest value of ν for which $y(t)$ reaches the value 10 at some time $t \in [0, 100]$?

Exercise 8.2. *RLC circuits and AM radio.* An AM radio station broadcasts radio waves consisting of a high-frequency carrier (say, 10^6 Hz) times a low-frequency oscillation (a few thousand Hz). This is equivalent to saying the signal is contained in a band of a few thousand hertz about 10^6 Hz. The radio is tuned by means of a resonant circuit that selects energy in this band. The simplest such circuit consists of a resistor of resistance R (in ohms), an inductor of inductance L (in henries), and a capacitor of capacitance C (in farads) in series. If $E(t)$ is the applied voltage (in volts) and $I(t)$ is the current (in amps) as functions of time, then I satisfies the ODE $LI'' + RI' + C^{-1}I = E'$. *(a)* Show that the natural frequency of oscillation (corresponding to R small enough to be negligible) is $(LC)^{-1/2}$. If $L = 1$ henry, what value of C is needed to tune in a station at 680 kHz? *(b)* Suppose it is desired to make the half-width of the resonance 1000 Hz in the sense that signals at 679 or 681 kHz generate responses of half the amplitude of a signal at 680 kHz. What's the right choice of R? Is this subcritical, critical, or supercritical damping?

Exercise 8.3. *1D analogue of Chladni patterns.* *(a)* Plot the solution of $y'' + 1000y = e^x$, $y(0) = y(\pi) = 0$. Why does it have such a regular shape, and why is the number of maxima what it is? Why does the shape become even more regular if 1000 is changed to 1020? *(b)* Answer the same questions for $y'''' - 10^6 y = e^x$, $y(0) = y''(0) = 0$, $y(\pi) = y''(\pi) = 0$, with 10^6 then changing to 1.05×10^6.

Exercise 8.4. *High tides in coastal cities.* *(a)* Find out the date of the next full or new moon in Honolulu, Lisbon, Sydney, and a fourth coastal city of your choosing. *(b)*

Find out the times of the two high tides in these cities on this date. For cities observing daylight saving time, be sure to correct appropriately so as to get high tides in standard local time. *(c)* Figure 8.12 suggests the high tides should be at approximately 6am and 6pm, whereas if the tidal bulges were aligned with the moon, it would be noon and midnight. Which of these scenarios do your data come closer to? How close?[37]

Exercise 8.5. Random forcing. Repeat Figure 8.7 but with the forcing function replaced by f = randnfun([0,200]), a smooth random function containing a wide range of wave numbers (see Chapter 12). Run the code three times so as to see responses to three random functions, and discuss the shape and size of the outputs.

Exercise 8.6. Beating. Figures 8.2 and 8.10 show beating effects that arise when two waves of nearby frequencies are added. *(a)* Use trigonometric identities to derive the formula $\cos(\omega t) + \cos((\omega + 2\varepsilon)t) = 2\cos((\omega + \varepsilon)t)\cos(\varepsilon t)$ for arbitrary constants ω and ε. *(b)* Relate this formula to one of these figures, and discuss what adaptation would be needed to relate it to the other.

Exercise 8.7. Damping and phase lag. Let $\omega = 1$ and $\varepsilon = 0.05$ and define a chebfun f for the denominator of (8.9) over the range $0.5 \leq \nu \leq 1.5$. Plot angle(1/f). Repeat for $\varepsilon = 0.005$ and relate the plots to the discussion about phase lag as a function of ν.

---

[37] In the final weeks of writing this book, author LNT visited the Holy Island of Lindisfarne just before the solar eclipse of August 21, 2017. When there is a solar eclipse, there must be a new moon syzygy, so Figure 8.12 suggests high tides at 6am and 6pm. Tides matter a great deal on Lindisfarne, because the causeway is underwater for ten hours each day! The actual high tide in the afternoon of August 21 was at 14:24, alas — not such a good match with the figure.

9. Second-order equations in the phase plane

Consider a second-order autonomous ODE, which may be linear or nonlinear,

$$y''(t) = f(y, y').\tag{9.1}$$

Given a pair of values y and y' at a particular time t, this equation tells us the rate of change of y' at t, and the rate of change of y itself is by definition y'. Thus with (9.1) we know the rates of change of both y and y', and we can represent this information pictorially by a diagram of the **phase plane**, in which the horizontal axis represents y and the vertical axis represents y'. For example, here is a "quiver plot" of the phase plane for the simple harmonic oscillator or linear pendulum equation $y'' = -y$.

```
L = chebop(@(t,y) diff(y,2) + y);
quiver(L,[-2.8 2.8 -1.1 1.1]), hold on, plot(0,0,'.')
```

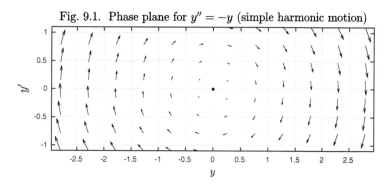

Fig. 9.1. Phase plane for $y'' = -y$ (simple harmonic motion)

At each point (y, y'), the arrow shows the direction and magnitude of the vector (y', y''). Solutions to the ODE will correspond to trajectories following the arrows around the plane. Note that for any equation (9.1), regardless of f, the arrows will always point rightward in the upper half-plane and leftward in the lower half-plane. The black dot at $y = y' = 0$ marks a *fixed point* (or *steady state*) of this equation, which means, a point at which $y' = y'' = 0$.

An image like Figure 9.1, while accurate, is sometimes not as compelling as one in which all the arrows are set to have the same length, giving a plot of a *direction field*. This can be done with the `quiver` option `'normalize'`.

```
quiver(L,[-2.8 2.8 -1.1 1.1],'normalize',1)
hold on, plot(0,0,'.')
```

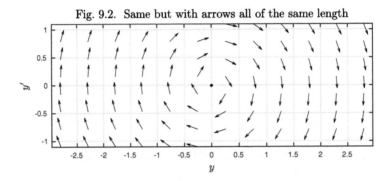

Fig. 9.2. Same but with arrows all of the same length

There is nothing more to the dynamics of an autonomous ODE than its phase plane. If an initial point (y, y') is specified, then all of the future trajectory is determined simply by the vector field.[38] This is the power of phase plane analysis: it reduces dynamics to geometry.

For example, let us now specify a t domain and an initial condition for the linear pendulum,

$$y'' = -y, \quad t \in [0, 1.8\pi], \ y(0) = 0, \ y'(0) = 1, \tag{9.2}$$

or in Chebfun,

```
L.domain = [0,1.8*pi]; L.lbc = [0;1];
```

Here we superimpose the trajectory corresponding to the solution of (9.2) on the vector field just displayed. The trajectory begins at the top of the unit circle with initial velocity 1 and initial acceleration 0, so the curve is oriented horizontally to the right. As y increases, y'' becomes negative, and the curve begins to bend around, describing a clockwise circle. Since the time interval runs 90% of the way to 2π, the circle is 90% complete.

```
y = L\0; hold on, arrowplot(y,diff(y))
```

---

[38]To be precise, this requires the solutions to be unique, which will be assured if f satisfies a condition of Lipschitz continuity. See Chapter 11.

Fig. 9.3. A trajectory added to the plot, the solution of (9.2)

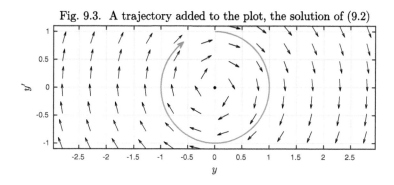

Let us dispense with the quiver arrows and collect trajectories with different initial values on a single plot. The next picture takes $b = 0.5, 0.8, \ldots, 2$, producing six circles of corresponding radii.

```
for b = .5:.3:2
  L.lbc = [0;b]; y = L\0; arrowplot(y,diff(y)), hold on
end
plot(0,0,'.')
```

Fig. 9.4. Six trajectories for (9.2)

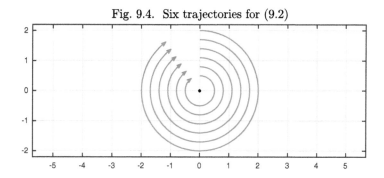

The phase plane can be informative about boundary-value problems, too. For example, suppose we change (9.2) to

$$y'' = -y, \quad t \in [0,3], \ y(0) = 1, \ y(4) = -1.5. \tag{9.3}$$

Here is the solution, shown as a seventh trajectory added to the previous plot (without an arrowhead since this is a BVP).

```
L = chebop(0,4); L.op = @(t,y) diff(y,2) + y;
L.lbc = 1; L.rbc = -1.5;
y = L\0; plot(y,diff(y))
```

Fig. 9.5. Solution of BVP (9.3)

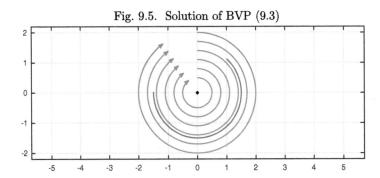

Equations (9.2) and (9.3) describe a linear pendulum without damping. Following Chapters 4 and 8, let us now add some damping in the form of a small multiple of y',

$$y'' = -y - \varepsilon y', \quad t \in [0, 1.8\pi], \ y(0) = 0, \ y'(0) = b, \qquad (9.4)$$

with $\varepsilon = 0.2$. If we follow the same six trajectories as before, we see that they now lose amplitude as they evolve, moving towards the fixed point $y = y' = 0$ as $t \to \infty$. This is a *stable* fixed point since all nearby trajectories stay close to it; we shall consider such definitions systematically in Chapter 15. The plot also shows the solution to the BVP variant of (9.4) with the same boundary conditions $y(0) = 1$, $y(4) = -1.5$ as in (9.3). Note that the solution starts from a greater velocity y' than before, necessary to compensate for the damping while still matching the boundary conditions.

```
L = chebop(0,1.8*pi); L.op = @(t,y) diff(y,2) + 0.2*diff(y) + y;
for b = .5:.3:2
  L.lbc = [0;b]; y = L\0; arrowplot(y,diff(y)), hold on
end
L = chebop(0,4); L.op = @(t,y) diff(y,2) + 0.2*diff(y) + y;
L.lbc = 1; L.rbc = -1.5;
y = L\0; plot(y,diff(y)), plot(0,0,'.')
```

Fig. 9.6. Damped linear pendulum (9.4)

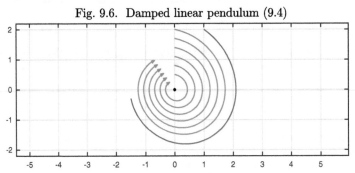

We stopped the flow at $t = 1.8\pi$, but of course this is not necessary. Here is a single trajectory carried to 9π. This represents a linear pendulum swinging back and forth 4 1/2 times, losing amplitude as it swings.

```
L = chebop(0,9*pi);
L.op = @(t,y) diff(y,2)+0.2*diff(y)+y; L.lbc = [0;2];
y = L\0; plot(y,diff(y)), hold on, plot(0,0,'.')
```

Fig. 9.7. A trajectory for (9.4) carried to longer time

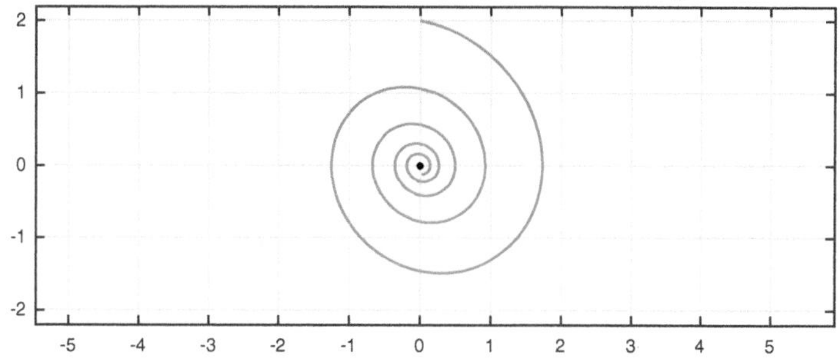

We mentioned that in the phase plane the position of a trajectory at any time t determines its future, which consists of following the unique path through that point. This uniqueness property depends on the equation being autonomous. If we solve a nonautonomous problem, such as

$$y'' = -y - 0.2y' - 2\cos(2t), \quad t \in [0, 1.8\pi], \ y(0) = 0, \ y'(0) = b, \qquad (9.5)$$

we can plot the solution in the y-y' plane, like this (now with different colors to help distinguish the curves):

```
L = chebop(0,1.8*pi);
L.op = @(t,y) diff(y,2)+0.2*diff(y)+y+2*cos(2*t);
for b = .5:.3:2
  L.lbc = [0;b]; y = L\0; arrowplot(y,diff(y)), hold on
end
plot(4.5,0,'X')
```

Fig. 9.8. Inhomogeneous problem — not truly a phase plane!

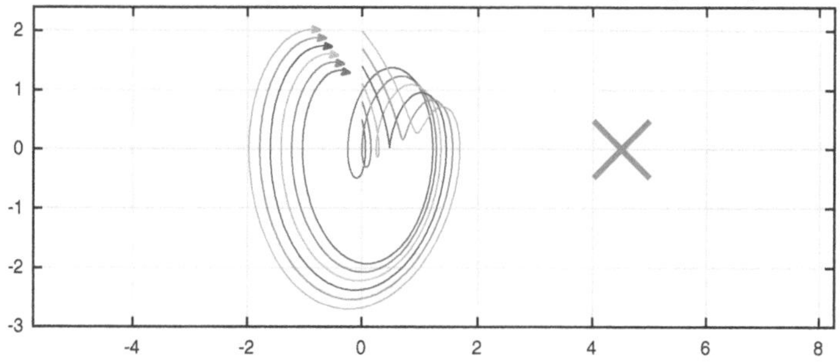

However, the point of planar analysis has been lost since the future of a trajectory is not determined by its current position in the plane, and the curves cross each other. The plot of trajectories has become merely a plot of trajectories, no longer an encapsulation of the dynamics of the system. Such plots can be interesting and informative; see for example Exercise 9.2 and the Duffing oscillator in Appendix B. They usually don't belong to phase plane analysis, however. An alternative in such cases is to include the time variable in the plot on an additional axis. Here, for example, we repeat the calculation on the longer interval $[0, 40]$, for a single trajectory, and plot the result in t-y-y' space.

```
L.domain = [0,40];
y = L\0; t = chebfun('t',[0 40]); plot3(t,y,diff(y))
```

Fig. 9.9. Trajectory in t-y-y' space

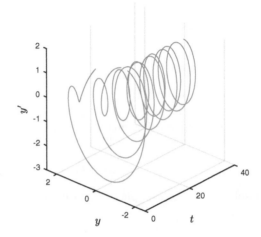

Returning to (9.4), in the language of Chapter 4, the damping with $\varepsilon = 0.2$ is *subcritical*: from (4.11) we see that the critical damping parameter for this equation is $\varepsilon = 2$. Here are images of subcritical, critical, and supercritical trajectories with $\varepsilon = 1, 2, 4$, now for $t \in [0, 1.5\pi]$. Note that it is the critically damped trio of trajectories that finishes closest to the origin, confirming that $\varepsilon = 2$ gives the most effective damping.

```
close all, L.domain = [0,1.5*pi];
subplot(1,3,1), L.op = @(t,y) diff(y,2)+diff(y)+y;
for b = 1:-.2:.6
  L.lbc = [0;b]; y = L\0; arrowplot(y,diff(y)), hold on
end
plot(0,0,'.'), subplot(1,3,2), L.op = @(t,y) diff(y,2)+2*diff(y)+y;
for b = 1:-.2:.6
  L.lbc = [0;b]; y = L\0; arrowplot(y,diff(y)), hold on
end
plot(0,0,'.'), subplot(1,3,3), L.op = @(t,y) diff(y,2)+4*diff(y)+y;
for b = 1:-.2:.6
  L.lbc = [0;b]; y = L\0; arrowplot(y,diff(y)), hold on
end
plot(0,0,'.')
```

Fig. 9.10. Subcritical, critical, and supercritical damping

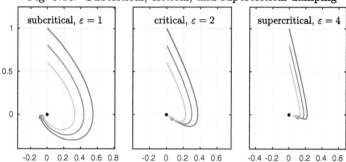

Phase plane analysis becomes particularly interesting for nonlinear ODEs. For example, the first nonlinear equation of this book is the van der Pol equation. With slightly different coefficients from (1.2), let us write this as

$$y'' + y - \mu(1 - y^2)y' = 0, \quad t \in [0, 10], \; y(0) = a, y'(0) = 0. \qquad (9.6)$$

Here are phase plane plots for $\mu = 0.125$ and $\mu = 1.5$. With the weak damping parameter $\mu = 0.0125$, the system is not far from the linear pendulum, with trajectories winding slowly in or out to an asymptotic curve known as a **limit cycle**. With the stronger damping parameter $\mu = 1.5$, trajectories converge to the limit cycle much faster, and its shape is far from circular, just as the van der Pol orbit plotted in Chapter 1 is far from a sine wave.

```
N = chebop(0,15);
for j = 1:2
  subplot(1,2,j), mu = 0.125; if j==2, mu = 1.5; end
  N.op = @(t,y) diff(y,2)-mu*(1-y^2)*diff(y)+y;
  for a = [1 3]
    N.lbc = [a;0]; y = N\0; arrowplot(y,diff(y)), hold on
  end
  plot(0,0,'.')
end
```

Fig. 9.11. Van der Pol equation

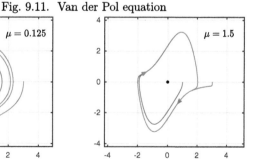

APPLICATION: NONLINEAR PENDULUM

The linear pendulum equation $y'' = -y$ describes oscillation in the context of Hooke's law, where the restoring force is proportional to the displacement — simple harmonic motion. When the amplitudes of motion are small, this is the right model for a spring or a pendulum and for many other vibrating systems, but when the amplitudes get bigger, the physics always becomes nonlinear. Different problems have different nonlinearities, but there is no doubt as to the archetypal problem of this kind: it is the **nonlinear pendulum**, corresponding to an idealized point mass moving in a circle at the end of a rigid weightless bar. The equation is

$$y'' = -\sin(y), \tag{9.7}$$

where $y(t)$ represents the angle from the vertical in radians at time t and constants are set to 1. For an entire book on the subject, see Baker and Blackburn, *The Pendulum*, Oxford University Press, 2005.

This is a perfect example for phase plane analysis. First we draw a quiver plot together with stable and unstable fixed points (black and red, respectively). There are stable fixed points at $(y, y') = (2\pi j, 0)$ for each integer j and unstable fixed points at the in-between locations $(2\pi(j + 1/2), 0)$.

```
N = chebop(0,1.8*pi); N.op = @(t,y) diff(y,2)+sin(y);
quiver(N,[-3 23 -6 6]), hold on, plot(pi*(0:7),0*(0:7),'.')
```

Fig. 9.12. Nonlinear pendulum (9.7)

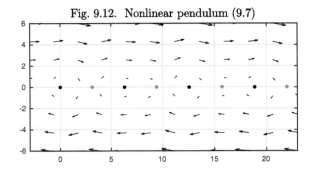

To see more, let us plot some trajectories. We start from $y = 0$ and $y'(0) = b = 1, 1.2, \ldots, 4$, calculating trajectories over the interval $t \in [0, 1.8\pi]$.[39]

```
plot(pi*(0:7),0*(0:7),'.'), hold on
for b = 1:.2:4
  N.lbc = [0;b]; y = N\0; arrowplot(y,diff(y))
end
```

---

[39] To us this looks like the hair of Botticelli's Venus; or is it the Starbucks logo?

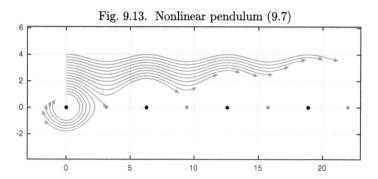

Fig. 9.13. Nonlinear pendulum (9.7)

Physically, these curves can be interpreted as follows. If $y'(0) = b < 2$, the pendulum does not have enough energy to swing over the top, and the trajectory goes around and around forever on a single loop in the phase plane, corresponding to the pendulum swinging back and forth, with the angle $y(t)$ remaining bounded. The loops are not circles, but they approach circles for small amplitude, where the distinction between y as in (9.2) and $\sin(y)$ as in (9.7) fades away. If $y'(0) = b > 2$, on the other hand, the pendulum has enough energy to swing over, and $y(t)$ keeps increasing monotonically. In the absence of damping, a pendulum that swings over once swings over infinitely many times as $t \to \infty$. The phase plane is 2π-periodic.

Notice the trajectory starting at $y'(0) = 2$. This one appears to stop at the y-axis, and that is exactly what it does. It has just enough energy to fly up toward the vertical configuration, with $y(t)$ approaching π as $t \to \infty$, but it never quite hits the top for any finite value of t.

Of course a real pendulum is sure to have some losses. Here is the same image corresponding to an equation with subcritical damping,

$$y'' = -\sin(y) - \mu y', \quad t \in [0, 1.8\pi], \ y(0) = 0, \ y'(0) = b, \qquad (9.8)$$

with $\mu = 0.1$. A curve is also added to the plot corresponding to the BVP defined by $y(0) = 0$, $y(1.95\pi) = 20$. We see that to reach $y = 20$ by the end of the time interval, a greater initial speed is needed.

```
N.op = @(t,y) diff(y,2)+sin(y)+.1*diff(y);
for b = 1:.2:4
  N.lbc = [0;b]; y = N\0; arrowplot(y,diff(y)), hold on
end
plot(pi*(0:7),0*(0:7),'.'), N.lbc = 0; N.rbc = 20;
y = N\0; plot(y,diff(y))
```

Fig. 9.14. Damped nonlinear pendulum (9.8)

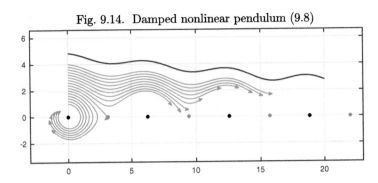

Now, a trajectory with sufficient initial energy swings over, but it keeps losing energy as it goes, so it may or may not swing over a second time. We can see more if we increase the time interval to $[0, 8\pi]$. The trajectory with initial velocity $y'(0) = 4$ swings over four times before eventually winding down to rest. As before, the function $f(y, y')$ defining the phase plane is 2π-periodic, though none of the individual trajectories are periodic.

```
N = chebop(0,8*pi); N.op = @(t,y) diff(y,2)+sin(y)+.1*diff(y);
plot(pi*(0:7),0*(0:7),'.'), hold on
for b = 1:.2:4
  N.lbc = [0;b]; y = N\0; arrowplot(y,diff(y))
end
```

Fig. 9.15. Longer time interval for (9.8)

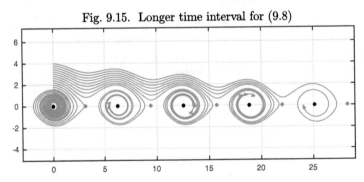

HISTORY. Four hundred years ago, Galileo understood the essentials of the linear pendulum. In his *Dialogues Concerning Two New Sciences* the character Salviati says, "As to the times of vibration of bodies suspended by threads of different lengths, they bear to each other the same proportion as the square roots of the lengths of the threads; or one might say the lengths are to each other as the squares of the times; so that if one wishes to make the vibration-time of one pendulum twice that of another, he must make its suspension four times as long."

OUR FAVORITE REFERENCE. When it comes to phase plane analysis, one of the oldest books is also one of the nicest: H. T. Davis, *Introduction to Nonlinear Differential and Integral Equations,* Dover, 1962 (first published in 1960).

For example, we enjoy Chapter 10 on "The phase plane and its phenomena," Chapter 11 on "Nonlinear mechanics," and Chapter 12 on "Some particular equations."

SUMMARY OF CHAPTER 9. *The phase plane for a second-order autonomous homogeneous ODE $y'' = f(y, y')$ is the plane with coordinates y and y'. The position of a solution at a particular time t determines its future trajectory as the unique curve passing through this point. Plotting phase plane trajectories gives a quick way to interpret behavior of ODEs, including nonlinear ones.*

Exercise 9.1. $y'' = y$. Draw phase plane trajectories or quiver arrows for the equation $y'' = y$ (either by hand or with the computer). Where in this image does the solution of Figure 5.3 lie? (It comes very close to following the *stable manifold* of the fixed point for 30 time units and then the *unstable manifold* for a further 30 times units; see Chapter 15.)

Exercise 9.2. Moving slowly in the phase plane. Consider the ODE $y'' + y = y^2$. *(a)* What are the fixed points? *(b)* Draw a quiver plot, choosing axes to make the plot as informative as possible. Based on this information, draw a sketch by hand of the key points of the phase plane dynamics. Describe qualitatively what orbits will remain bounded, and how they will behave; also what orbits will diverge to ∞, and how they will behave. *(c)* Find two distinct solutions that satisfy $y(0) = y(10) = 2$. Plot them both as functions of t and in the phase plane. What are the values of $y'(0)$ for these two solutions?

Exercise 9.3. Region-filling orbits. (Adapted from Davis, *Introduction to Nonlinear Differential and Integral Equations,* section 10.4.) *(a)* Use the method of undetermined coefficients to find the analytical solution of the IVP $y'' + 2y = -2\cos(2t)$, $y(0) = 1$, $y'(0) = \sqrt{2}$. *(b)* This solution has a curious property in the phase plane: the curve eventually gets arbitrarily close to every point in a near-elliptical region. Plot the solution over $t \in [0, 100]$ to see the effect. (This is fun to watch using `comet` as well.) *(c)* The solution just considered is nonperiodic. Periodic solutions are obtained from the same initial conditions, on the other hand, if $\cos(2t)$ is replaced by $\cos(kt)$ for certain values of $k > 0$. Find the smallest three such values analytically, and produce the corresponding plot for $t \in [0, 100]$.

Exercise 9.4. Period of the nonlinear pendulum. The code

```
y = @(s) chebop(@(y) diff(y,2)+sin(y),[0 15-5*log(pi-s)],[s;0],[])\0;
T = @(s) 2*min(diff(roots(y(s)))));
```

produces two anonymous functions y and T applicable for values $s \in (0, \pi)$. Explain what these functions compute and how they do it. Make a plot of $T(s)$ for $s \in [0.1, 3.14]$ and explain its principal features. Explain in a general way (not necessarily with mathematical details) the role of the quantity $15 - 5\log(\pi - s)$.

10. Systems of equations

Up to this point, our discussion has concerned scalar ODEs. In this chapter we begin to talk about systems of equations, which involve more than one dependent variable, or equivalently, a dependent variable that is a vector rather than a scalar.

All our vector problems will be of first order. A general first-order ODE can be written

$$\mathbf{y}'(t) = \mathbf{f}(t, \mathbf{y}) \tag{10.1}$$

for a linear or nonlinear function $\mathbf{f}$, where for each t, $\mathbf{y}(t)$ represents a vector of dimension n,

$$\mathbf{y}(t) = \begin{pmatrix} y_1(t) \\ \vdots \\ y_n(t) \end{pmatrix}, \quad \mathbf{f}(t, \mathbf{y}) = \begin{pmatrix} f_1(t, \mathbf{y}) \\ \vdots \\ f_n(t, \mathbf{y}) \end{pmatrix}.$$

The dependent variables are thus $y_1, \ldots, y_n$, and we could write the system out explicitly like this:

$$y_1'(t) = f_1(t, y_1(t), \ldots, y_n(t)),$$

$$\vdots$$

$$y_n'(t) = f_n(t, y_1(t), \ldots, y_n(t)).$$

For systems of small size we will usually find it convenient to use variable names without subscripts, such as u, v, w. The reason we can restrict the discussion to first order is that any higher-order ODE can be written as a system of first-order ODEs by introducing additional variables, as outlined in Exercise 1.5. In FLASHI nomenclature, any fS$\cdots$ can be turned into an Fs$\cdots$.[40]

To fully specify an ODE problem from (10.1), one normally needs n additional conditions. In an initial-value problem, we prescribe the value of $\mathbf{y}$ at a fixed time such as $t = 0$,

$$\mathbf{y}(0) = \mathbf{a}. \tag{10.2}$$

This amounts to specifying each of the n components,

$$y_1(0) = a_1, \quad \ldots, \quad y_n(0) = a_n.$$

In a boundary-value problem, different components of $\mathbf{y}$ or combinations thereof may be specified at different points, for a total normally of n conditions altogether. Exactly what specifications may lead to a well-posed BVP for a system of equations is not always a straightforward matter. For IVPs, however, existence and uniqueness are guaranteed so long as $\mathbf{f}$ is continuous with respect to t and $\mathbf{y}$ and Lipschitz continuous with respect to $\mathbf{y}$, as we shall prove in the next chapter (Theorem 11.2).

For example, consider the two-variable autonomous system

$$u' = -v - u(u^2 + v^2), \quad v' = u - v(u^2 + v^2). \tag{10.3}$$

Here are the trajectories of u and v for $t \in [0, 30]$ with $u(0) = 1$, $v(0) = 0$.[41]

```
N = chebop(0,30); N.lbc = [1; 0];
N.op = @(t,u,v) [diff(u)+v+u*(u^2+v^2); diff(v)-u+v*(u^2+v^2)];
[u,v] = N\0; plot([u v])
```

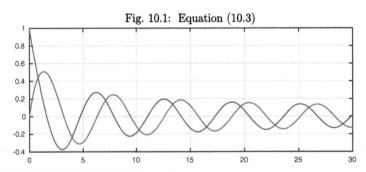

Fig. 10.1: Equation (10.3)

---

[40]This doesn't mean that, in practice, higher-order systems are necessarily reduced to first-order form. For example, the Solar System Dynamics Group at the Jet Propulsion Laboratory in California solves systems of hundreds of ODEs numerically to track the moon and planets and other bodies: when the media tell you there's going to be an eclipse, the computations probably came from JPL. The methods used by the SSD Group are based on a second-order formulation, without reduction to first order.

[41]For plots like this showing multiple components, we revert to MATLAB's built-in color tables rather than the light/dark green and blue colors usually used in this book for linear/nonlinear IVPs and BVPs.

We see two interlocking oscillations, decaying rapidly in amplitude at first but then much more slowly.

Since (10.3) is autonomous, the whole future of the system is determined by the values of u and v at any given time. Thus it makes sense to plot this solution in the **phase plane**, with u on the horizontal axis and v on the vertical axis. This is a straightforward generalization of the phase plane of the last chapter, where the two axes represented y and y'. Here, however, trajectories need not point rightward in the upper half-plane.

```
arrowplot(u,v), hold on, plot(0,0,'.')
```

Fig. 10.2. Solution of (10.3) in the phase plane

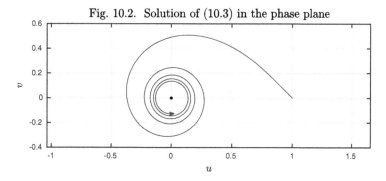

The dot at the center marks the fixed point of the system, corresponding to the constant solution $u(t) = v(t) = 0$. In general, a **fixed point** of an autonomous ODE $\mathbf{y}' = \mathbf{f}(\mathbf{y})$ is any point $\mathbf{y}_0$ such that $\mathbf{f}(\mathbf{y}_0) = \mathbf{0}$, implying that the constant $\mathbf{y}(t) = \mathbf{y}_0$ is a solution. The dynamics of this problem is angularly symmetric, as can be confirmed by converting $\mathbf{f}$ to polar coordinates.

As in the last chapter, we may think of the trajectory as following the arrows of a direction field:

```
quiver(N,[-.7 1.1 -.4 .6])
```

Fig. 10.3. Same with quiver arrows added

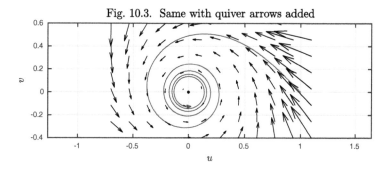

One way to understand the motion is to interpret the nonlinear terms of (10.3) as linear terms with varying coefficients. For a positive constant κ, the system

$$u' = -v - \kappa u, \quad v' = u - \kappa v$$

describes a simple oscillation with damping. Locally, near any particular point $(u(t), v(t))$, (10.3) will behave in just this way with $\kappa = u(t)^2 + v(t)^2$. This explains the behavior of the two images above: we start with a damping coefficient $\kappa = 1$, but, at the end of the trajectory, κ is about 60 times smaller:

```
kappa = u(end)^2 + v(end)^2
```

```
kappa = 0.0164
```

We emphasized in the last chapter that phase plane or more generally phase space analysis (for $n \geq 3$) is appropriate only for a system that is autonomous, so that the state $\mathbf{y}$ at a fixed time determines fully the future solution $\mathbf{y}(t)$.[42] A fundamental property of phase space analysis is that *distinct trajectories can never meet* (assuming $\mathbf{f}$ is continuous with respect to t and $\mathbf{y}$ and Lipschitz continuous with respect to $\mathbf{y}$). This follows from the uniqueness of solutions, for if an autonomous ODE has two solutions $\mathbf{y}_1(t)$ and $\mathbf{y}_2(t)$ such that $\mathbf{y}_1(t_1) = \mathbf{y}_2(t_2)$ for some t_1 and t_2, then if solutions are unique, we must have $\mathbf{y}(t_1 + t) = \mathbf{y}_2(t_2 + t)$ for all t, positive and negative. So the trajectories corresponding to $\mathbf{y}_1$ and $\mathbf{y}_2$ must be the same.

For another example, let us consider the two-variable system known as the **predator–prey** or **Lotka–Volterra** equations. We suppose an environment in which there is a prey species, say rabbits, whose population as a function of time is $u(t)$, and a predator species, say foxes, whose population as a function of time is $v(t)$.[43] In the absence of foxes, the rabbit population grows exponentially thanks to abundant vegetation, but it is decreased by fatal encounters with foxes at a rate proportional to the product uv,

$$u' = u - uv. \tag{10.4}$$

The fox population, on the other hand, decays exponentially in the absence of rabbits to eat but expands when they are available,

$$v' = -\tfrac{1}{5}v + uv. \tag{10.5}$$

(The constant $1/5$ is included to make the dynamics nontrivial. In a serious application one would have dimensional constants in front of each term, based on measurements of field data.) Combining the two equations with initial conditions, we obtain the Lotka–Volterra IVP

$$u' = u - uv, \quad v' = -\tfrac{1}{5}v + uv, \quad t \geq 0, \quad u(0) = u_0, \quad v(0) = v_0. \tag{10.6}$$

A quiver plot looks like this:

---

[42] A nonautonomous system of size n can, however, be written as an autonomous one of size $n + 1$ by introducing a new dependent variable τ equivalent to t, governed by the equation $\tau' = 1$ and the initial value $\tau(0) = 0$. See Figure 9.9.

[43] Volterra's original application of 1926 involved fish populations in the Adriatic Sea. Danby writes in *Computer Modeling: From Sports to Spaceflight... From Order to Chaos:* "Presentations of this model include many pairs: birds and worms, wolves and deer, sharks and tuna, to name a few. I have found that my students prefer foxes and rabbits, so I shall refer to these. After all, who identifies with a worm?"

```
N = chebop(0,60); N.lbc = [1;1];
N.op = @(t,u,v) [diff(u)-u+u*v; diff(v)+.2*v-u*v];
quiver(N,[0 1.5 0 3])
```

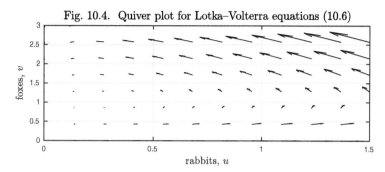

Fig. 10.4. Quiver plot for Lotka–Volterra equations (10.6)

This problem has periodic solutions, where the rabbit population oscillates between large and (very) small and the fox population oscillates between large and (not so) small, with a phase lag since a large rabbit population leads to a growing fox population. Here is the periodic solution that evolves from the initial populations $u(0) = v(0) = 1$.

```
[u,v] = N\0; plot([u v])
hold on, plot([0 0;60 60],[.2 1; .2 1],'--')
```

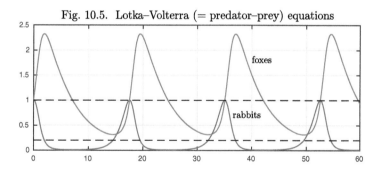

Fig. 10.5. Lotka–Volterra (= predator–prey) equations

The period is about 17.5.

```
[~,m] = max(v,'local'); period = diff(m)

period =
   17.5262
   17.5262
   17.5262
```

To understand the Lotka–Volterra dynamics, again it is helpful to interpret the nonlinear terms of (10.4)–(10.5) as linear terms with varying coefficients. Equation (10.4) can be written $u' = (1 - v)u$, showing that, locally, u will decrease exponentially for $v > 1$ (the fox curve lies above the upper dashed line) and increase exponentially for $v < 1$ (it lies below the upper dashed line). Thus the rabbit population has an exponential growth tendency that shuts off as v rises above 1. Similarly, equation (10.5) can be written $v' = (u - 1/5)v$, showing that the fox population has an exponential decay tendency but grows whenever there are enough rabbits, $u > 1/5$ (the rabbit curve lies above the lower dashed line).

Here is the orbit just computed in the phase plane, winding around counterclockwise several times.

```
arrowplot(u,v), hold on, quiver(N,[0 1.5 0 3])
plot([.2 0;.2 1.5],[0 1; 3 1],'--')
```

Fig. 10.6. Lotka–Volterra cycle in the phase plane

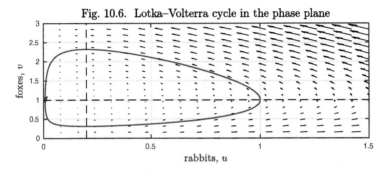

Let us superimpose several orbits in a single plot, corresponding to the solutions arising from various initial populations of rabbits.

```
for s = .4:.2:1.4
  N.lbc = [s; 1]; [u,v] = N\0; arrowplot(u,v), hold on
end
plot([.2 0;.2 1.5],[0 1; 3 1],'--')
```

Fig. 10.7. Superposition of six orbits

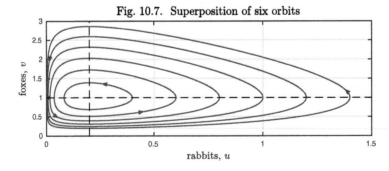

The figures show that in the Lotka–Volterra model the effects of the initial conditions last forever: some fox-rabbit oscillations have great amplitude while others move little. At the center is obviously a fixed point, which we may confirm by setting $u' = v' = 0$ in (10.6). This gives the equations

$$u = uv, \quad \tfrac{1}{5}v = uv,$$

implying that these equations in fact have two fixed points: one at $(1/5, 1)$ and the other at $(0, 0)$. Let us mark them in the plot.

```
hold on, plot([0 .2],[0 1],'.')
```

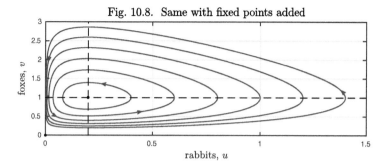

Fig. 10.8. Same with fixed points added

The Lotka–Volterra equations are perhaps the most famous system of two ODEs, appearing in every ODE textbook. Turning now to three dimensions, it is only fitting that we should begin with the most famous system of three ODEs, the **Lorenz equations**. In 3D, a new possibility opens up for reasons we shall explain in a moment: the dynamics of an ODE may be *chaotic*. The Lorenz equations are the archetypal chaotic system, consisting of three coupled first-order equations,

$$u' = 10(v - u), \quad v' = u(28 - w) - v, \quad w' = uv - (8/3)w. \tag{10.7}$$

The coefficients 10, 28, and 8/3 are arbitrary, and it is not necessary to use exactly these values. However, so much study of the Lorenz equations has been based on these parameter choices that they have become standard.

Equations (10.7) may look complicated at first glance, but in fact the nonlinearities here are rather simple: the equation for u' is linear, and the equations for v' and w' are quadratic, their only nonlinearities consisting of the term $-uw$ in the equation for v' and the term uv in the equation for w'. To make an IVP, we impose initial conditions such as

$$u(0) = v(0) = -15, \quad w(0) = 20. \tag{10.8}$$

Here is the solution of (10.7)–(10.8) up to time $t = 30$, showing the three components together.

```
N = chebop(0,30); N.lbc = [-15; -15; 20];
N.op = @(t,u,v,w) [diff(u)-10*(v-u); ...
    diff(v)-u*(28-w)+v; diff(w)-u*v+(8/3)*w];
[u,v,w] = N\0; plot([u v w])
```

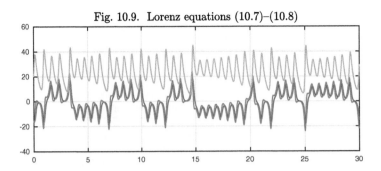

Fig. 10.9. Lorenz equations (10.7)–(10.8)

To focus on just one component of the solution, here is a plot of $v(t)$. Note the characteristic property of chaos: apparent randomness in a deterministic system. We shall discuss chaos more fully in Chapter 13.

```
plot(v)
```

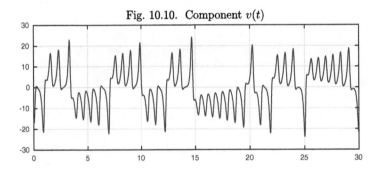

Fig. 10.10. Component $v(t)$

The Lorenz equations are autonomous, so they can be represented in a phase space, which will have three dimensions. Here is a phase space plot of the trajectory just computed. The plot includes dots showing the fixed points, which are the solutions of the equations we obtain by setting $u' = v' = w' = 0$ in (10.7),

$$v = u, \quad 28u - uw = v, \quad uv = 8w/3.$$

There are three fixed points, one at $(u, v, w) = (0, 0, 0)$ and the others at

$$(u, v, w) = (\pm 6\sqrt{2}, \pm 6\sqrt{2}, 27).$$

```
plot3(u,v,w), c = 6*sqrt(2); hold on
plot3([0 c -c],[0 c -c],[0 27 27],'.')
```

Fig. 10.11. 3D phase space for the Lorenz eqs.

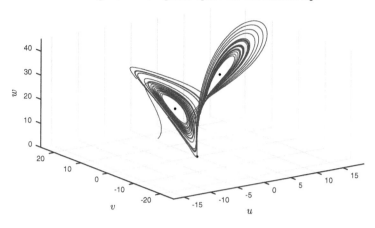

Ideas related to phase spaces and their trajectories are at the heart of the rich subject of *dynamical systems,* and a great deal is known about the mathematics and application of these notions. The traditional method of this analysis is to begin by finding fixed points and then examine the behavior near these points by approximating the nonlinear problem locally by a linear problem. As we shall see in Chapter 14, linear analysis makes sense at any point of a phase space, not just a fixed point; locally, any smooth nonlinear ODE might as well be linear. What makes the fixed points particularly interesting is that trajectories interact in nontrivial ways at such points, and to see the overall dynamics in a phase space, it is often fruitful to start from the fixed points and see how they may be connected by various trajectories. See Chapter 15.

One of the fundamental things one can learn from this kind of geometrical reasoning is that trajectories can get tangled up in 3D, but not in 2D. In 2D, since trajectories cannot cross, tangling is not possible. Therefore, chaos can appear in autonomous systems with $n \geq 3$ but never with $n = 2$.[44] Another point is that, since a linear system of ODEs behaves in essentially the same way at every point of phase space, its trajectories look essentially the same everywhere. So they can't get tangled up either, and chaos can never appear in a linear problem, no matter how many variables there are. Since we have not given a mathematical definition of chaos, these observations must be regarded as heuristic, but they can be made precise.

Let us finish with an example of a three-variable problem that is not chaotic, analyzed in pp. 202–204 of Bender and Orszag, *Advanced Mathematical Methods for Scientists and Engineers,*

$$u' = vw, \quad v' = -2uw, \quad w' = uv. \tag{10.9}$$

It can be shown that along any trajectory, the quantity $u(t)^2 + v(t)^2 + w(t)^2$ is constant, and thus trajectories lie on spheres. Here is a plot showing some of them.

---

[44]A precise formulation of this idea is provided by the *Poincaré–Bendixson theorem.*

```
close all, N = chebop(0,10);
N.op = @(t,u,v,w) [diff(u)-v*w; diff(v) + 2*u*w; diff(w)-u*v];
for theta = -1.5:.2:1.5
  N.lbc = [cos(theta); sin(theta); 0];
  [u,v,w] = N\0; plot3(u,v,w), hold on
  plot3(-u,v,w), plot3(w,v,u), plot3(w,v,-u)
end
plot3([0 0 0 0 1 -1],[0 0 1 -1 0 0],[1 -1 0 0 0 0],'.')
```

Fig. 10.12. Phase space for (10.9)

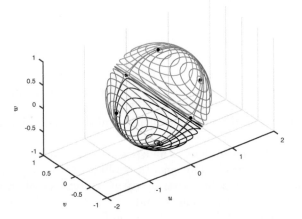

As explained by Bender and Orszag, this example is related to the mechanical phenomenon known as *Eulerian wobble* and can be used to explain why, if you toss a book in the air, you can make it spin stably around the shortest axis or the longest, but not the middle one: it will somersault. This is also called the *tennis racket theorem* or the *Dzhanibekov effect*.

APPLICATION: SIR MODEL FOR EPIDEMICS

A major advance in epidemiology dates to a 1927 study by W. O. Kermack and A. G. McKendrick of a 1906 outbreak of bubonic plague in Bombay, now Mumbai ("A contribution to the mathematical theory of epidemics," *Proceedings of the Royal Society of London A*). Kermack and McKendrick proposed what is now called the *SIR model* for the spread of disease. Although the SIR model is now considered too simplistic for quantitative tracking of real epidemics, it exhibits several important properties and remains the foundation for more comprehensive models.

This is a *compartment model,* in which one imagines members of a population making the transition continuously from a box labeled S for *susceptible* to another box I for *infected* and eventually to a box R for *recovered* or *removed* (possibly by death). In nondimensional form the system is

$$S' = -\beta SI, \quad I' = (\beta S - \gamma)I, \quad R' = \gamma I, \qquad (10.10)$$

where $\beta, \gamma > 0$ are parameters and $S(t)$, $I(t)$, and $R(t)$ denote the proportions of the population in the three compartments. These equations model the dynamics of the transitions $S \to I$ and $I \to R$. First, S decreases and I increases at the rate βSI (so S is monotonically nonincreasing). This product corresponds to infected people coming into contact with susceptible ones with infection rate β per contact (high for measles, low for AIDS). Second, R increases and I decreases at the rate γI (so R is monotonically nondecreasing). This represents the approximation that infected people come to the end of their infections, whether through death or recovery, in a random fashion at a steady rate (again high for measles, low for AIDS).

Note that (10.10) is nonlinear because of the product SI. Note also how easily we can spot factors that are omitted from the model. For example, (10.10) says nothing about the course of the infection; an infected patient is simply assumed to recover or die at random with a probability that does not vary from day to day. Also, the model assumes the populations are perfectly mixed, with no spatial or social aspect to the epidemic. In actuality, spatial and socioeconomic factors can be very important, as was made famous by John Snow's study of the cholera outbreak linked to a certain public water pump in a crowded quarter of London in 1854.

The equations (10.10) have two obvious steady states. If $S = 1$ and $I = R = 0$, nobody is infected and the disease never gets going. If $S = I = 0$ and $R = 1$, the whole population is recovered or removed and the epidemic has passed into history. The nontrivial dynamics emerges when we begin with a nonzero infected fraction I_0,

$$S(0) = 1 - I_0, \quad I(0) = I_0, \quad R(0) = 0.$$

Here we show the course of the epidemic with $\beta = 2$, $\gamma = 1$, and $I_0 = 0.0001$.

```
beta = 2; gamma = 1; I0 = 0.0001; N = chebop([0 30]); close all
N.op = @(t,S,I,R) [ diff(S) + beta*S*I
                    diff(I) - beta*S*I + gamma*I
                    diff(R) - gamma*I ];
N.lbc = [1-I0; I0; 0];
[S,I,R] = N\0;  plot([S,I,R]), hold on, plot(S+I+R,'--')
```

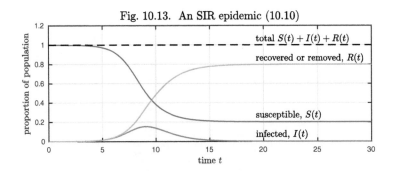

Fig. 10.13. An SIR epidemic (10.10)

The model may be simple, but there are some remarkable things to see in these curves. First of all, note how a disease may be active in a small fraction of a population for a long time, exponentially growing but at an amplitude so low that it may go unnoticed.[45]

Why does it grow at all? As mathematicians, we may say that the fixed point $(S, I, R) = (1, 0, 0)$ is unstable. Looking at (10.10), we see that the equation giving exponential growth is the second one, $I' = (\beta S - \gamma)I$. If $\beta S > \gamma$, the coefficient is positive and we can expect I to grow exponentially at the rate $\beta S - \gamma$. For our choice of parameters, this is indeed the case at $t = 0$, with $\beta S - \gamma = 1$. As epidemiologists, we can interpret this condition as follows: each newly infected person, on average, infects more than 1 additional person before ceasing to be infective.

Eventually, on the other hand, the epidemic shuts off. As soon as S falls to the point where $\beta S \leq \gamma$, $I(t)$ begins to diminish and the epidemic starts fading out. In this example this occurs at the point t_c where $S(t_c) = 0.5$.

```
tc = roots(S-0.5)

tc = 9.0718
```

Note that although the infected population begins to diminish after this point, the epidemic has by no means yet run its course. In the end, most of the population has had the disease:

```
Rinfty = R(end)

Rinfty = 0.7968
```

But not all. This is a fascinating and important aspect of epidemiology. For a population to be safe from a certain pathogen, it is not necessary that everybody be immune. It suffices for a high enough fraction to be immune so that further infections will not spread. This is the celebrated effect of *herd immunity*. And here we realize that the two "obvious" fixed points of this system noted earlier are not the only ones. In fact, any values S_∞ and $R_\infty = 1 - S_\infty$ in $[0, 1]$ may be combined with $I_\infty = 0$ to make a fixed point.

As β increases, the peak of $I(t)$ comes both sooner and higher:

---

[45]What do you suppose is happening in a carton of milk in your refrigerator when its "best before" date is still a week away?

```
for beta = [1.3 1.6 2 2.8]
    N.op = @(t,S,I,R) [ diff(S) + beta*S*I
                        diff(I) - beta*S*I + gamma*I
                        diff(R) - gamma*I ];
    [S,I,R] = N\0; plot(I), hold on, [val,pos] = max(I);
end
```

Fig. 10.14. SIR epidemic for different infection rates

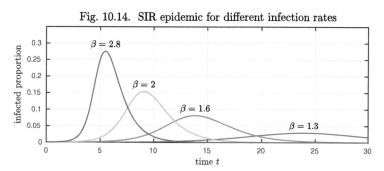

Epidemiological equations are not just used to track biological diseases. Similar compartment models have been used to study the spread of computer malware as well as other items that travel across networks — like a rumor, or a meme. See our favorite reference at the end of Chapter 15.

HISTORY. Systems of differential equations were studied by d'Alembert and Lagrange in the mid-18th century, but vector notation was not yet available in those days. Vector formulations became customary with the work of Peano and others near the end of the 19th century.

OUR FAVORITE REFERENCE. J. D. Murray's wide-ranging book *Mathematical Biology* did much to create the field of mathematical biology as it is known today. In its later extension to two volumes (Springer, 2001), the book focuses in volume 1 on systems of ODEs modeling biological systems, including insect populations, fishery management, tumor cell growth, divorce rates, biological oscillators, propagation of neural signals, and much more. The biology is varied, and the dynamical effects in the ODEs are equally varied, combining to give a deeply satisfying illustration of the power of mathematics in understanding our world.

SUMMARY OF CHAPTER 10. *Any system of ODEs can be reduced to a first-order system of the form* $\mathbf{y}'(t) = \mathbf{f}(t, \mathbf{y})$. *An n-variable autonomous system* $\mathbf{y}'(t) = \mathbf{f}(\mathbf{y})$ *has an n-dimensional phase space. If $n \geq 3$ and the equations are nonlinear, there is the possibility of chaos.*

Exercise 10.1. Four bugs on a rectangle. In Chapter 3, using the complex arithmetic trick, we considered a scalar ODE in which a lion chases an antelope, always moving directly towards it. Now consider a problem of four bugs starting at four corners of a rectangle, each chasing the one counterclockwise from it at speed 1. *(a)* Suppose the bugs begin at the corners of the square $(\pm 1, \pm 1)$. Draw a figure showing the evolution to time $t = 1.99995$, and report the locations at that time of the four bugs. (This part of the problem could be reduced to a scalar ODE — indeed it can easily be solved analytically — but the next part is necessarily a system.) *(b)* Now suppose the bugs begin at the four corners of the rectangle $(\pm 1.01, \pm 0.99)$. Answer the same questions as in part *(a)*. To learn about the extraordinary paths followed by the bugs as $t \to 2$, see Chapman, Lottes, and Trefethen, "Four bugs on a rectangle," *Proceedings of the Royal Society*, 2011.

Exercise 10.2. *Oregonator.* The Oregonator, or Field–Noyes model, is an approximation to the dynamics of the Belousov–Zhabotinskii chemical reaction, which exhibits periodic oscillations of its reagents. (You can see a video of the reaction at `https://youtu.be/wxSa9BMPwow?t=3m9s`.) In nondimensional form the equations are

$$\varepsilon u' = qv - uv + u(1 - u), \quad \delta v' = -qv - uv + w, \quad w' = u - w,$$

where q, ε, and δ are parameters. For this exercise use the values $q = 8 \times 10^{-4}$, $\varepsilon = 0.05$, and $\delta = 0.02$. (These are not physically realistic for the BZ reaction. For realistic values, the system is considered "stiff" and requires a change in the numerical solver Chebfun uses, as illustrated in example 43 of Appendix B.) Solve the system with Chebfun for $u(0) = w(0) = 0$, $v(0) = 1$, and plot the three components as functions of time. (A particularly interesting way to see the dynamics is `comet3(u,v,w)`.)

Exercise 10.3. *Nonautonomous.* Suppose that a first-order, two-variable ODE system has unique solutions for any initial data and one of its solutions is $u(t) = \sin(t)$, $v(t) = \sin(2t)$. Sketch this orbit in the phase plane and explain why this ODE cannot be autonomous.

Exercise 10.4. *Matrix eigenvalues via ODE isospectral flow.* Suppose $\mathbf{A} = [a \ b; \ b \ c]$ is a 2×2 real symmetric matrix. The eigenvalues of $\mathbf{A}$ can be determined from $\lim_{t \to \infty} a(t)$ and $\lim_{t \to \infty} c(t)$ in the ODE $a' = 2b^2$, $b' = b(c - a)$, $c' = -2b^2$. *(a)* Try this for the matrix $[3 \ 2; \ 2 \ 1]$, plotting deviations from their limiting values as a function of $t \in [0, 2]$. How close are $a(t)$ and $c(t)$ at $t = 1$ and 2 to their final values? *(b)* Do the same for the matrix $[1 \ 2; \ 2 \ 3]$. What is qualitatively different in this case? *(c)* What are the fixed points of this ODE? (If you are curious to learn more about isospectral flows in linear algebra, including the case of $n \times n$ matrices and connections with standard algorithms for computing matrix eigenvalues, see Deift, Nanda, and Tomei, "Ordinary differential equations and the symmetric eigenvalue problem," *SIAM Journal on Numerical Analysis* 20 (1983), pp. 1–22.)

Exercise 10.5. *Energy conservation for Eulerian wobble.* Show analytically that the quantity $u^2 + v^2 + w^2$ is independent of time for solutions of the system (10.9).

Exercise 10.6. *Four kinds of fixed points* (from Hairer, Nørsett, and Wanner). *(a)* Draw a quiver plot of the system $u' = (u - v)(1 - u - v)/3$, $v' = u(2 - v)$. Determine the four fixed points analytically and include them in the plot. *(b)* Calculate the eigenvalues of the Jacobian at these points and show that one is a sink, one is a source, one is a saddle point, and one is a spiral.

Exercise 10.7. *Phase plane for SIR model.* *(a)* Suppose a solution of (10.10) satisfies $S(0) + I(0) + R(0) = 1$. Show that $S(t) + I(t) + R(t) = 1$ for all t. Using this conservation property, we can eliminate S or I or R from the system and thus obtain a two-variable system that can be analyzed in the phase plane. *(b)* Elimination of R is particularly trivial. Write down the resulting two-variable system. Solve it for the same parameters as in Figure 10.13 and make an arrowplot of the trajectory in the S-I plane. Where are the fixed points in this plane?

11. The fundamental existence theorem

More than most mathematical fields, the subject of ODEs is founded on a key theorem: solutions to an IVP $y' = f(t, y)$, $y(0) = y_0$ exist and are unique so long as f is continuous with respect to both variables and Lipschitz continuous with respect to y, as defined below. (If $\partial f / \partial y$ exists and is uniformly bounded, that is enough to imply Lipschitz continuity, since a bound on $|\partial f / \partial y|$ will serve as a Lipschitz constant.) The theorem applies to systems as well as scalars, which means that, by the usual addition of extra variables, it applies to higher-order as well as first-order equations. We rely on this result throughout this book. In this chapter we present one of the standard proofs, due to Picard and Lindelöf.[46]

Since an ODE prescribes the slope of a curve at each point, it may seem obvious that a unique solution must always exist. However, we saw examples in Chapter 3 showing this is not the case. The problem $y' = y^2$, $y(0) = 1$ of (3.9) has the solution $y(t) = 1/(1 - t)$ on $[0, d]$ for $d < 1$, but no solution exists for $d \geq 1$; y^2 fails to be Lipschitz continuous as $y \to \infty$. The problem $y' = y^{1/2}$, $y(0) = 0$ of (3.16) has the distinct solutions $y(t) = 0$ and $y(t) = t^2/4$, as well as many others; $y^{1/2}$ is not Lipschitz continuous for $y \approx 0$. So existence and uniqueness cannot be taken for granted.

For simplicity, we will state and prove the theorem first in the scalar case, and then indicate the modest changes needed for the generalization to systems.

Theorem 11.1. Existence and uniqueness for a first-order scalar

---

[46]We emphasize that this theorem and proof represent just one particularly noteworthy item from the theory of existence and uniqueness for ODEs. In fact, there is a whole book on the subject: R. P. Agarwal and V. Lakshmikantham, *Uniqueness and Nonuniqueness Criteria for Ordinary Differential Equations*, World Scientific, 1993.

ODE IVP (FlaShl). *If f is continuous with respect to t and y and Lipschitz continuous with respect to y, then the IVP*

$$y'(t) = f(t, y), \quad t \in [0, d], \ y(0) = y_0 \tag{11.1}$$

has a solution, and it is unique.

By a solution to the IVP, we mean a continuously differentiable function $y(t)$ satisfying (11.1). The condition that f is **Lipschitz continuous** with respect to y means that there exists a constant K such that for all $t \in [0, d]$ and $y \in \mathbf{R}$, $|f(t, y_2) - f(t, y_1)| \le K|y_2 - y_1|$. Although our discussion assumes $d > 0$ for simplicity, (11.1) is actually symmetric with respect to t, and the same result holds for $t \in [d, 0]$ with $d < 0$.

The standard proof of Theorem 11.1 is based on the process known as **Picard iteration**. We note that integration of (11.1) yields the equation[47]

$$y(t) = y_0 + \int_0^t f(s, y(s))\, ds. \tag{11.2}$$

In the Picard iteration, we consider the sequence of functions defined by $y^{(0)} = y_0$ and then

$$y^{(k+1)}(t) = y_0 + \int_0^t f(s, y^{(k)}(s))\, ds, \quad k = 0, 1, 2, \dots, \tag{11.3}$$

or as we may write abstractly for an operator N,

$$y^{(k+1)} = N(y^{(k)}), \quad k = 0, 1, 2, \dots. \tag{11.4}$$

The proof consists of showing that, under the given assumptions, this successive substitution process converges to a unique solution of (11.1), at least on some smaller interval $[0, d/m]$. By a succession of m such steps we reach all of $[0, d]$.

Before presenting the mathematical argument, let us see the construction in action. The problem

$$y' = \sin(y) + \sin(t), \quad t \in [0, 8], \ y(0) = 1 \tag{11.5}$$

is an example of a nonlinear IVP whose defining function $f(t, y)$ is continuous with respect to both variables and Lipschitz continuous with respect to y; the Lipschitz constant can be taken as $K = 1$. Here is a plot of iterates $k = 0, \dots, 4$:

```
d = 8; t = chebfun('t',[0 d]); y0 = 1; y = y0 + 0*t;
for k = 0:4
   plot(y), hold on, y = y0 + cumsum(sin(y)+sin(t));
end
```

---

[47] This is an example of a *Volterra integral equation*.

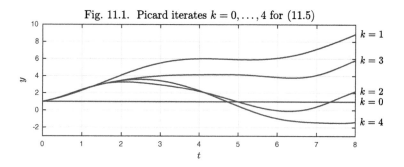

Fig. 11.1. Picard iterates $k = 0, \ldots, 4$ for (11.5)

A second plot shows $k = 5, \ldots, 9$.

```
for k = 5:9
  plot(y), hold on, y = y0 + cumsum(sin(y)+sin(t));
end
```

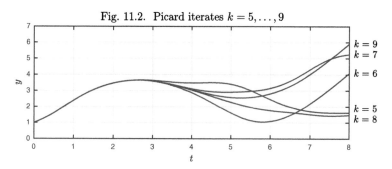

Fig. 11.2. Picard iterates $k = 5, \ldots, 9$

A third plot shows $k = 10, \ldots, 14$, and this time we include the true solution (a dashed lined in red, mostly hidden under the green curves) to confirm that the iteration is converging successfully.

```
N = chebop(0,d); N.op = @(t,y) diff(y) - sin(y); N.lbc = y0;
yexact = N\sin(t); plot(yexact,'--'), hold on
for k = 10:14
  plot(y), y = y0 + cumsum(sin(y)+sin(t));
end
```

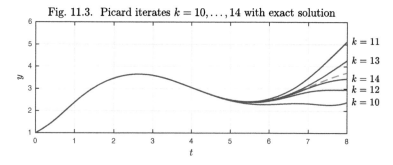

Fig. 11.3. Picard iterates $k = 10, \ldots, 14$ with exact solution

These figures give a vivid impression of how convergence works for the Picard iteration: *from left to right.* On a short interval like $[0, 1]$, the convergence for this example is rapid, whereas on the longer interval $[0, 8]$ the rate is not so good. In fact, the successive iterates satisfy

$$y^{(0)}(t) - y(t) = O(t), \quad y^{(1)}(t) - y(t) = O(t^2), \quad y^{(2)}(t) - y(t) = O(t^3), \dots. \quad (11.6)$$

These estimates apply even if f is not smooth with respect to t or y (Exercise 11.7). For our example, the powers are readily confirmed on the computer by plotting the errors of $y^{(0)}, \dots, y^{(4)}$ as functions of t on a log-log plot. (The vertical bars correspond to points where the error happens to cross through zero.)

```
y = y0 + 0*t; tt = logspace(-2,log10(8),1200);
for k = 0:4
  err = abs(y(tt)-yexact(tt));
  for j = 10:1000
    if err(j)<=min(err(j-1:j+1)), err(j)=1e-20; end
  end
  loglog(tt,err), hold on, y = y0 + cumsum(sin(y)+sin(t));
end
```

Fig. 11.4. Errors of iterates $0, \dots, 4$ for (11.5)

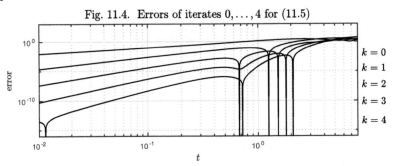

One way to prove Theorem 11.1 is to make (11.6) quantitative. (See, for example, Chapter 12 of Süli and Mayers, *An Introduction to Numerical Analysis,* Cambridge, 2003.) We follow here the more abstract and elegant approach of regarding the mapping N of (11.4) as a *contraction map* in the Banach space $C([0, d])$ of continuous functions on $[0, d]$ with the supremum norm.[48] More precisely, it may be necessary to restrict the interval to $[0, d/m]$ for some m and take m steps.

Proof of Theorem 11.1. As described above, we set $y^{(0)} = y_0$ and iterate with the formula (11.3). By induction it follows that $y^{(k)}$ is well-defined and continuously differentiable for each k. From (11.2) we compute

$$y^{(k+1)}(t) - y^{(k)}(t) = \int_0^t \left[f(s, y^{(k)}(s)) - f(s, y^{(k-1)}(s)) \right] ds.$$

---

[48]Do we really need Banach spaces? Not really — see p. 4 of Hastings and McLeod, *Classical Methods in Ordinary Differential Equations with Applications to Boundary Value Problems,* American Mathematical Society, 2012.

Since $t \leq d$, this equation implies

$$\|y^{(k+1)} - y^{(k)}\|_\infty \leq dK\|y^{(k)} - y^{(k-1)}\|_\infty, \tag{11.7}$$

where K is the Lipschitz constant. Now suppose $dK < 1$. Then (11.7) asserts that the map N of (11.4) is a *contraction* in the Banach space $C([0,d])$ of continuous functions on $[0,d]$ with norm $\|\cdot\|_\infty$. By a standard result known as the *Banach fixed-point theorem* or the *contraction mapping principle*, a contraction map has a unique fixed point, i.e., a point y with $N(y) = y$, and the iteration converges to it. In our context, this means that the iteration converges to a unique function $y \in C([0,d])$ that satisfies $N(y) = y$, i.e., (11.2). From (11.2) it follows that y is in fact continuously differentiable and satisfies (11.1).

This completes the proof if $dK < 1$. What if $dK > 1$? In this case we may pick an integer m such that $dK/m < 1$ and use the same argument to establish a unique solution in $C([0, d/m])$. From here, a second application of the fixed-point theorem gives a unique solution in $C([d/m, 2d/m])$, and so on for m steps. ∎

Theorem 11.1 extends in an immediate manner to a first-order system of n equations.

Theorem 11.2. Existence and uniqueness for a first-order system of ODEs (FlashI). *If* **f** *is continuous with respect to t and* **y** *and Lipschitz continuous with respect to* **y***, then the IVP*

$$\mathbf{y}'(t) = \mathbf{f}(t, \mathbf{y}), \quad t \in [0, d], \; \mathbf{y}(0) = \mathbf{y}_0 \tag{11.8}$$

has a solution, and it is unique.

The same proof works as before, with the Banach space $C([0,d])$ generalized to $C^n([0,d])$ and with $\|\mathbf{y}\|_\infty$ now defined as the supremum for $t \in [0,d]$ of $\|\mathbf{y}(t)\|$, where $\|\cdot\|$ is any fixed norm on $\mathbf{R}^n$. Lipschitz continuity is also defined with respect to the latter norm. We say that $\mathbf{f}(t, \mathbf{y})$ is Lipschitz continuous with respect to **y** if there exists a constant K such that for all $t \in [0, d]$ and $y \in \mathbf{R}^n$, $\|f(t, \mathbf{y}_2) - f(t, \mathbf{y}_1)\| \leq K\|\mathbf{y}_2 - \mathbf{y}_1\|$. Since all norms are equivalent on a finite-dimensional space, this definition is independent of the choice of norm.

$$* \quad * \quad *$$

The main business of this chapter is finished: the statement and proof of Theorems 11.1 and 11.2, which assume that $f(t, y)$ is continuous in t and Lipschitz continuous in y. Let us now explore around the edges a little. Although these theorems mark a center point of this field, there is more to be said about both existence and uniqueness.

The most important matter to note is that continuity of f with respect to t is a stronger assumption than necessary for the Picard iteration argument. The simplest next step, sufficient for the examples explored in this book such as those of Figures 2.3 and 2.8, is to suppose that f is piecewise continuous as in Theorems 2.2 and 2.3. When we say that the bivariate function $f(t, y)$

is piecewise continuous with respect to t, we mean that it is continuous with respect to t except for at most a finite set of jump discontinuities at points $t_1, \ldots, t_k$ that are independent of y. The proof by Picard iteration then goes through essentially as before, with the Banach space $C([0, d])$ generalized to the Banach space of piecewise continuous functions with jump discontinuities only at the same points $t_1, \ldots, t_k$, again with norm $\| \cdot \|_\infty$.

Theorem 11.3. Existence and uniqueness for discontinuous ODEs (Flashl). *The conclusions of Theorems 11.1 and 11.2 also hold if **f** is piecewise continuous with respect to t as defined above and Lipschitz continuous with respect to **y**.*

For an extensive treatment of existence theorems for discontinuous ODEs, see A. F. Filippov, *Differential Equations with Discontinuous Righthand Sides*, Kluwer, 1988. One theme in this theory is to extend results like Theorem 11.3 to coefficients that are just integrable with respect to t. More generally, one may also weaken the condition that f is Lipschitz continuous with respect to y. One line of such results takes f to be continuous but not necessarily Lipschitz continuous, which is enough to guarantee existence of a solution at least locally, on some interval $[0, \delta]$ with $\delta > 0$; this is the *Peano existence theorem*. The solution need not be unique, however. A standard example is equation (3.16), $y' = y^{1/2}$, and here is another example, taken from Ince's *Ordinary Differential Equations*:

$$y' = f(t, y), \quad f(t, y) = \begin{cases} 0, & t = y = 0, \\ \dfrac{4t^3 y}{y^2 + t^4} & \text{otherwise.} \end{cases} \tag{11.9}$$

The function f is continuous with respect to t and y for all t and y, and away from the point $t = y = 0$ it is (locally) Lipschitz continuous with respect to y, ensuring existence and uniqueness of solutions so long as they stay away from this point and $\pm\infty$. Here is a display of some such solutions.

```
N = chebop(0,1); N.op = @(t,y) diff(y) - 4*t^3*y/(y^2+t^4);
for y0 = [-1.4:.2:-.2 .2:.2:1.4]
  N.lbc = y0; y = N\0; plot(y), hold on
end
```

Fig. 11.5. Solutions of (11.9) that avoid the point $t = y = 0$

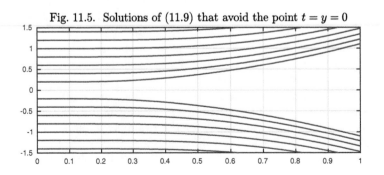

The interesting matter is what happens with solutions that do touch the point $t = y = 0$. We can quickly spot three such solutions, $y(t) = -t^2$, $y(t) = 0$, and $y(t) = t^2$. We add dashed black curves for $-t^2$ and t^2 to the figure.

```
t = chebfun('t',[0,1]); plot([t^2 -t^2],'--')
```

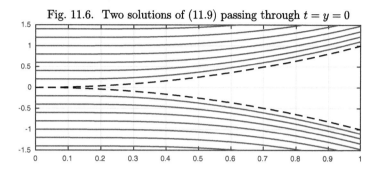

Fig. 11.6. Two solutions of (11.9) passing through $t = y = 0$

Between these two black curves, there is a continuum of solutions, all passing through the point $t = y = 0$. We compute some numerically by marching backwards from $t = 1$ to $t = 0.01$, plotting the results in orange.

```
N.domain = [.01 1]; N.lbc = [];
for y0 = [-.85:.17:.85]
  N.rbc = y0; y = N\0; plot(y)
end
plot([t^2 -t^2],'--')
```

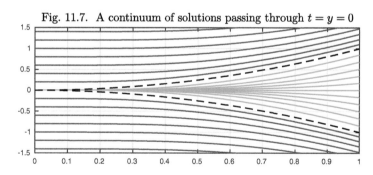

Fig. 11.7. A continuum of solutions passing through $t = y = 0$

Actually, this problem has an analytic solution. For any c, the function

$$y(t) = c^2 - (t^4 + c^4)^{1/2} \tag{11.10}$$

satisfies (11.9) and takes the value $y(0) = 0$. The negative of (11.10) is also a solution.

In an image like Figure 11.7, nonuniqueness takes the form of multiple solutions emanating from a single point t and $y(t)$. It is interesting to consider the same effect in reverse time, solving the same ODE, for example, from $t = 1$ to

$t = 0$, as we discussed for the "leaky bucket" problem of Chapter 3. (We also reversed time to generate Figure 11.7.) Here, we see multiple trajectories that coalesce — not just approximately but exactly. In an ODE problem driven by a Lipschitz continuous function f, two distinct solutions can never coalesce, so in some sense information about the initial condition can never be completely lost. Non-Lipschitz problems like the leaky bucket viewed backward in time, however, are different. One might say that the adjoint of nonuniqueness is extinction.

APPLICATION: DESIGNER NONUNIQUENESS

From examples like (3.16) and (11.9), one may get the impression that nonuniqueness is elusive, to be found only if one knows how to look in just the right hiding places. In fact, generating nonunique solutions is as easy at sketching curves on a sheet of paper, and Figure 11.7 shows us the sort of curves that are needed. Take this diagram of functions $a(\sin(\pi t))^2$ with $-1 \le a \le 1$, for example.

```
t = chebfun('t',[-2,2]);
for a = -1:.2:1
  y = a*sin(pi*t)^2; plot(y), hold on
end
```

Fig. 11.8. Sketching nonunique solution trajectories

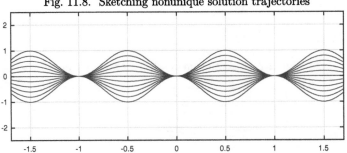

Each of these curves $y(t)$ is smooth, with a well-defined derivative at each point, which we may call $f(t,y)$. So the curves are solutions of $y'(t) = f(t,y)$ for this choice of f. Yet the trajectory emanating from $t = 0$, $y = 0$ is obviously nonunique, as is the trajectory emanating from $t = k$, $y = 0$ for any integer k.

In the figure, suppose we imagine that trajectories have been specified as indicated for each value $a \in [-1, 1]$. If the ODE is to be defined for all t and y, we need to fill in the regions above the top curve and below the bottom one. This can be done in any number of ways, and here is one of them, based on functions $\pm[b + (\sin(\pi t))^2]$ with $b > 1$.

```
for b = .2:.2:1
  y = b + sin(pi*t)^2; plot([y; -y])
end
```

Fig. 11.9. Filling in the whole t-y plane

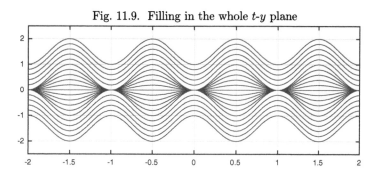

If b is regarded as taking all values $1 < b < \infty$, then we have completed a specification of a function $f(t,y)$ that is continuous with respect to both variables for all t and y. Since it has nonunique trajectories through certain points, it cannot possibly be Lipschitz continuous with respect to y. And indeed it is not, at least when t ranges over any interval that includes one of the integers (Exercise 11.6).

Once we start sketching trajectories in the plane, we can see that all kinds of effects are possible. Here is a function `pinch` that has the effect of "pinching" a square of diameter $2d$ centered at (t_0, y_0) so as to introduce nonuniqueness at this point.

```
pinch = @(t,y,t0,y0,d) y - (abs(y-y0)<d).*(abs(t-t0)<d).* ...
   cos(pi*(t-t0)/(2*d)).^2.*sign(y-y0).*(d/2-abs(abs(y-y0)-d/2));
```

Rather than talk through the algebra, we visualize the effect of applying `pinch(t,y,0,0,1)` to a set of horizontal trajectories:

```
t = linspace(-2,2,200)';
for ys = -2:.05:2
   y = ys + 0*t; y = pinch(t,y,0,0,1); plot(t,y), hold on
end
```

Fig. 11.10. Pinching trajectories gives nonuniqueness

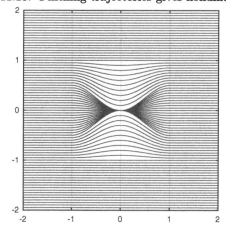

By pinching the plane at the middle point, we have introduced nonuniqueness there. With a few more pinches we can introduce more points of nonuniqueness.

```
for ys = -2:.05:2
  y = ys + 0*t;
  y = pinch(t,y,0,0,1);
  y = pinch(t,y,1.3,1.3,.5); y = pinch(t,y,-1.3,-1.3,.5);
  y = pinch(t,y,1,-1,.3); y = pinch(t,y,-1,1,.3);
  plot(t,y), hold on
end
```

Fig. 11.11. Multiple pinch points

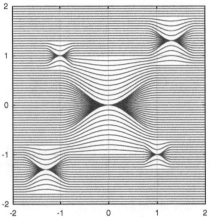

In a paper published in 1963, based on an earlier publication by Lavrentieff in 1925, P. Hartman took this idea to a fascinating limit with a fractal flavor ("A differential equation with non-unique solutions," *American Mathematical Monthly*). By introducing infinitely many pinches on successively smaller scales, he showed that one can construct a flow field with pinch points falling arbitrarily close to every value (t, y). This implies a remarkable consequence: there is an ODE $y' = f(t, y)$ with the property that, for every choice of initial point (t_0, y_0), the equation has more than one solution on every interval $[t_0, t_0 + \varepsilon]$.

HISTORY. Theorem 11.2 is often called the Picard–Lindelöf theorem, following publications by Picard in 1890 and Lindelöf in 1894; another landmark was Goursat's *Cours d'analyse mathématique* of 1908. It is also called the Cauchy–Lipschitz theorem, and an early publication was by Liouville in 1838. Peano's local existence theorem, without the Lipschitz requirement or the assertion of uniqueness, appeared in 1890 and was elaborated in his *Traité d'Analyse*, though the idea of successive substitution is much older. Banach's fixed-point theorem appeared in 1922, and Carathéodory in 1927 published one of the first local existence theorems for ODEs defined by discontinuous coefficient functions **f**.

OUR FAVORITE REFERENCE. Discontinuous right-hand sides are ubiquitous in applications, and their dynamical consequences are explored in di Bernardo,

Budd, Champneys, and Kowalczyk, *Piecewise-smooth Dynamical Systems: Theory and Applications,* Springer, 2008.

Summary of Chapter 11. *The fundamental existence theorem of ODEs asserts that an ODE $\mathbf{y}' = \mathbf{f}(t, \mathbf{y})$ subject to initial data $\mathbf{y}(0) = \mathbf{y}_0$ has a unique solution for all t if $\mathbf{f}$ is continuous with respect to t and Lipschitz continuous with respect to $\mathbf{y}$. This result applies to systems as well as scalars and thus covers higher-order ODEs too if appropriate conditions are specified on derivatives. Both existence and uniqueness can fail if $\mathbf{f}$ is merely continuous with respect to $\mathbf{y}$, though existence still holds locally.*

Exercise 11.1. Cleve Moler's favorite ODE. Consider the IVP $(y')^2 + y^2 = 1$, $y(0) = 0$ with the additional constraint $-1 \le y \le 1$. *(a)* Show that there are exactly two solutions for $t \in [0, 1]$ and state formulas for them. *(b)* Show that there are infinitely many solutions for $t \in [0, 2]$.

Exercise 11.2. From an integral equation to an IVP. Convert the integral equation $y(t) = e^t + 4 \int_0^t (t-s) y(s) ds$ to an ODE IVP (including the initial condition). Determine the solution analytically.

Exercise 11.3. Differentiability and Lipschitz continuity. Prove that if a function $f(t, y)$ has a uniformly bounded derivative $|\partial f / \partial y|$ for all t and y, then it is Lipschitz continuous.

Exercise 11.4. Value of m for our example. For the example (11.5) of the opening pages of this chapter, the Picard iteration converges over the whole interval $[0, 8]$. However, our proof of Theorem 11.1 subdivides the interval into m subintervals. For this example, what is the smallest allowed number m?

Exercise 11.5. A first-order two-point BVP. *(a)* Sketch the solution curves of $y' = |y|^{1/2}$ in the (t, y) plane. How do nonuniqueness and extinction effects appear in this plot? *(b)* Suppose $y(0) = -1$ and $y(6) = 1$. There exists a unique solution for $t \in [0, 6]$ for these data (an unusual situation in that this is a first-order equation with two boundary conditions!). Determine this solution analytically.

Exercise 11.6. Figure 11.9. *(a)* Verify that the function f described by Figure 11.9 is not Lipschitz continuous. *(b)* Exactly how many solutions are there on $[-2, 2]$ to the ODE described by this figure that satisfy $|y(t)| = 1$ for $t = -1.5, -0.5, 0.5, 1.5$?

Exercise 11.7. Nonsmooth f. In the text it was mentioned that the estimates (11.6) apply even if f is not smooth. Verify this experimentally by reproducing Figure 11.4 with f changed to *(a)* $\sin(y) + \text{sign}(\sin(50t))$ and *(b)* $|\sin(10y)| + \sin(t)$. It is enough to work with the time interval $[0, 1]$.

Exercise 11.8. A growing exponent. A function $y(t)$ is continuously differentiable, nonnegative, and unbounded for $t \in (0, 4)$, where it satisfies $y' = y^t$. For what subinterval of $(0, 4)$ is y identically zero? (*Hint.* Try integrating backward in time from $t = 4$ to $t = 1$ with a boundary condition $y(4) = 4$ or 8.)

12. Random functions and random ODEs

One of the most fascinating themes in the mathematical sciences, whose importance is growing every year, is randomness. In this chapter we say a word about how randomness plays into the subject of ODEs.

To begin the discussion, here are two examples of random functions produced by the Chebfun `randnfun` command.

```
rng(1), lam1 = 1; lam2 = 0.1; dom = [0 10];
f1 = randnfun(lam1,dom); subplot(2,1,1), plot(f1)
f2 = randnfun(lam2,dom); subplot(2,1,2), plot(f2)
```

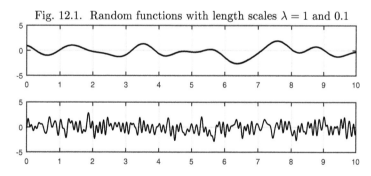

Fig. 12.1. Random functions with length scales $\lambda = 1$ and 0.1

At the end of the chapter we will explain the precise mathematical definition, but for the moment the main thing to note is that these are smooth functions defined on a prescribed interval and with a prescribed length scale λ. The first function, with $\lambda = 1$, has a typical distance on the order of 1 between maxima, whereas the second, with $\lambda = 0.1$, wiggles ten times as fast. The vertical scales are the same, and in fact, at each fixed point t, each function produced by randnfun takes values corresponding to samples from the standard normal distribution $N(0,1)$, with mean 0 and variance 1.

Like so many commands in Chebfun, randnfun provides a continuous analogue of a familiar discrete object. In MATLAB, randn(n,1) generates an n-vector of random entries from $N(0,1)$. Similarly randnfun(lam,[a,b]) produces a smooth random function of typical wavelength λ on the interval $[a,b]$.

As our first random ODE problem, let us consider the simplest ODE IVP of all,

$$y'(t) = f(t), \quad y(0) = 0, \tag{12.1}$$

whose solution is just the indefinite integral of f,

$$y(t) = \int_0^t f(s)\,ds. \tag{12.2}$$

If we take f to be the two functions plotted above, we get these results. We call a curve like these a **smooth random walk**.

```
y1 = cumsum(f1); subplot(2,1,1), plot(y1)
y2 = cumsum(f2); subplot(2,1,2), plot(y2)
```

Fig. 12.2. Their indefinite integrals: smooth random walks

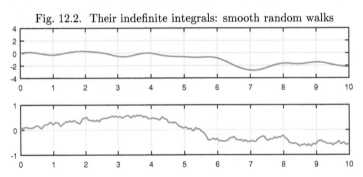

Note that the first curve has a larger amplitude than the second. The reason for this is a familiar matter of statistics associated with cancellation of random signs. These indefinite integrals are essentially the average value of the integrand (times 10, when we reach $t = 10$), and, according to the law of large numbers, this average converges to 0 as the number of samples approaches ∞, which in our context means as λ approaches zero. Moreover, the convergence will be in proportion to $\lambda^{1/2}$. So in fact our second curve should be expected to be on the order of $\sqrt{10}$ times smaller than the first. To eliminate this dependence on λ we can renormalize f by dividing it by $\lambda^{1/2}$, and in Chebfun this (approximately) is what is done if randnfun is called with the 'big' flag. From now on we will always use 'big'.

Here are three smooth random walks with $\lambda = 0.1$.

```
lam = 0.1;
for k = 1:3
  f = randnfun(lam,dom,'big');
  y = cumsum(f); subplot(1,3,k), plot(y)
end
```

Fig. 12.3. Smooth random walks with $\lambda = 0.1$

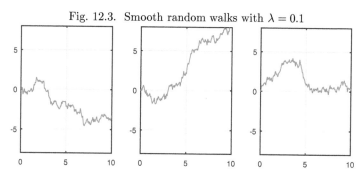

Here are three smooth random walks with $\lambda = 0.01$.

```
lam = 0.01;
for k = 1:3
  f = randnfun(lam,dom,'big');
  y = cumsum(f); subplot(1,3,k), plot(y)
end
```

Fig. 12.4. Smooth random walks with $\lambda = 0.01$

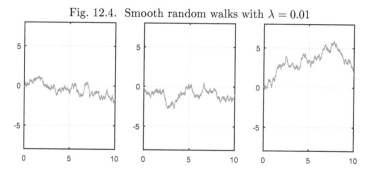

The sample paths we have shown in Figs. 12.2–12.4 are smooth, but as $\lambda \to 0$, the smoothness goes away. In this limit we get the precisely defined mathematical notion of *Brownian motion*, where the sample paths are continuous but not smooth. A Brownian motion trajectory is also called a *Wiener path*, and probabilists say that a Wiener path is a sample from the *Wiener process*. We can show the convergence as $\lambda \to 0$ by superimposing three paths for successively smaller values of λ, all based on the same random number seed set by MATLAB's **rng** command.[49]

---

[49]In MATLAB as in other programming languages, successive calls to **randn** give new random numbers, but one can reinitialize the sequence for repeatability with the command **rng(k)**, where k is a fixed integer. Chebfun's **randnfun** works the same way. This feature has been crucial for us in writing this chapter, since we need reproducible random curves if we are to comment on their particular features.

```
for lam = [1 1/4 1/16]
  rng(3), f = randnfun(lam,dom,'big');
  y = cumsum(f); plot(y), hold on
end
```

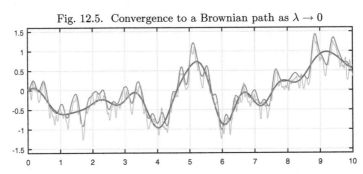

Fig. 12.5. Convergence to a Brownian path as $\lambda \to 0$

Here is a smooth random walk over a longer time scale, up to $t = 500$. Note that the maximal amplitude is a bigger than before, and yet the trajectory comes back repeatedly to zero — whereupon, of course, it "starts over." In an infinitely long trajectory, the path will cross zero infinitely often, and yet the amplitudes will grow.[50] Probability theory is full of such paradoxes.

```
lam = 0.1; rng(1)
f = randnfun(lam,[0 500],'big');
y = cumsum(f); plot(y)
```

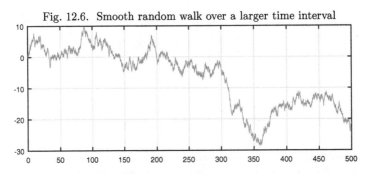

Fig. 12.6. Smooth random walk over a larger time interval

Here are $n = 10$ smooth random walks up to $t = 100$, together with their mean, shown as a thicker curve in black. As the sample size n approaches ∞, the mean will approach the function $\varphi(t)$ that is the *expected* value of $f(t)$ at each point t. For this simple example, $\varphi(t) = 0$.

```
lam = 0.1; F = randnfun(lam,[0 100],10,'big'); Y = cumsum(F);
plot(Y), hold on, plot(mean(Y,2))
```

---

[50]Statements like this hold "with probability 1" or "almost surely." In principle a Brownian path could be any function at all, and thus, for example, might remain bounded by 1 forever, or even identically zero, but the probability of such events will be zero. With probability 1, a Brownian path is everywhere continuous and nowhere differentiable.

Fig. 12.7. Ten smooth random walks and their mean

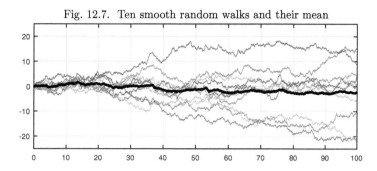

For a second random ODE problem, let us consider an indefinite integral as before, but now a system of equations in two variables y_1 and y_2,

$$y_1'(t) = f_1(t), \ y_2' = f_2(t), \quad y_1(0) = y_2(0) = 0, \qquad (12.3)$$

where f_1 and f_2 are independent random functions, normalized again by division by $O(\lambda^{1/2})$. The two variables are uncoupled, so in a sense there is nothing new here. On the other hand, the trajectories now take the interesting form of two-dimensional smooth random walks, which in the limit $\lambda \to 0$ would become 2D Brownian motion. Here are two sample paths with $\lambda = 0.1$ on $[0, 10]$.

```
rng(2)
for k = 1:2
  f1 = randnfun(lam,dom,'big')/sqrt(2); y1 = cumsum(f1);
  f2 = randnfun(lam,dom,'big')/sqrt(2); y2 = cumsum(f2);
  subplot(1,2,k), plot(y1,y2)
end
```

Fig. 12.8. 2D smooth random walks to $t = 10$

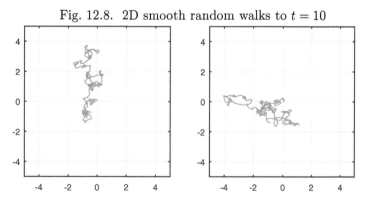

Following our usual trick in 2D, we could equally well have generated these images using a single complex random function instead of two real ones:

```
for k = 1:2
  f = randnfun(lam,dom,'big','complex');
  y = cumsum(f); subplot(1,2,k), plot(y)
end
```

Fig. 12.9. 2D smooth random walks via complex arithmetic

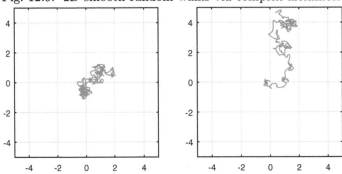

These trajectories look different, but only because we have rolled the dice again. Beneath the superficial distinction of complex scalars vs. real 2-vectors, these are independent sample paths from the same distribution.

Our random ODEs so far have been trivial, just indefinite integrals. Let us explore some more substantial examples, which will give an idea of some of the fascination of the field of **stochastic differential equations (SDEs)**. In all of the next six figures, f is a smooth random function of some small fixed time scale and amplitude on the interval $[0, 5]$. In each case several sample trajectories are plotted.

First we look at an equation featuring *additive noise*,

$$y' = y + f, \quad y(0) = 0. \tag{12.4}$$

Without f, the solution would be $y(t) = 0$, but the noise term breaks this symmetry. At first, so long as $|y|$ is small, trajectories look like random walks, with signs varying from $+$ to $-$, but as $|y|$ gets larger the exponential element overwhelms the random one, and a path shoots off to $-\infty$ or ∞ with probability 1. By symmetry, it is clear that both fates are equally likely.

```
rng(0), lam = 0.1; dom = [0 5];
L = chebop(dom); L.op = @(y) diff(y) - y; L.lbc = 0;
for k = 1:6
  f = randnfun(lam,dom,'big');
  y = L\f; plot(y), hold on
end
```

Fig. 12.11. Six solutions to (12.4): unstable

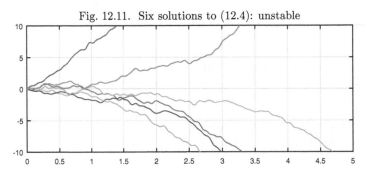

On a larger vertical scale the same curves look simply like exponentials.

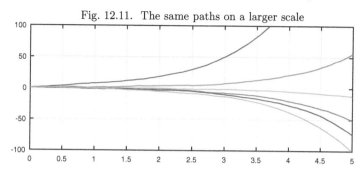

Fig. 12.11. The same paths on a larger scale

Next, we reverse the sign in (12.4) and consider

$$y' = -y + f, \quad y(0) = 0. \tag{12.5}$$

Now the process is stable, showing random oscillations about 0 that remain bounded as t increases.

```
L.op = @(y) diff(y) + y; L.lbc = 0;
for k = 1:6
  f = randnfun(lam,dom,'big');
  y = L\f; plot(y), hold on
end
```

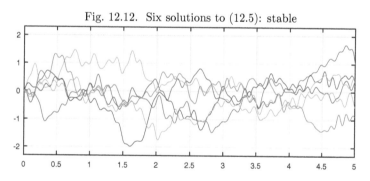

Fig. 12.12. Six solutions to (12.5): stable

Now let us change (12.4) into an equation with *multiplicative noise*,

$$y' = fy, \quad y(0) = 1, \tag{12.6}$$

where f is again random. We find that the amplitudes of the solutions of this new equation vary widely.

```
dom = [0 5]; rng(1), L = chebop(dom); L.lbc = 1;
for k = 1:6
  f = randnfun(lam,dom,'big'); L.op = @(t,y) diff(y) - f*y;
  y = L\0; plot(y), hold on
end
```

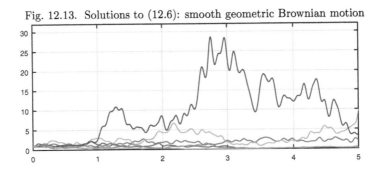

Fig. 12.13. Solutions to (12.6): smooth geometric Brownian motion

The greatly differing amplitudes may seem surprising at first, but in fact (12.6) is nothing more than the exponential of (12.1). We can verify this by rewriting (12.6) as $y'/y = f$, that is,

$$(\log y)' = f, \quad \log y(0) = 0. \tag{12.7}$$

So for any given f, the solution y of (12.6) is the exponential of the solution y of (12.1).

Equations (12.5) and (12.6) are first-order linear equations of type FLAShI and FLaSHI, respectively. Of course, equations involving $ay'' + by' + cy$ as in (7.10) in which the coefficients a, b, c all vary with t can also be considered, as can nonlinear equations. Let us consider a nonlinear example with a bistable flavor. Without the random term f, the equation

$$y' = y - y^3 + f \tag{12.8}$$

would have stable fixed points $y = \pm 1$. Taking 20 trajectories from the initial value $y = 0$, and putting the amplitude scale of f at 0.2, we find that about half end up oscillating about each of these values. By symmetry, the positive and negative behaviors must be must be equally likely. (These fates are not permanent. Since Gaussians take arbitrarily large values, though rarely, further sign flips will happen with probability 1 for sufficiently large values of t.)

```
N = chebop(dom); rng(0)
N.lbc = 0; N.op = @(t,y) diff(y) - y + y^3;
for k = 1:20
  f = 0.2*randnfun(lam,dom,'big');
  y = N\f; plot(y), hold on
end
```

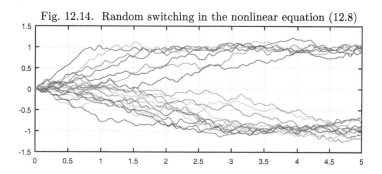

Fig. 12.14. Random switching in the nonlinear equation (12.8)

On the other hand, suppose we bias the switch slightly by taking the initial value $y(0) = 0.20$. Both positive and negative fates are again possible, but among twenty test trajectories, just two now go negative.

```
N.lbc = 0.2;
for k = 1:20
  f = 0.2*randnfun(lam,dom,'big');
  y = N\f; plot(y), hold on
end
```

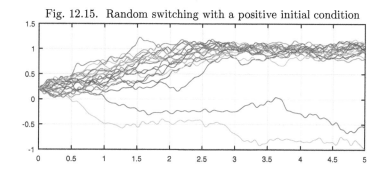

Fig. 12.15. Random switching with a positive initial condition

We promised at the beginning to explain the definition of the smooth random functions delivered by randnfun. The essential idea here is the use of finite Fourier series with normally distributed random coefficients all of equal variance. We start from the notion of a periodic function on the interval $[0, L]$, defined by a Fourier series

$$f(t) = a_0 + \sqrt{2} \sum_{k=1}^{m} \left[a_k \cos\left(\frac{2\pi kt}{L}\right) + b_k \sin\left(\frac{2\pi kt}{L}\right) \right], \qquad (12.9)$$

where each a_k and b_k is an independent sample from the $N(0, 1/(2m+1))$ distribution, i.e., with mean 0 and variance $1/(2m+1)$. The space scale λ is fixed by setting m to be the largest integer $\leq L/\lambda$. In the "big" mode as specified in Chebfun by the 'big' flag, we have the same formula but with a_k and b_k coming from a distribution whose variance does not diminish as $m \to \infty$

for fixed L. Such a series almost surely does not converge as $m \to \infty$, but its integrals almost surely do, such as the indefinite integral

$$\int^t f(s)\,ds = a_0 t + \frac{L}{\sqrt{2}\pi} \sum_{k=1}^{m} k^{-1}\left[a_k \sin\left(\frac{2\pi k t}{L}\right) - b_k \cos\left(\frac{2\pi k t}{L}\right)\right]. \quad (12.10)$$

Random infinite series of the form (12.10) go back to Paley, Wiener, and Zygmund in the 1920s and 1930s, and both (12.9) and (12.10) could be called *finite Fourier–Wiener series*. To generate a nonperiodic random function, `randnfun` first constructs a periodic one on a larger interval and then restricts it to the interval prescribed.

Without fully describing any of the mathematics, let us at least mention some of the terminology that appears when our smooth random ODEs are related to SDEs via the limit $\lambda \to 0$. A random function f is a sample from a certain **Gaussian process** dependent on the parameter λ. Suppose we write an ODE involving f in the form

$$y'(t) = \mu(t, y(t)) + \sigma(t, y(t))f(t) \quad (12.11)$$

for some functions μ and σ. As $\lambda \to 0$, this ODE approaches an **SDE** that would normally be written as

$$dX_t = \mu(t, X_t)dt + \sigma(t, X_t) \circ dW_t. \quad (12.12)$$

The two terms on the right are sometimes labeled *drift* and *diffusion* (or *volatility*), respectively. If μ is of the form of a constant times X_t and σ is a constant, as in (12.4) and (12.5), the SDE is a **Langevin equation**, and its solution is the **Ornstein–Uhlenbeck process**. If μ and σ are both of the form of a constant times X_t, as in (12.6), we have the SDE of **geometric Brownian motion**. The small circle in (12.12) indicates that this is an SDE of **Stratonovich** type. The alternative of an **Itô** SDE has a different definition and the notation

$$dX_t = \tilde{\mu}(t, X_t)dt + \sigma(t, X_t)dW_t. \quad (12.13)$$

We have changed μ to $\tilde{\mu}$ because although (12.12) and (12.13) have different meanings, they define the same stochastic process provided $\tilde{\mu}$ and μ are related by

$$\tilde{\mu}(t, X_t) = \mu(t, X_t) + \frac{1}{2}\sigma(t, X_t)\frac{\partial \sigma}{\partial x}(t, X_t). \quad (12.14)$$

Details of the usual formulations of Itô and Stratonovich calculus can be found in many books of stochastic analysis. Results about the convergence of random ODEs to SDEs stem from two papers by E. Wong and M. Zakai in 1966; see also Sussmann, "On the gap between deterministic and stochastic ordinary differential equations," *The Annals of Probability*, 1978.

APPLICATION: METASTABILITY, RADIOACTIVITY, AND TUNNELING

Many systems in physics, chemistry, biology, and social sciences have what are known as *metastable states*, which means, states that may appear stable for a long time but then suddenly undergo a transition. Examples include financial bubbles, supercooled liquids, and radioactive nuclei. Often the effect can be explained by noting that there is a stable fixed point of a noise-free system, but when noise is present it eventually kicks the system out of the stable state. We can illustrate the effect with the IVP

$$y' = y^3 - y + \varepsilon f(t), \quad y(0) = 0, \tag{12.15}$$

where f is a smooth random function and ε is a noise amplitude parameter. (Note that the signs are opposite to those in (12.8).) Here are three solutions for $t \in [0, 100]$ with $\varepsilon = 0.35$. In the absence of the noise term, $y = 0$ is a stable fixed point and $y = \pm 1$ are unstable fixed points. When noise is added, however, the stable state will eventually be left behind.

```
lam = 1; rng(11)
N = chebop(0,100); N.op = @(y) diff(y) - y^3 + y; N.lbc = 0;
N.maxnorm = 10; ep = 0.35;
f1000 = randnfun(lam,[0 1000],'big',3); f = f1000{0,100};
for k = 1:3
  y = N\(ep*f(:,k)); plot(y), hold on
end
```

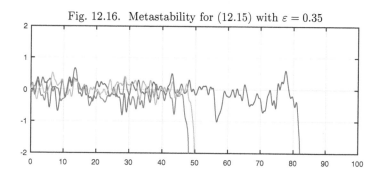

Fig. 12.16. Metastability for (12.15) with $\varepsilon = 0.35$

Note that each trajectory stays near the stable state for a while, and then at some moment escapes. We cannot predict the precise moment of escape, though it would appear that, for this example, it happens on a time scale in the range 10–100. To put it another way, the *half-life* of the system is evidently in this range, where the half-life is defined (as in the Application of Chapter 2) as the expected time $t_{1/2}$ by which the probability of escape has risen to $1/2$. A related notion is that of a *mean exit time*.[51]

Intuitively speaking, a system will escape from a metastable state when the random fluctuations, by chance, happen to deviate by an exceptionally large amount from their usual state. The mathematical theory of *large deviations* is used to analyze such effects. One phenomenon one finds in this subject is that a small change in a parameter may have a large effect on the lifetime. Here, for example, we reduce ε from 0.35 to 0.30 and find that none of the three trajectories escapes.

```
ep = 0.30;
for k = 1:3
  y = N\(ep*f(:,k)); plot(y), hold on
end
```

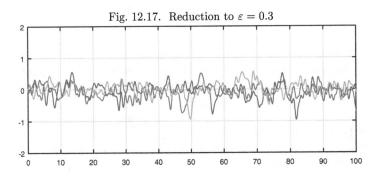

Fig. 12.17. Reduction to $\varepsilon = 0.3$

Eventually, trajectories will still escape, as we can see if we show results over all of $t \in [0, 1000]$.

```
N.domain = [0 1000];
for k = 1:3
  y = N\(ep*f1000(:,k)); plot(y), hold on
end
```

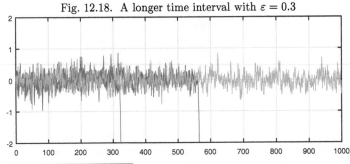

Fig. 12.18. A longer time interval with $\varepsilon = 0.3$

---

[51] For such definitions to be mathematically precise, they must be based on a precise definition of when a particle has escaped. The definition implicit in the N.maxnorm setting of our Chebfun code is that a particle escapes when $|y|$ reaches the value 10.

Thanks to the power of exponentials, half-lives of radioactive isotopes have been estimated ranging over more than 50 orders of magnitude, from less than 10^{-24} seconds to more than 10^{22} years. Three famous examples are uranium-238, with a half-life of 4.5 billion years, uranium-235 at 700 million years, and carbon-14 at 5700 years. In quantum physics the process of decay from a metastable state is called *tunneling*.

HISTORY. The approach to stochastic differential equations taken in this chapter, via smooth random functions, is nonstandard. After foundational works of Bachelier (1900), Einstein (1905 and 1906), Smoluchowski (1906), Langevin (1906), and Perrin (1909), it became usual at least among mathematicians since the work of Wiener (1923) to regard randomness as intrinsically nonsmooth, involving independent, instantaneous noise increments injected at each instant of time. An advantage of this point of view is that it is mathematically beautiful and just right as an idealization, even if the physical world does not contain elements on all scales down to infinitesimal. A disadvantage is that it is mathematically advanced, so that any discussion of randomness is faced with technical challenges of measure theory and functional analysis (or an apology for their omission) from page 1. Indeed, one cannot even write SDEs in the usual form $y'(t) = f(t, y)$, since y' does not exist — it would represent white noise, which to be truly white must have infinite amplitude. Therefore new notations as in eqs. (12.12) and (12.13) are used instead. Along with new notation go new theories of SDEs above and beyond the usual theory of deterministic ODEs (Itô, Stratonovich), and these in turn must be solved by numerical methods above and beyond the usual ones (Euler–Maruyama, Milstein, . . .).

OUR FAVORITE REFERENCE. Jean-Pierre Kahane (1926–2017) was an expert in Taylor and Fourier series with random coefficients. As our favorite reference, we would like to highlight his review paper "A century of interplay between Taylor series, Fourier series, and Brownian motion," *Bulletin of the London Mathematical Society* 29 (1997), pp. 257–279. The opening pages tell the fascinating story of how an infinite Taylor series with random coefficients from $N(0, 1)$, for example, defines an analytic function in the open complex unit disk $|z| < 1$ and hence a smooth function of θ for $z = re^{i\theta}$ for any $r < 1$ (see Exercise 12.2). As $r \to 1$, such functions approach white noise.

SUMMARY OF CHAPTER 12. *Smooth random functions with specified length scale λ can be defined via finite Fourier series with random coefficients. Integrals of such functions give smooth random walks, and random ODEs can incorporate such functions either as forcing terms or as coefficients. As $\lambda \to 0$, smooth random ODEs approach stochastic differential equations (SDEs) of the Stratonovich variety.*

Exercise 12.1. *Tracking a random signal.* Let f be the function on $[0, 50]$ defined by `rng(0)`, `randnfun(1,[0,50])`, and consider the IVP $y' = -a(y(t) - f(t))$, $y(0) = 0$, where $a > 0$ is a constant. Plot f together with the solutions y for $a = 0.1$, 1, and 10 and discuss the results. Intuitively speaking, what is happening here?

Exercise 12.2. Random and lacunary Taylor series. *(a)* Define $f(z) = \sum_{k=0}^{n} c_k z^k$, where $c_0, \ldots, c_n$ are independent random samples from $N(0, 1)$, with n chosen big enough so that it is equivalent to ∞ to plotting accuracy. For a particular choice of random coefficients, plot $\mathrm{Re}(f(z))$ as a function of θ for $z = re^{i\theta}$ with $r = 0.5, 0.9, 0.99$. *(b)* Another way to generate an analytic function in the unit disk with a natural boundary on the unit circle is by means of a *lacunary series* (i.e., one with long gaps), an idea going back to Weierstrass. Make the same plots as in *(a)* but now with $c_j = 1$ when j is a power of 2 and $c_j = 0$ otherwise.

Exercise 12.3. Unbounded variation of a Brownian path. White noise has unbounded 1-norm with probability 1; so its integral, Brownian motion, has unbounded variation. Make a log-log plot of the 1-norms of big smooth random functions on $[-1, 1]$ as a function of wavelength parameter λ for $\lambda = 1, 1/2, \ldots, 1/256$. What rate of increase do you see as a function of λ?

Exercise 12.4. Cumulative maximum of a Brownian path. Plot four smooth random walks with $\lambda = 0.1$ on $[0, 50]$ together with their cumulative maxima calculated with `cummax(f)`. Describe qualitatively what you see.

Exercise 12.5. Roots of a Brownian path. Calculate smooth random walks on $[0, 50]$ for $\lambda = 16, 8, 4, \ldots, 1/16$, initializing the random number seed with `rng(1)` in each case. Plot each function and calculate its roots. Describe qualitatively how the sets of roots behave as $\lambda \to 0$. Find a way to show this graphically. (With probability 1, the zero set of a Brownian path is an uncountably infinite closed set with no isolated points and fractal dimension $1/2$. For this and many other properties of Brownian paths, see Mörters and Peres, *Brownian Motion,* Cambridge, 2010.)

Exercise 12.6. Winding number of a Brownian path. *(a)* Construct ten complex smooth random walks starting from $z = 1$ rather than $z = 0$ for $t \in [0, 100]$ with $\lambda = 0.1$. How many of the paths complete a circuit 360° around the origin at some point of the trajectory? (Use the Chebfun `angle` command.) It can be shown that, with probability 1, a Brownian path will wind around the origin infinitely often as $t \to \infty$, yet the expected time for each circuit is ∞. *(b)* The expected time for the path to reach an angle of 30° from the positive axis, however, is finite. Estimate it numerically to 1 or 2 digits of accuracy.

13. Chaos

Having just considered functions that are truly random, at least in principle, we now turn to the celebrated phenomenon of solutions of ODEs that "look random" even though they are not. Besides this property, two other hallmarks of chaos are *sensitive dependence on initial conditions* and *strange attractors*. In this chapter we explore these notions, connecting them with the number known as the Lyapunov exponent.

We begin with the Lorenz equations as given in equation (10.7),

$$u' = 10(v - u), \quad v' = u(28 - w) - v, \quad w' = uv - (8/3)w. \qquad (13.1)$$

In Figure 10.11 we plotted the trajectory for $t \in [0, 30]$ emanating from the initial data

$$u(0) = v(0) = -15, \ w(0) = 20. \qquad (13.2)$$

Here is an image of this trajectory in phase space, seen from the angle that amounts to a projection onto the u–w plane.

```
N = chebop(0,30); N.lbc = [-15; -15; 20];
N.op = @(t,u,v,w) [diff(u)-10*(v-u); ...
    diff(v)-u*(28-w)+v; diff(w)-u*v+(8/3)*w];
[u,v,w] = N\0; plot(u,w)
c = 6*sqrt(2); hold on, plot([0 c -c],[0 27 27],'.')
```

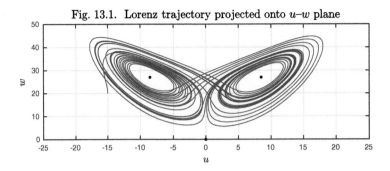

Fig. 13.1. Lorenz trajectory projected onto u–w plane

This image reveals the famous "butterfly" structure of the **strange attractor** for the Lorenz equations.[52] What it means to be a strange attractor is that typical orbits rapidly approach this set, which is not a simple curve or surface but has the form of a fractal. For the Lorenz equations, the fractal dimension is approximately 2.06, so the butterfly is just a little bit thicker than a two-dimensional manifold.[53]

Now let us look at dependence on initial conditions. Here the function $v(t)$ just computed is plotted in green, as in Chapter 10. In addition, another function $\tilde{v}(t)$ is plotted in red that arises from the very slightly perturbed initial data

$$u(0) = v(0) = -15, \quad w(0) = 20.00001. \tag{13.3}$$

```
N.lbc = [-15; -15; 20.00001]; [u2,v2,w2] = N\0;
plot(v2), hold on, plot(v)
```

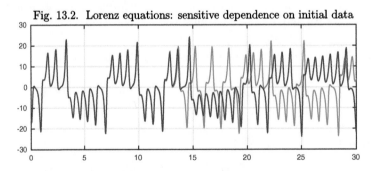

Fig. 13.2. Lorenz equations: sensitive dependence on initial data

The two initial conditions differ by less than one part in 10^6, so one would expect v and $\tilde{v}$ to be close to one another, and for about 13 time units, so they are. But throughout that time, the trajectories are steadily (on average) separating, and eventually the differences are of size $O(1)$ and the functions

---

[52]Not to be confused with the *butterfly effect* that also originates with Lorenz (not his famous 1963 paper, but a later one from 1969). If a butterfly flaps its wings in the Amazon, thanks to sensitive dependence of the earth's weather on initial conditions, might that cause a hurricane in Texas?

[53]The *fractal dimension* of a set is a precisely defined mathematical quantity that may take any nonnegative real value, not just an integer.

become completely uncoupled. An initial difference of size 10^{-5} has grown by
six orders of magnitude in 15 time units.

Everything in this problem is smooth, differentiable, and indeed analytic.
For example, the derivative of the value $v(30)$ with respect to the third initial
condition $w(0)$ is a perfectly well-defined number — it is just that it is a very
big one! Here is an approximation to the derivative of $v(5)$ with respect to $w(0)$:

```
(v2(5)-v(5))/(w2(0)-w(0))
ans = -30.9180
```

Here is the analogous approximation to the derivative of $v(10)$ with respect to
$w(0)$:

```
(v2(10)-v(10))/(w2(0)-w(0))
ans = 7.6882e+04
```

Note that these numbers are rapidly growing with t. If we compute the corresponding finite difference at $t = 30$, we get

```
(v2(30)-v(30))/(w2(0)-w(0))
ans = 2.5687e+06
```

but this greatly underestimates the actual derivative of $v(30)$ with respect to
$w(0)$, which is on the order of 10^{13}. We can explain the underestimation by
noting that the initial perturbation by 0.00001 is not nearly small enough to
grow by 13 orders of magnitude before reaching size $O(1)$, at which point it
stops growing.

To see more of this effect, it is interesting to plot $\|\tilde{\mathbf{y}}(t) - \mathbf{y}(t)\|$ on a log scale,
where $\mathbf{y}$ and $\tilde{\mathbf{y}}$ are the 3-component vector solutions resulting from the original
and the perturbed initial conditions. (The norm $\| \cdot \|$ we use is the square root
of the sum of the squares of the components $u(t), v(t), w(t)$.) Here is such a
plot, and it reveals two distinct regimes. For $t < 15$, the perturbations grow
exponentially. For $t > 15$, they reach size $O(1)$ (numbers roughly in the range
10–100) and stop growing.

```
tt = linspace(0,30,400);
err = sqrt((u2(tt)-u(tt)).^2+(v2(tt)-v(tt)).^2+(w2(tt)-w(tt)).^2);
semilogy(tt,err)
```

Fig. 13.3. Exponential growth of perturbations to scale $O(1)$

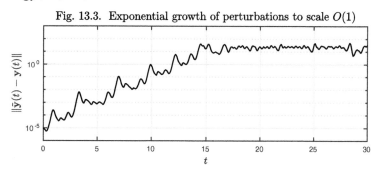

The growth rate of this initial phase is known as the **Lyapunov exponent**, λ, for this ODE. We can approximate it by a least-squares fit to the data for $t \in [0, 15]$.

```
ii = find(tt<=15);
c = polyfit(tt(ii),log(err(ii)),1); e0 = c(2); lam = c(1)

lam = 0.9052
```

The significance of this number is that, approximately speaking, perturbations in the Lorenz trajectories typically grow at the rate

$$\|\tilde{\mathbf{y}}(t) - \mathbf{y}(t)\| \approx C e^{0.91t}.$$

We can plot this fit to the data as a dashed line.

```
hold on, semilogy([0 18],exp(e0+lam*[0 18]),'--')
```

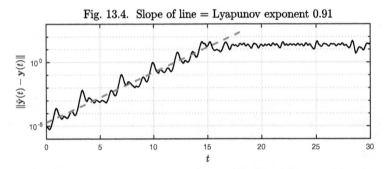

Fig. 13.4. Slope of line = Lyapunov exponent 0.91

In this experiment, we started from a finite perturbation, which grew exponentially over a finite time span. The mathematical definition of a Lyapunov exponent is based on infinitesimal perturbations, which may grow forever. To be precise, λ is defined by this formula, involving a supremum over all initial perturbations $\delta\mathbf{y}(0)$:

$$\lambda = \lim_{t \to \infty} \; \limsup_{\|\delta\mathbf{y}(0)\| \to 0} \; t^{-1} \log \frac{\|\delta\mathbf{y}(t)\|}{\|\delta\mathbf{y}(0)\|}. \tag{13.4}$$

In principle this number might vary from one initial point $\mathbf{y}(0)$ to another, in which case one would typically be interested in the supremum over all $\mathbf{y}(0)$.[54]

The Lyapunov exponent for the Lorenz equations is known to be about 0.9056. By chance, our experiment has matched this number more closely than should really be expected, statistically speaking (see Exercise 13.1).

---

[54]A further complication is that what we have called the Lyapunov exponent should more properly be termed the *maximal* Lyapunov exponent. For an n-dimensional dynamical system, imagine initial conditions in the form of an infinitesimal spherical cloud or blob centered at a point $\mathbf{y}(0)$. As $t \to \infty$, the blob will elongate and compress into an ellipsoid, with the lengths of the axes of the ellipsoid growing or decaying at different exponential rates on average as $t \to \infty$ in a manner that can be made precise by the tool known as the singular value decomposition. These growth and decay rates are the Lyapunov exponents of the system.

The article that launched the study of chaos was published by Edward Lorenz in 1963 with the title "Deterministic nonperiodic flow," and is one of the most important scientific publications of the 20th century.[55] The fact that it took until after 1963 for the phenomenon to be widely recognized can be attributed to the invention of computers. Chaos is not an unusual behavior at all in nonlinear systems of ODEs, but it could not be easily seen in the closed form solutions that were available in the days of hand calculation.

The historical side of our next example is particularly interesting. Among the most important ODEs of all scientifically are the equations of the **n-body problem**, by which we mean the equations that govern the trajectories of n point masses attracting each other gravitationally and moving according to Newton's laws. In its simplest form this is a set of $3n$ ODEs of second order: for each body, there are three spatial coordinates, and the differential equations express the fact that the acceleration of each body is equal to the sum of the inverse-square attractions to the others. For problems confined to a plane, the count reduces to $2n$ variables, an x and a y coordinate for each body. We are going to look at such a problem, and for convenience we will employ our usual trick of encoding x and y as a complex variable $z = x + iy$, as first introduced in Chapter 3. This brings us to a second-order system of ODEs in n complex unknowns:

$$z_j'' = -\sum_{i \neq j} \frac{z_j - z_i}{|z_j - z_i|^3}, \quad 1 \leq j \leq n. \tag{13.5}$$

The analytic solution to the 2-body problem goes back to Kepler and Newton, and it involves stable ellipses (as in Exercise 4.1). But there is no analytic solution for the 3-body problem, let alone for the n-body problem with $n > 3$.

For a long time, mathematicians and physicists have asked, is our solar system stable? Might its regular orbits one day break down? This problem proved theoretically intractable but has led to a great deal of important mathematics along the way. Even today, after extensive computational investigations, there is some controversy over whether or not the solar system is stable or chaotic, but the difficulty of this question is a result of a special circumstance: the mass of the sun is much greater than that of the planets, and acts as a strong regulating influence. The sun's mass is so dominant that, to first approximation, each planet's orbit is just the solution of a 2-body problem involving itself and the sun. By contrast, if you look at the trajectories of n attracting bodies of equal masses in the absence of a heavy sun to act as a policeman, chaos is the rule. Before computers, nobody could look at such trajectories.

The idealized configuration we shall examine consists of three planets in a plane with no sun, initially positioned with zero velocity at the vertices of a 3-4-5 right triangle. The following commands compute the orbits up to $t = 150$.

```
u0 = 0; v0 = 3; w0 = 4i; N = chebop(0,150);
N.op = @(t,u,v,w) [ ...
```

---

[55]The term "chaos" came later, coined by Jim Yorke in 1975.

```
      diff(u,2) + (u-v)/abs(u-v)^3 + (u-w)/abs(u-w)^3; ...
      diff(v,2) + (v-u)/abs(v-u)^3 + (v-w)/abs(v-w)^3; ...
      diff(w,2) + (w-u)/abs(w-u)^3 + (w-v)/abs(w-v)^3];
N.lbc = @(u,v,w) [u-u0; v-v0; w-w0; diff(u); diff(v); diff(w)];
[u,v,w] = N\0;
```

To begin with we plot the orbits just up to $t = 20$.

```
plot([u v w],'interval',[0 20])
```

Fig. 13.5. Orbits of three planets to $t = 20$

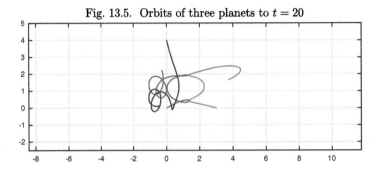

In this image the red, green, and blue curves show paths of the three planets as t increases. At first they are well separated, but soon two close red-blue flybys are observed. Here are the distance and time of the closest approach:

```
[closest_distance,closest_time] = min(abs(u{0,20}-v{0,20}))
```

```
closest_distance = 0.0039
closest_time = 7.3318
```

Plotting the orbits up to $t = 50$ gives a picture hard to interpret in detail. It is clear, however, that the planets are swinging around each other in an effectively random fashion.

```
plot([u v w],'interval',[0 50])
```

Fig. 13.6. Orbits continued to $t = 50$

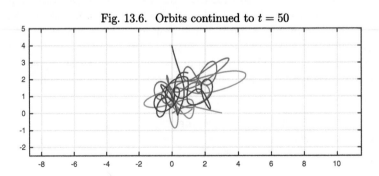

One might expect this behavior to continue forever, but, in fact, it doesn't. Around $t = 86$, the three-body system breaks up ("self-ionizes"), with the red planet shooting off to the northwest and the green and blue ones spiraling off together to the southeast. This curious effect is revealed in the plot below of the orbits up to $t = 100$, looking like ribbons on a birthday present. Thus the 3-body problem for an initial 3-4-5 triangle turns out to exemplify what is known as *transient chaos*.

```
plot([u v w],'interval',[0 100])
```

Fig. 13.7. Orbits to $t = 100$, with self-ionization near $t = 86$

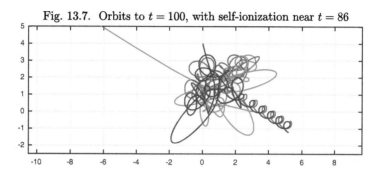

Here, for example, is the time at which the red planet passes through coordinate $x = -2$:

```
t_escape = roots(real(v)+2)

t_escape = 90.1543
```

Just as we did with the Lorenz equations, let us examine the effect of a small perturbation in one component of the initial data. Changing the initial coordinate $w(0)$ from $4i$ to $3.9999i$ gives the following orbit up to $t = 100$, which is similar to the former one for a while but then begins to differ completely. This time there is no self-ionization.

```
N.lbc = @(u,v,w) [u-u0; v-v0; w-3.9999i; diff(u); diff(v); diff(w)];
[u2,v2,w2] = N\0; plot([u2 v2 w2],'interval',[0 100])
```

Fig. 13.8. Slightly perturbed orbits to $t = 100$

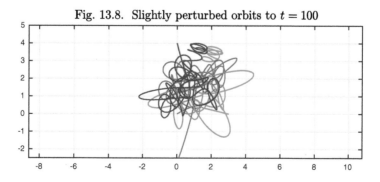

A plot shows $\|\tilde{\mathbf{y}}(t) - \mathbf{y}(t)\|$ as a function of t and the estimated Lyapunov exponent $\lambda \approx 0.15$.

```
tt = linspace(0,150,400);
err = sqrt(abs(u2(tt)-u(tt)).^2 + abs(v2(tt)-v(tt)).^2 + ...
      abs(w2(tt)-w(tt)).^2);
semilogy(tt,err), ii = find(tt<=70);
c = polyfit(tt(ii),log(err(ii)),1); e0 = c(2); lam = c(1)
hold on, semilogy([0 80],exp(e0+lam*[0 80]),'--')
```

```
lam = 0.1524
```

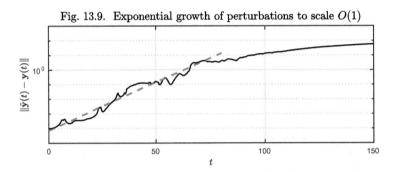

Fig. 13.9. Exponential growth of perturbations to scale $O(1)$

Note the transition from the chaotic exponential phase to smooth algebraic growth at a rate $O(t)$ after the bodies have separated.

Our third example of a chaotic system is the **Rössler equations**,

$$u' = -v - w, \quad v' = u + \tfrac{1}{5}v, \quad w' = \tfrac{1}{5} + w(u - c), \tag{13.6}$$

where the constant $1/5$ has been fixed arbitrarily and c is a parameter. This system is even simpler than the Lorenz equations (13.1) in that only one of the three equations is nonlinear. The Rössler equations illustrate the phenomenon of *period doubling* as a route to chaos. First, here we solve (13.6) for $t \in [0, 300]$ with $c = 2$ with initial conditions $u(0) = 2$ and $v(0) = w(0) = 0$. The image on the left shows the trajectory in the three-dimensional u-v-w phase space, which settles down to a regular oscillation, a limit cycle. The image on the right shows the same trajectory projected onto the u-v plane, just the part for $t > 200$. The initial transient has died away, and thus all one sees is the 2D projection of the limit cycle.

```
N = chebop(0,300); N.lbc = [2; 0; 0];
N.op = @(t,u,v,w) [diff(u)+v+w; diff(v)-u-.2*v; diff(w)-.2-w*(u-2)];
[u,v,w] = N\0; subplot(1,2,1), plot3(u,v,w)
subplot(1,2,2), plot(u{200,300},v{200,300})
```

Fig. 13.10. Rössler system (13.6), $c = 2$

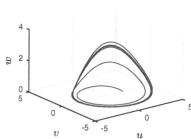
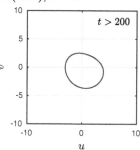

As the parameter c is increased, a change takes place: a bifurcation (see Chapter 17). At around $c = 2.8$, the limit cycle undergoes **period doubling**, with the trajectory unfolding into a double loop. The image for $c = 3.5$ shows this "period 2" solution.

```
N.op = @(t,u,v,w) ...
       [diff(u)+v+w; diff(v)-u-.2*v; diff(w)-.2-w*(u-3.5)];
[u,v,w] = N\0; subplot(1,2,1), plot3(u,v,w)
subplot(1,2,2), plot(u{200,300},v{200,300})
```

Fig. 13.11. Rössler system (13.6), $c = 3.5$

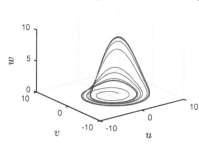
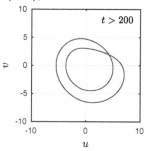

As c increases further, more bifurcations take place. A second period doubling to a "period 4" solution occurs around $c = 3.7$, and here is a pair of images for $c = 4$.

```
N.op = @(t,u,v,w) ...
       [diff(u)+v+w; diff(v)-u-.2*v; diff(w)-.2-w*(u-4)];
[u,v,w] = N\0; subplot(1,2,1), plot3(u,v,w)
subplot(1,2,2), plot(u{200,300},v{200,300})
```

Fig. 13.12. Rössler system (13.6), $c = 4$

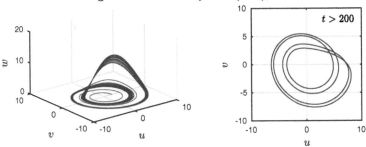

The phenomenon of period doubling was made famous in the 1970s by Mitchell Feigenbaum, who showed that it is a route to chaos in many problems. As c increases further (the next transition is around $c = 4.1$), the period doubles again and again, infinitely often. Each time interval from one doubling to the next is asymptotically 4.6692... times shorter than the last; this is *Feigenbaum's constant*. Finally, for c greater than about 4.2, the system is chaotic. The following images for $c = 5$ show the chaotic regime, with the orbits settling down not to a limit cycle but to a strange attractor.

```
N.op = @(t,u,v,w) ...
        [diff(u)+v+w; diff(v)-u-.2*v; diff(w)-.2-w*(u-5)];
[u,v,w] = N\0; subplot(1,2,1), plot3(u,v,w)
subplot(1,2,2), plot(u{200,300},v{200,300})
```

Fig. 13.13. Rössler system (13.6), $c = 5$

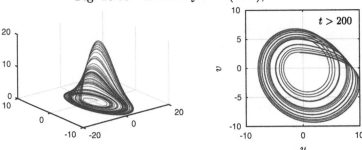

Our final example of chaos is governed by a nonautonomous equation due to Moon and Holmes, a chaotic *nonlinear forced oscillator*. The equation is

$$y'' + \tfrac{1}{4}y' - y + y^3 = 0.4\cos(t). \qquad (13.7)$$

As always, the constants here are somewhat arbitrary and could be adjusted. This is just a second-order ODE, so in the absence of the nonautonomous forcing function, the trajectories could not be chaotic. The forcing function, however, makes this system equivalent to a first-order autonomous system in three variables y, y', and t (see footnote 40 in Chapter 10). Thus the dimension is great enough for chaos to be a possibility, and a computation confirms its appearance.

```
t = chebfun('t',[0 300]); N = chebop(0,300);
N.op = @(t,y) diff(y,2) + .25*diff(y)-y+y^3;
N.lbc = [0;0]; rhs = 0.4*cos(t);
y = N\rhs; plot(y)
```

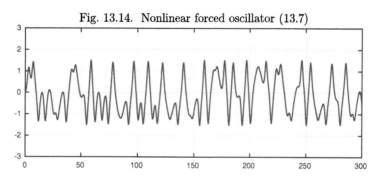

Fig. 13.14. Nonlinear forced oscillator (13.7)

We have not defined chaos! This is because there is no universally accepted definition, though the features of sensitive dependence and strange attractors are important. Note that exponential divergence of trajectories alone cannot be enough, since the solutions of $y' = y$ diverge at the rate e^t but nobody would call this equation chaotic. One needs the exponential divergence to be combined with some kind of global boundedness associated with nonlinearity, and this is where the strange attractors come in.

APPLICATION: CHAOS IN A FOOD WEB

In Chapter 10 we saw that a simple model of the interactions between rabbits and foxes led to limit cycles in their populations. If we introduce a third species into the fray, this can transform the dynamics completely. This possibility was discovered by Bob May (later Lord May) in the 1970s, a story made famous in the book *Chaos: Making a New Science* by James Gleick.

Rabbits need to eat too! Suppose in addition to the populations of rabbits, $u(t)$, and foxes, $v(t)$, we consider the population of carrots, $c(t)$. We suppose that, left on their own, these tend to grow logistically (see Exercises 3.15 and 3.16). Now rabbits consume carrots, and foxes consume rabbits, and neither animal species can be sustained without food. A reasonable model of the system is

$$c' = c(1-c) - f_1(c)u, \quad u' = f_1(c)u - f_2(u)v - d_1 u, \quad v' = f_2(u)v - d_2 v, \quad (13.8)$$

with $f_i(z) = a_i z/(1 + b_i z)$ for $i = 1, 2$. The consumption interactions are little different from those in the Lotka–Volterra equations. They include a saturation effect for the consumer species, accounting for extra competition as populations grow large. This model was proposed by Hastings and Powell in "Chaos in a three-species food chain," *Ecology*, 1991, where the parameter choices were

$a_1 = 5$, $a_2 = 0.1$, $b_2 = 2$, $d_1 = 0.4$, $d_2 = 0.01$. The parameter b_1 was allowed to vary.

Increasing b_1 increases the effect of competition between rabbits. Here is what happens to the rabbits with $b_1 = 2.5$, a nonchaotic regime.

```
a1 = 5; a2 = 0.1; b2 = 2; d1 = 0.4; d2 = 0.01;
f1 = @(z,b1) a1*z./(1+b1*z);   f2 = @(z) a2*z./(1+b2*z);
N = chebop(0,3000); b1 = 2.5;
N.op = @(t,c,u,v) [ diff(c)-(c*(1-c)-f1(c,b1)*u);
                    diff(u) - (f1(c,b1)*u-f2(u)*v-d1*u);
                    diff(v) - (f2(u)*v-d2*v) ];
N.lbc = [.4;1;9]; [c,u,v] = N\0; plot(u{2000,3000})
```

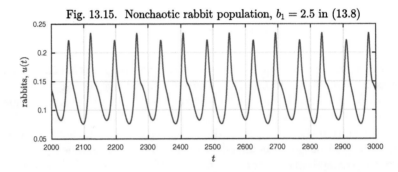

Fig. 13.15. Nonchaotic rabbit population, $b_1 = 2.5$ in (13.8)

At first glance this may look somewhat irregular. But in phase space we see an ordinary limit cycle of doubled period, just as in Figure 13.11.

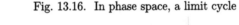

```
plot3(c{2000,3000},u{2000,3000},v{2000,3000})
```

Fig. 13.16. In phase space, a limit cycle

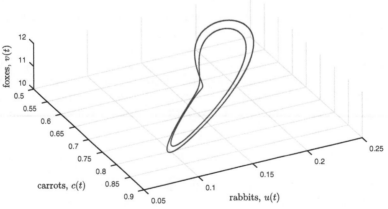

If we set $b_1 = 3.5$, increasing the competition between rabbits, the picture changes fundamentally.

```
b1 = 3.5;
N.op = @(t,c,u,v) [ diff(c)-(c*(1-c)-f1(c,b1)*u);
                    diff(u) - (f1(c,b1)*u-f2(u)*v-d1*u);
                    diff(v) - (f2(u)*v-d2*v) ];
[c,u,v] = N\0; plot3(c{2000,3000},u{2000,3000},v{2000,3000})
```

Fig. 13.17. Chaotic rabbit population, $b = 3.5$ in (13.8)

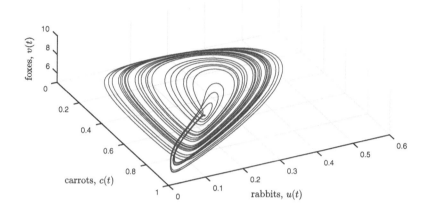

Looking again at the rabbit population, we see repeated but aperiodic crashes in the population, separated by a variable number and size of shorter cycles of boom and bust.

```
close all, plot(u{2000,3000})
```

Fig. 13.18. Chaotic rabbit population

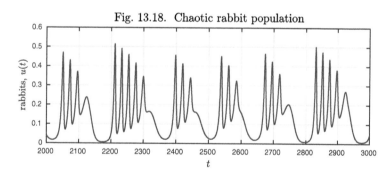

Obviously real food webs can be far more complex than this. But this example shows that the change from two species to three can have a quantum effect, and for reasons that are mathematical, not biological.

HISTORY. The roots of chaos are often traced to Poincaré and Hadamard in the 1890s, long before the days of computers, but the subject did not become widely studied until the work of Lorenz, May, Yorke, Feigenbaum, and others in the 1960s and 1970s. Chaos became known to the public with James Gleick's

1987 book *Chaos: Making a New Science* mentioned earlier and the 1993 movie *Jurassic Park*.

OUR FAVORITE REFERENCE. One of the best mathematical textbooks ever written is S. H. Strogatz, *Nonlinear Dynamics and Chaos: With Applications to Physics, Biology, Chemistry, and Engineering,* Westview Press, 2015 (first published in 1994). Strogatz combines marvelous clarity with a precise presentation of the mathematics of this fascinating subject.

SUMMARY OF CHAPTER 13. *Many nonlinear ODEs with three or more variables are chaotic, though this fact was not widely recognized until the last third of the 20th century. Chaos is characterized by the property that perturbations may grow exponentially with time, yet global orbits remain bounded. The maximal rate of exponential growth is known as the Lyapunov exponent.*

Exercise 13.1. *Lucky Lyapunov exponents.* It was mentioned in the text that the estimate 0.9052 of the Lyapunov exponent was fortuitously close to the true value. Confirm this by computing the name number based on data for $t \in [0, 14]$ and $t \in [1, 15]$ instead of $t \in [0, 15]$.

Exercise 13.2. *Smaller perturbation of the Lorenz equations.* In the text we perturbed the Lorenz equations by changing the value of $w(0)$ from 20 to $20+10^{-5}$. *(a)* Reproduce Figures 13.2 and 13.3 with the smaller perturbation $20 + 10^{-9}$ and comment on the results. *(b)* Also repeat the finite-difference estimates of the derivatives of $v(5)$, $v(10)$, and $v(30)$ with respect to $w(0)$, and comment on the results.

Exercise 13.3. *Alternative choices of the Lorenz coefficient* 28. In the Lorenz equations, let r denote the parameter that traditionally takes the value 28. Starting from our usual initial conditions, make plots of $u(t)$ against $w(t)$ as in Figure 13.1 for $t \in [0, 100]$ with $r = 20, 22, 24$; also make plots in each case of $u(t)$ against t as in Figure 13.2. Which case seems to be chaotic? Which one gives the clearest example of transient chaos?

Exercise 13.4. *Lorenz equations with a breeze.* In the Lorenz equations (13.1), let the first equation be changed to $u' = 10(v - u) - a$, where a is a parameter. As in the last exercise, make plots of $u(t)$ against $w(t)$ and of $u(t)$ against t for $t \in [0, 30]$ with $a = 20, 25, 30$. Comment on the solutions.

Exercise 13.5. *Two electrons and a nucleus.* Consider the highly idealized problem of two electrons of mass 1 and charge -1 orbiting a nucleus of charge $+2$ fixed at the origin of the x-y plane. Let $z(t)$ and $w(t)$ be the positions of the electrons represented with the usual complex variable trick. Consider trajectories for $t \in [0, 20]$ starting from initial conditions $z = i$, $z' = 1$, $w = -i$, $w' = a$. *(a)* Write down the ODE governing the evolution of $w(z)$ and $z(t)$ assuming an inverse-square electrostatic force law with constant 1. The electrons repel each other while being attracted to the nucleus. *(b)* Plot the two trajectories in the case $a = 1$. The configuration is symmetric, and the symmetry should be preserved for all t. *(c)* Now make similar plots for $a = 0.5, 0.6, 0.7, 0.8, 0.9,$ and 0.99. Discuss the results.

Exercise 13.6. *Chaos and cellular automata.* Discrete processes, in which no real numbers are involved, can also exhibit chaotic properties. Illustrate this by simulating the "Rule 30" cellular automaton described in Stephen Wolfram's 2002 book *A New Kind of Science*.[56] To do this, let n be a positive even integer and initialize an $n \times n$ matrix $\mathbf{A}$ to zero apart from the value 1 in the middle of the top row, $a_{1,n/2} = 1$. Now sweep from rows 2 to n, updating each entry according to the following rule: a_{ij} is changed to the value 1 if the three entries above it, $a_{i-1,j-1:j+1}$, correspond to the binary representation of one of the numbers $1, 2, 3, 4$ rather than $0, 5, 6, 7$. (The numbers in columns 1 and n can be left unchanged.) Take $n = 200$ and use the MATLAB **spy** command to plot the matrix at the end. Note that the structure is completely deterministic yet has apparently random properties. For another view of the randomness, plot $a_{i,n/2}$ as a function of i.

Exercise 13.7. *Random Fibonacci sequence.* Here, on the other hand, is an example of a discrete process with true randomness. Suppose $x_0 = x_1 = 1$ and, for $k \geq 1$, $x_{k+1} = x_{k-1} + x_k$. Then it is well known that x_k grows asymptotically at a rate determined by ϕ^k, where ϕ is the golden ratio $(1 + \sqrt{5})/2 \approx 1.618$. Consider the *random Fibonacci sequence* defined by $x_{k+1} = \pm x_{k-1} \pm x_k$, where at each step each sign is independently $+$ or $-$ with probability 0.5. On a semilogy scale, make plots of $|x_k|$ vs. k up to the maximum values $k = 100$ and 5000. Numerically estimate the *Lyapunov constant* for this process; that is, the constant C such that with probability 1 the sequence grows in absolute value at a rate C^k as $k \to \infty$. (If you are curious to learn more, see D. Viswanath, "Random Fibonacci sequences...," *Mathematics of Computation* 69 (2000), pp. 1131–1155.)

---

[56]On p. 27 of the original edition Wolfram calls this "probably the single most surprising scientific discovery I have ever made."

14. Linear systems and linearization

Much of mathematics springs from two topics: calculus and linear algebra. The subject of ODEs is obviously rooted in calculus, and it has a fundamental linear algebra side too. If an ODE is linear, then it is "all" linear algebra. If it is nonlinear, then linear algebra still determines its local behavior near each point of a trajectory.

Let us start with the linear case. If $\mathbf{A}$ is an $n \times n$ matrix, a first-order linear ODE with n variables can be defined by

$$\mathbf{y}'(t) = \mathbf{A}\mathbf{y}(t), \tag{14.1}$$

a special case of the general system (10.1). Conversely, any first-order linear, autonomous, homogeneous n-variable system of ODEs ("FLAsH") can be written in this form for some matrix $\mathbf{A}$. If $\mathbf{y}_0$ is an n-vector, then one solution of (14.1) is

$$\mathbf{y}(t) = e^{t\mathbf{A}}\mathbf{y}_0, \tag{14.2}$$

where $e^{t\mathbf{A}}$ is the **matrix exponential**, defined by

$$e^{t\mathbf{A}} = \mathbf{I} + t\mathbf{A} + \frac{1}{2!}(t\mathbf{A})^2 + \frac{1}{3!}(t\mathbf{A})^3 + \cdots. \tag{14.3}$$

This series always converges, providing a well-defined matrix exponential for any $\mathbf{A}$ and t.[57] In fact, (14.3) is the Taylor series of $e^{t\mathbf{A}}$ about $t = 0$, and from

---

[57] A proof can be based on the observation that, for any t, the powers $(t\mathbf{A})^k$ grow at most geometrically as $k \to \infty$, whereas the factorials $k!$ grow faster than geometrically.

the theory of analytic functions it is known that the series can be differentiated term by term, yielding

$$\frac{d}{dt}e^{t\mathbf{A}} = \mathbf{A}e^{t\mathbf{A}}.$$

This formula confirms that (14.2) is a solution of (14.1). Equations (14.1)–(14.2) are matrix generalizations of equations (2.1)–(2.2) of Chapter 2.

So linear, autonomous, homogeneous systems of ODEs are all about exponentials of matrices. We record this conclusion as a theorem formulated for IVPs.

Theorem 14.1. Solution of first-order linear autonomous homogeneous IVP system (FLAsHI). *The problem*

$$\mathbf{y}'(t) = \mathbf{A}\mathbf{y}(t), \quad \mathbf{y}(0) = \mathbf{y}_0, \tag{14.4}$$

where $\mathbf{y}_0$ is an n-vector and $\mathbf{A}$ is an $n \times n$ matrix, has the unique solution

$$\mathbf{y}(t) = e^{t\mathbf{A}}\mathbf{y}_0 \tag{14.5}$$

valid for all t, $-\infty < t < \infty$.

Proof. We have just outlined an argument for existence, and uniqueness follows from Theorem 11.2. A suitable Lipschitz constant for (14.4) is $K = \|\mathbf{A}\|$; as explained in Chapter 11, the choice of norm does not matter. ∎

A small extension of (14.1) is to make the ODE inhomogeneous ("FLAsh"),

$$\mathbf{y}'(t) = \mathbf{A}\mathbf{y}(t) + \mathbf{g},$$

where $\mathbf{g}$ is a fixed n-vector. We might call this an **affine** autonomous system of equations, though most of the time we will just say "linear." Following Theorem 2.4 for the scalar case, we readily derive the solution as follows.

Theorem 14.2. Solution of first-order linear autonomous IVP system with constant inhomogeneity (FLAshI). *The problem*

$$\mathbf{y}'(t) = \mathbf{A}\mathbf{y}(t) + \mathbf{g}, \quad \mathbf{y}(0) = \mathbf{y}_0, \tag{14.6}$$

where $\mathbf{y}_0$ and $\mathbf{g}$ are n-vectors and $\mathbf{A}$ is an $n \times n$ matrix, has the unique solution

$$\mathbf{y}(t) = e^{t\mathbf{A}}\mathbf{y}_0 + \int_0^t e^{(t-s)\mathbf{A}}\mathbf{g}\,ds. \tag{14.7}$$

If A is nonsingular this reduces to

$$\mathbf{y}(t) = e^{t\mathbf{A}}\mathbf{y}_0 + \mathbf{A}^{-1}(e^{t\mathbf{A}} - \mathbf{I})\mathbf{g}. \tag{14.8}$$

Proof. It can be verified explicitly that (14.7) and (14.8) are solutions of (14.6), and uniqueness again follows from Theorem 11.2. ∎

Theorem 14.2 assumes a constant inhomogeneity, but the variable case is also straightforward (again "FLAsh"):

$$\mathbf{y}'(t) = \mathbf{A}\mathbf{y}(t) + \mathbf{g}(t),$$

where $\mathbf{g}(t)$ is a n-vector function of t. Here is a systems generalization of a result midway between Theorems 2.3 and 2.4 (since $\mathbf{g}$ but not $\mathbf{A}$ has been made t-dependent). As in those theorems, the ODE is understood to hold everywhere except at any points of discontinuity.

Theorem 14.3. Solution of first-order linear autonomous inhomogeneous IVP system (FLAshI). *The problem*

$$\mathbf{y}'(t) = \mathbf{A}\mathbf{y}(t) + \mathbf{g}(t), \quad \mathbf{y}(0) = \mathbf{y}_0, \tag{14.9}$$

where $\mathbf{y}_0$ is an n-vector, $\mathbf{g}(t)$ is an n-vector piecewise continuous function of t, and $\mathbf{A}$ is an $n \times n$ matrix, has the unique solution

$$\mathbf{y}(t) = e^{t\mathbf{A}}\mathbf{y}_0 + \int_0^t e^{(t-s)\mathbf{A}}\mathbf{g}(s)ds. \tag{14.10}$$

Proof. Again the formulas are readily verified and uniqueness comes from Theorem 11.2. ∎

The discussion above is confined to autonomous problems, but nonautonomous linear equations of the form $\mathbf{y}' = \mathbf{A}(t)\mathbf{y} + \mathbf{g}(t)$ are important too. In this situation the matrix exponential $e^{t\mathbf{A}}$ generalizes to a so-called *fundamental matrix* $\mathbf{Y}(t)$, discussed in equations (19.17)–(19.18) of Chapter 19. The special case $\mathbf{g} = \mathbf{0}$ also appears in equation (14.32) below.

Some ODEs are linear to start with, but the greatest importance of linear ODEs comes from the fact that a nonlinear ODE can be *linearized*. By this we mean that locally, near a given time t_0, the solution of a nonlinear ODE

$$\mathbf{y}'(t) = \mathbf{f}(t, \mathbf{y}(t)) \tag{14.11}$$

will evolve approximately like that of a linear one. In fact, every autonomous ODE looks locally like an affine autonomous system of the form (14.6), so long as the coefficients are twice differentiable. We now work out the details of such approximations, which are a matter of multivariate calculus. As usual, we keep the formulas simple by assuming $t_0 = 0$, even though in an application we may linearize about values $t_0 \neq 0$.

Suppose we have an autonomous ODE

$$\mathbf{y}'(t) = \mathbf{f}(\mathbf{y}(t)) \tag{14.12}$$

and are interested in the behavior of solutions $\mathbf{y}(t)$ near a particular point $\mathbf{y}_*$. Specifically, we consider the solution of the IVP

$$\mathbf{y}'(t) = \mathbf{f}(\mathbf{y}(t)), \quad \mathbf{y}(0) = \mathbf{y}_0 \tag{14.13}$$

for some initial value $\mathbf{y}_0$ close to or equal to $\mathbf{y}_*$. We use the abbreviation

$$\mathbf{f}_* = \mathbf{f}(\mathbf{y}_*) \tag{14.14}$$

and suppose that $\mathbf{f}$ is twice differentiable at $\mathbf{y} = \mathbf{y}_*$. The partial derivative $\partial\mathbf{f}/\partial\mathbf{y}$ is an $n \times n$ **Jacobian matrix**,

$$\mathbf{J} = \frac{\partial\mathbf{f}}{\partial\mathbf{y}} = \begin{pmatrix} \dfrac{\partial f_1}{\partial y_1} & \cdots & \dfrac{\partial f_1}{\partial y_n} \\ \vdots & & \vdots \\ \dfrac{\partial f_n}{\partial y_1} & \cdots & \dfrac{\partial f_n}{\partial y_n} \end{pmatrix}.$$

We abbreviate the value of $\mathbf{J}$ at $\mathbf{y} = \mathbf{y}_*$ by

$$\mathbf{J}_* = \mathbf{J}(\mathbf{y}_*). \tag{14.15}$$

We now calculate from the definition of $\mathbf{J}_*$

$$\mathbf{f}(\mathbf{y}(t)) = \mathbf{f}_* + \mathbf{J}_*(\mathbf{y}(t) - \mathbf{y}_*) + O(\|\mathbf{y}(t) - \mathbf{y}_*\|^2). \tag{14.16}$$

This equation tells us that up to an error $O(\|\mathbf{y}(t) - \mathbf{y}_*\|^2)$, any autonomous ODE can be regarded as linear, or rather affine, as in (14.6). Here $\|\cdot\|$ can denote any norm on the space of n-vectors, since all norms on a finite-dimensional space are equivalent.

The formulas will be simpler if we work with the difference variables

$$\delta\mathbf{y}(t) = \mathbf{y}(t) - \mathbf{y}_*, \quad \delta\mathbf{y}_0 = \mathbf{y}_0 - \mathbf{y}_*.$$

With these definitions, (14.8) and (14.16) give us the following conclusions.

Theorem 14.4. Linearization of an autonomous system of ODEs (FIAsHI). *Let $\mathbf{y}_*$ be fixed and assume $\mathbf{f}$ is twice differentiable at $\mathbf{y} = \mathbf{y}_*$ with Jacobian $\mathbf{J}_*$. The solution of (14.13) satisfies*

$$\delta\mathbf{y}'(t) = \mathbf{f}_* + \mathbf{J}_*\delta\mathbf{y}(t) + O(\|\delta\mathbf{y}(t)\|^2) \tag{14.17}$$

and if $\mathbf{J}_*$ is nonsingular,

$$\delta\mathbf{y}(t) = e^{t\mathbf{J}_*}\delta\mathbf{y}_0 + (\mathbf{J}_*)^{-1}(e^{t\mathbf{J}_*} - \mathbf{I})\mathbf{f}_* + O(t\Delta(t)^2) \tag{14.18}$$

if $\Delta(t)$ is an upper bound on $\|\delta\mathbf{y}(s)\|$ for $0 \le s \le t$. If $\mathbf{y}_0 = \mathbf{y}_*$, then $\delta\mathbf{y} = \mathbf{0}$, and this estimate becomes

$$\delta\mathbf{y}(t) = (\mathbf{J}_*)^{-1}(e^{t\mathbf{J}_*} - \mathbf{I})\mathbf{f}_* + O(t^3). \tag{14.19}$$

Sketch of proof. Equation (14.17) is a restatement of (14.16). Equation (14.18) follows by applying Theorem 14.2 to (14.17) with $\mathbf{A} = \mathbf{J}_*$ and $\mathbf{h} = \mathbf{f}_*$. Equation (14.19) follows from (14.18) together with the estimate $\Delta(t) = O(t)$ in the special case $\delta\mathbf{y}(0) = \mathbf{0}$. (In this outline we are assuming that the $O(\cdot)$ terms behave in the obvious matter, with a small perturbation of an ODE resulting in a small perturbation of its solution. A careful argument could justify such steps by the use of a lemma known as *Gronwall's inequality*.) ▮

We now explore three examples of Theorem 14.4 in action, first for a scalar first-order problem, then for a scalar second-order problem analyzed by reduction to a first-order system, then for a two-variable first-order system.

For the scalar first-order example, we recall the IVP (3.9),

$$y'(t) = y(t)^2, \quad y(0) = 1, \tag{14.20}$$

whose solution $y(t) = (1 - t)^{-1}$ blows up to ∞ at $t = 1$. Here is a solution plotted as in Chapter 3.

```
N = chebop(0,1); N.op = @(t,y) diff(y) - y^2;
N.lbc = 1; N.maxnorm = 25;
y = N\0; plot(y), hold on, plot([1 1],[0 30],'--')
```

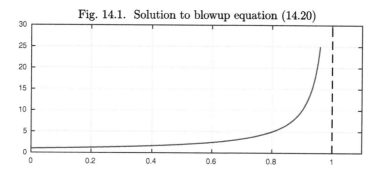
Fig. 14.1. Solution to blowup equation (14.20)

The Jacobian for this equation is the scalar $J(y) = 2y$, which takes the value $J_* = 2y_0$ at $y_* = y_0$, so Theorem 14.4 gives the following linear approximation for $t \approx 0$, $y \approx y_0$:

$$y'(t) \approx (y_0)^2 + 2y_0(y(t) - y_0), \quad y(0) = y_0,$$

or near a possibly nonzero time t_0,

$$y'(t) \approx (y_0)^2 + 2y_0(y(t) - y_0), \quad y(t_0) = y_0. \tag{14.21}$$

Let us add dotted arcs to the plot corresponding to solutions of this linear equation emanating from $t_0 = 0.5$ and 0.8.

```
for t0 = [0.5 0.8]
  y0 = y(t0); f0 = y0^2; J0 = 2*y(t0); L = chebop(t0,t0+.22);
  L.op = @(t,u) diff(u) - f0 - J0*(u-y0); L.lbc = y0;
  u = L\0; plot(u,':'), plot(t0,y0,'.')
end
```

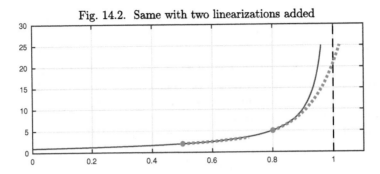
Fig. 14.2. Same with two linearizations added

Each linearized solution is shown over an interval of length 0.22. At the initial point, as asserted by (14.19), the linearization matches both the slope and the curvature. The approximation starting at $t = 0.5$ tracks the true solution closely over the interval shown, whereas the approximation starting at $t = 0.8$ loses accuracy more quickly. Note that as the solution to a linear problem, it will exist for all t, unlike the underlying nonlinear problem with its blowup.

Next we look at an example involving a second-order scalar ODE. This is such an important situation that it is worth spelling out the special form Theorem 14.4 takes in this case. Suppose we have a second-order scalar autonomous problem

$$u''(t) = F(u(t), u'(t)), \quad u(0) = u_0, \quad u'(0) = v_0. \tag{14.22}$$

Setting $v(t) = u'(t)$, we can write this as a first-order system in the variable $\mathbf{y}(t) = (u(t), v(t))^T$:

$$u'(t) = v(t), \quad v'(t) = F(u(t), v(t)), \quad u(0) = u_0, \quad v(0) = v_0.$$

The Jacobian $\mathbf{J}_*$ is

$$\mathbf{J}_* = \begin{pmatrix} 0 & 1 \\ \partial F/\partial u & \partial F/\partial v \end{pmatrix},$$

and (14.17) becomes $u'(t) = v(t)$ together with

$$v'(t) = F(u_*, v_*) + \frac{\partial F}{\partial u}(u(t) - u_*) + \frac{\partial F}{\partial v}(v(t) - v_*).$$

Translating this back to the original second-order scalar context gives this variant of Theorem 14.4, with $\delta u(t) = u(t) - u_*$ and $\delta v(t) = u'(t) - v_*$.

Theorem 14.5. Linearization of an autonomous second-order scalar ODE (flASHI). *Let the function F defining the scalar second-order IVP (14.22) be twice differentiable with respect to its first and second arguments at $u = u_*$, $u' = v_*$, and define*

$$F_* = F(u_*, v_*), \quad a_* = \frac{\partial F}{\partial u}(u_*, v_*), \quad b_* = \frac{\partial F}{\partial u'}(u_*, v_*).$$

Then $u(t)$ satisfies

$$(\delta u(t))'' = F_* + a_* \delta u(t) + b_* \delta v(t) + O((\delta u(t))^2) + O((\delta v(t))^2). \tag{14.23}$$

If $u_0 = u_*$ and $v_0 = v_*$, this becomes

$$(\delta u(t))'' = F_* + a_* \delta u(t) + b_* \delta v(t) + O(t^2). \qquad (14.24)$$

For an example, we turn to our friend the van der Pol equation, as in (8.8):

$$u'' = 5(1 - u^2)u' - u, \quad t \in [0, 15], \quad u(0) = 1, \ u'(0) = 0. \qquad (14.25)$$

```
N = chebop(0,15); N.lbc = [1;0];
N.op = @(t,u) diff(u,2) - 5*(1-u^2)*diff(u) + u;
u = N\0; plot(u), hold on
```

Fig. 14.3. Van der Pol equation (14.25)

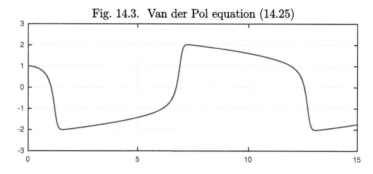

By Theorem 14.5, the linearized approximation near a point t_0 with $u(t_0) = u_*$ and $u'(t_0) = v_*$ is

$$u''(t) \approx 5(1 - (u_0)^2)v_0 - u_0(10u_0v_0 + 1)(u(t) - u_0) + 5(1 - u_0^2)(u'(t) - v_0).$$

We use this result to add three curves to the plot corresponding to times $t_0 = 3$, 6.9, and 11.5.

```
for t0 = [3 6.9 11.5]
  u0 = u(t0); v0 = deriv(u,t0);
  F0 = 5*(1-u0^2)*v0-u0; a0 = -(10*u0*v0+1); b0 = 5*(1-u0^2);
  L = chebop(t0,t0+1.5); L.lbc = [u0; v0];
  L.op = @(t,w) diff(w,2) - F0 - a0*(w-u0) - b0*(diff(w)-v0);
  w = L\0; plot(w,':'), plot(t0,u0,'.')
end
```

Fig. 14.4. Same with three linearizations added

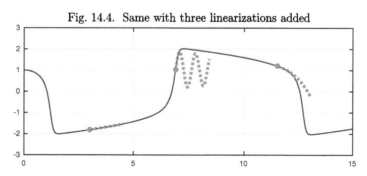

According to (14.24), the linearization of this problem captures u'' with accuracy $O(t^2)$. It follows that u itself is captured with accuracy $O(t^4)$: in the figure, the dotted lines match not just $y(0)$, $y'(0)$, and $y''(0)$, but also $y'''(0)$ (see Exercise 14.3). Yes, the oscillatory middle approximation is correct!

Now we consider an example to illustrate Theorem 14.5 with a generic autonomous system of two equations, that is, one not obtained from a second-order scalar problem. Here are the Lotka–Volterra equations (10.6):

$$u' = u - uv, \quad v' = -\tfrac{1}{5}v + uv, \quad t \geq 0, \ u(0) = u_0, \ v(0) = v_0. \qquad (14.26)$$

In Chapter 10 we plotted a limit cycle solution.

```
N = chebop(0,20); N.lbc = [1;1];
N.op = @(t,u,v) [diff(u)-u+u*v; diff(v)+.2*v-u*v];
[u,v] = N\0; arrowplot(u,v), hold on, plot([0 .2],[0 1],'.')
```

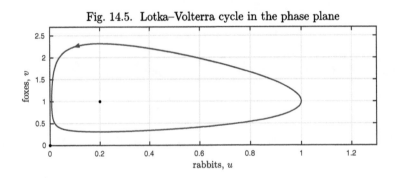

Fig. 14.5. Lotka–Volterra cycle in the phase plane

The Jacobian for (14.25) is

$$\mathbf{J}_0 = \begin{pmatrix} 1 - v & -u \\ v & u - 1/5 \end{pmatrix}.$$

This enables us to add dotted linearized trajectories as before.

```
for t0 = [0 2 14]
    u0 = u(t0); v0 = v(t0); f01 = u0-u0*v0; f02 = -v0/5+u0*v0;
    L = chebop(t0,t0+1); L.lbc = [u0; v0];
    L.op = @(t,U,V) [diff(U)-f01-(1-v0)*(U-u0)+u0*(V-v0); ...
                     diff(V)-f02-v0*(U-u0)-(u0-1/5)*(V-v0)];
    [U,V] = L\0; plot(U,V,':'), plot(u0,v0,'.')
end
```

Fig. 14.6. Same with three linearizations added

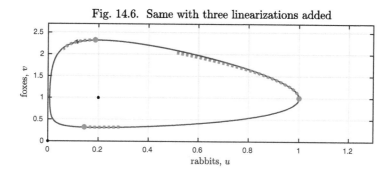

APPLICATION: LINEARIZED LORENZ TRAJECTORIES

Chaos is the quintessential nonlinear effect, yet at each point of time, a chaotic ODE, like any other ODE, behaves linearly. Let us explore this effect for the Lorenz equations (13.1),

$$u' = 10(v - u), \quad v' = u(28 - w) - v, \quad w' = uv - (8/3)w. \tag{14.27}$$

Suppose at some time t_0 a trajectory $\mathbf{y}(t)$ of (14.27) takes the values $\mathbf{y}(t_0) = \mathbf{y}_* = (u_*, v_*, w_*)^T$. If we define as usual $\delta\mathbf{y} = \mathbf{y} - \mathbf{y}_*$, then from Theorem 14.4 we have

$$\delta\mathbf{y}' \approx \mathbf{f}_* + \mathbf{J}_*\delta\mathbf{y}, \tag{14.28}$$

where we can calculate the Jacobian as

$$\mathbf{J}(u, v, w) = \begin{pmatrix} -10 & 10 & 0 \\ 28 - w & -1 & -u \\ v & u & -8/3 \end{pmatrix}. \tag{14.29}$$

This gives us a linear model of the local behavior near the given time and solution values.

Let us focus on what the model tells us about perturbations. If $\mathbf{y}(t)$ is the given trajectory, let $\mathbf{y}(t) + \Delta\mathbf{y}(t)$ be another nearby trajectory. Then by subtracting (14.28) applied to one solution from (14.28) applied to the other, we obtain

$$\Delta\mathbf{y}' \approx \mathbf{J}_*\Delta\mathbf{y}. \tag{14.30}$$

This approximation is valid near the given time t_0, but if we let $\mathbf{J}$ vary with t, so that it always corresponds to the local Jacobian along the trajectory, we get

$$\Delta\mathbf{y}' \approx \mathbf{J}(t)\Delta\mathbf{y}. \tag{14.31}$$

If $\Delta\mathbf{y}$ is infinitesimal, this becomes an equality,

$$\Delta\mathbf{y}' = \mathbf{J}(t)\Delta\mathbf{y} \quad (\Delta\mathbf{y} \text{ infinitesimal}). \tag{14.32}$$

This kind of linearization is applicable to all nonlinear problems. *Infinitesimal perturbations of a nonlinear ODE evolve according to a linear, homogeneous, nonautonomous equation.* In other words, infinitesimal perturbations are a problem of type FLasHI.

We can look at the Jacobians for the Lorenz equations numerically. Starting from our usual initial values, we run the system up to time $t = 10$ and make a function J that evaluates $\mathbf{J}(t)$ for any $t \in [0, 10]$.

```
N = chebop(0,10);
N.op = @(t,u,v,w) [diff(u)+10*u-10*v; ...
     diff(v)-(28-w)*u+v ; diff(w)-u*v+(8/3)*w];
N.lbc = [-15; -15; 20]; [u,v,w] = N\0;
J = @(t) [-10 10 0; 28-w(t) -1 -u(t); v(t) u(t) -8/3];
```

Here for example is $\mathbf{J}(t)$ at $t = 4$, a number big enough that initial transients have died away and the solution is close to the strange attractor.

```
J(4)
```

```
ans =
   -10.0000    10.0000          0
    -5.9316    -1.0000    12.2391
   -10.2430   -12.2391    -2.6667
```

Now here is something curious. We look at the eigenvalues of this matrix,

```
eig(J(4))
```

```
ans =
  -12.5350 + 0.0000i
   -0.5658 +15.2951i
   -0.5658 -15.2951i
```

They all have negative real part! This is a surprise because the Lorenz equations are chaotic, meaning that infinitesimal perturbations grow exponentially. In fact, we saw in Chapter 13 that on average they grow approximately at the rate $\exp(0.91t)$. Yet eigenvalues with negative real part correspond to exponential decay, not growth. What's going on?

The explanation is that, even though a chaotic system is characterized by exponential growth of perturbations on average, there can be points along its trajectories where the perturbations are shrinking. This is just what happens with the Lorenz equations. To see the effect, we can plot the *spectral abscissa* of $\mathbf{J}(t)$, the maximum real part of its eigenvalues, as a function of t.

```
spec_absc = chebfun(@(t) max(real(eig(J(t)))),[4,10], ...
    'splitting','on'); plot(spec_absc)
```

Fig. 14.7. Spectral abscissa of Lorenz eqs. Jacobian

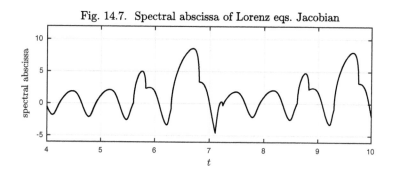

Most of the time, the spectral abscissa is positive, and its mean is positive,

```
mean(spec_absc)
```

```
ans = 1.4455
```

Nevertheless, it regularly dips below zero. If the nonlinear problem were frozen with fixed linear dynamics at such a time, then perturbations would eventually decay rather than grow.

As a fine point of linear algebra, let us say a little more of what it means for a matrix $\mathbf{J}$ to have all its eigenvalues in the complex left half-plane. This implies that solutions to the constant-coefficient problem $\mathbf{y}' = \mathbf{J}\mathbf{y}$ must decay as $t \to \infty$. It does not imply that they must decay even at the start, for small t. A different condition of linear algebra is needed to ensure this stronger property, namely that the *numerical abscissa* of the matrix is negative. The numerical abscissa of $\mathbf{J}$ is the maximum eigenvalue of $(\mathbf{J} + \mathbf{J}^T)/2$, and here we add another curve to the plot showing how this quantity varies for our Lorenz trajectory.

```
numer_absc = chebfun(@(t) max(eig((J(t)+J(t)')/2)),[4,10],...
   'splitting','on'); hold on, plot(numer_absc)
```

Fig. 14.8. Numerical abscissa of Lorenz eqs. Jacobian

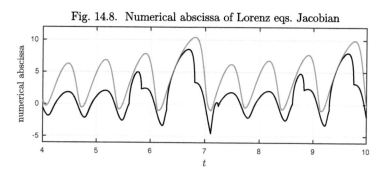

Evidently even the numerical abscissa dips below zero intermittently, implying that at certain times the behavior of the Lorenz equations is locally dissipative by any definition, though chaos reigns at large scale. Analogous effects can be found in atmospheric dynamics and other scientific problems and are sometimes quantified by means of a "local Lyapunov exponent."

HISTORY. Perhaps the most extreme case of linearization in the history of science was reported in *Physical Review Letters* in February 2016 in the paper "Observation of gravitational waves from a binary black hole merger," which won the Nobel Prize for Barish, Thorne, and Weiss just a year later.[58] Einstein's ten coupled partial differential equations of general relativity, from 1915, are forbiddingly nonlinear. In 1916, however, Einstein proposed that when linearized to small amplitudes, the equations predict the possibility of propagation of *gravitational waves*. Meanwhile, 1.3 billion years earlier, two black holes had merged together in an event so cataclysmic that for a fraction of a second it radiated energy with greater power than all the stars in the observable universe combined. For 1.3 billion years the gravitational waves flew outward at the speed of light, losing amplitude in the usual inverse-radius fashion, and they reached the earth on September 14, 2015, when the minute oscillations were detected by the LIGO project nearly simultaneously in Louisiana and Washington State, USA. One might fancifully say that the merger of the black holes was the most nonlinear event ever observed by mankind, and the signal by which it was ultimately observed was the most linear. The amplitude of that signal was almost unimaginably small, as is reflected in the astonishing label of the y-axis in Figure 1 of the 2016 paper, which informs the reader that the figure shows relative deflections in units of 10^{-21}.

OUR FAVORITE REFERENCE. A classic textbook with a great emphasis on the linear algebra side of ODE theory was Hirsch and Smale, *Differential Equations, Dynamical Systems, and Linear Algebra*, published in 1974 by Academic Press. Later a third author was added, Devaney, and the title was changed to *Differential Equations, Dynamical Systems, and an Introduction to Chaos* (third edition, Elsevier, 2013). The books are quite different, with less about the linear algebra side in the later edition, and both are very interesting.

SUMMARY OF CHAPTER 14. *An autonomous ODE* $\mathbf{y}'(t) = \mathbf{f}(\mathbf{y}(t))$ *with a sufficiently smooth function* $\mathbf{f}$ *can be approximated near a particular time* t_0 *and value* $\mathbf{y}_*$ *by the affine equation* $\delta\mathbf{y}'(t) \approx \mathbf{f}_* + \mathbf{J}_*\delta\mathbf{y}(t)$, *where* $\mathbf{f}_*$ *and* $\mathbf{J}_*$ *are the function* $\mathbf{f}$ *and Jacobian matrix* $\partial\mathbf{f}/\partial\mathbf{y}$ *frozen at* $t = t_0$ *and* $\mathbf{y} = \mathbf{y}_*$ *and* $\delta\mathbf{y}(t) = \mathbf{y}(t) - \mathbf{y}_*$. *Globally over a range of values of* t, *infinitesimal perturbations to a nonlinear trajectory evolve according to the linear homogeneous nonautonomous ODE* $\Delta\mathbf{y}' = \mathbf{J}(t)\Delta\mathbf{y}$, *where* $\mathbf{J}(t)$ *is the Jacobian matrix at time* t *for the given nonlinear trajectory.*

Exercise 14.1. Exponential of a matrix and linear systems of BVPs. (a) Find formulas for the powers $\mathbf{A}^k$ of the 2×2 matrix $\mathbf{A} = $ [0 1; -1 0] (MATLAB notation). *(b)* Using the results of (a) and familiar formulas for Taylor series, find a formula for

---

[58]It is one of the most compellingly written papers we have seen — exciting reading for anyone interested in science. The first three of the 1011 authors, incidentally, are Abbott, Abbott, and Abbott, and the last three are Zucker, Zuraw, and Zweizig.

$\exp(t\mathbf{A})$. *(c)* What is the smallest $t > 0$ for which $\exp(t\mathbf{A})$ is skew-diagonal, that is, having zeros in the positions on the diagonal? Call this number T. What is the matrix $\exp(T\mathbf{A})$? *(d)* Show that the BVP $\mathbf{y}' = \mathbf{A}\mathbf{y}$ with boundary conditions $y_1(0) = a$, $y_2(T) = b$ is ill-posed, having either no solutions or infinitely many solutions depending on the values of a and b. *(e)* Show on the other hand that if $\mathbf{A}$ is any diagonal matrix, this BVP is well-posed, with a unique solution for each a and b.

Exercise 14.2. Affine autonomous systems. Verify that (14.7) is a solution of (14.6).

Exercise 14.3. Confirming fourth-order accuracy. According to the text, the dashed red lines in Figure 14.4 match the green curve they approximate to accuracy $O(t^4)$, or more precisely $O((t-t_0)^4)$ for an approximation near $t = t_0$. Confirm this numerically for the oscillatory middle curve by means of an appropriate log-log plot.

Exercise 14.4. Exponential of a nonnormal matrix. Let $\mathbf{A}$ be the 6×6 bidiagonal matrix with $-0.5, -0.6, \ldots, -1$ on the main diagonal, $2, 2, \ldots, 2$ on the first super-diagonal, and 0 everywhere else. *(a)* Calculate the spectral abscissa and numerical abscissa of $\mathbf{A}$. *(b)* Make a semilogy plot of $\|e^{t\mathbf{A}}\|$ as a function of $t \in [0, 40]$, where $\|\cdot\|$ is the 2-norm. (In MATLAB the appropriate command is expm.) Superimpose appropriate dashed lines to indicate how this curve matches the results of *(a)*.

15. Stable and unstable fixed points

The last chapter dealt with linearization of ODEs. One of the most important applications of linearization is the analysis of fixed points.

Consider an autonomous equation

$$\mathbf{y}'(t) = \mathbf{f}(\mathbf{y}(t)). \tag{15.1}$$

As defined in Chapters 9 and 10, a **fixed point** of (15.1) is a vector $\mathbf{y}_*$ such that $\mathbf{f}(\mathbf{y}_*) = \mathbf{0}$. We saw in those chapters that a fruitful way of understanding the behavior of an autonomous ODE is to begin by examining its fixed points in the phase plane (if $n = 2$) or more generally in phase space. If $\mathbf{y}_*$ is a fixed point, then the term $\mathbf{f}_*$ in Theorem 14.4 vanishes. Equation (14.17) becomes

$$\delta\mathbf{y}'(t) = \mathbf{J}_*\delta\mathbf{y}(t) + O(\|\delta\mathbf{y}(t)\|^2), \tag{15.2}$$

with $\delta\mathbf{y}(t) = \mathbf{y}(t) - \mathbf{y}_*$ as before. Near a fixed point, therefore, an ODE behaves approximately like the equation $\mathbf{y}' = \mathbf{A}\mathbf{y}$ with which we began the last chapter — not just affine, but linear, with $\mathbf{A}$ being the Jacobian matrix $\mathbf{J}_*$.

To illustrate the structure of some linearizations at fixed points in the phase plane, here are two plots showing solutions of (15.2) (without the "O" term) corresponding to the diagonal matrices

$$\mathbf{J}_* = \begin{pmatrix} -1 & 0 \\ 0 & -1 \end{pmatrix}, \begin{pmatrix} -2 & 0 \\ 0 & -1 \end{pmatrix}. \tag{15.3}$$

Each plot shows trajectories emanating from 16 equally spaced initial points on the unit circle, which is drawn in black.

```
th = (pi/8)*(1:16) + .0001; u0 = cos(th); v0 = sin(th);
L = chebop(0,1.4);
op = @(J) @(t,u,v) [diff(u)-J(1,1)*u-J(1,2)*v; ...
                    diff(v)-J(2,1)*u-J(2,2)*v];
subplot(1,2,1), plot(0,0,'.'), hold on
c = chebfun('exp(1i*pi*x)'); plot(c)
J = [-1 0; 0 -1]; L.op = op(J);
for k = 1:16
  L.lbc = [u0(k); v0(k)]; [u,v] = L\0; arrowplot(u,v)
end
subplot(1,2,2), plot(0,0,'.'), hold on, plot(c)
J = [-2 0; 0 -1]; L.op = op(J);
for k = 1:16
  L.lbc = [u0(k); v0(k)]; [u,v] = L\0; arrowplot(u,v)
end
```

Fig. 15.1. Fixed points for the matrices (15.3)

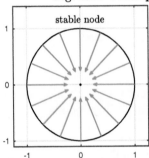 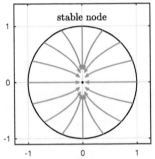

In both figures, all trajectories are converging to the origin. This is because both eigenvalues of $\mathbf{J}_*$, which in this case are simply the diagonal entries, are negative. If all the eigenvalues of the Jacobian at a fixed point are negative, or more generally satisfy $\mathrm{Re}\,\lambda < 0$ and thus lie in the open left half of the complex plane, then $\mathbf{y}_*$ is called a **sink**. This implies that all orbits starting sufficiently close to $\mathbf{y}_*$ converge to $\mathbf{y}_*$ at an exponential rate. The image on the left above may be the first one that comes to mind when one thinks about sinks, but the image on the right is more typical: most trajectories approach a sink along special directions corresponding to the eigenvectors associated with eigenvalues of least negative real part. In this example the eigenvectors are $(1,0)^T$, the direction of exponential decay at the rate e^{-2t}, and $(0,1)^T$, the direction of slower decay at the rate e^{-t}. As t increases, the component in the $(1,0)^T$ direction becomes negligible compared with the component in the $(0,1)^T$ direction, so trajectories approach the origin along the latter, vertical axis.

But still we have diagonal matrices, so these pictures do not show the general behavior. To illustrate some further possibilities, here are figures for two nondiagonal matrices,

$$\mathbf{J}_* = \begin{pmatrix} -1 & 1 \\ -1 & -1 \end{pmatrix}, \quad \begin{pmatrix} -2 & 2.5 \\ 0 & -1 \end{pmatrix}, \tag{15.4}$$

whose eigenvalues are $\{-1+i, -1-i\}$ and $\{-2, -1\}$, respectively. Again the eigenvalues are in the left half-plane, so $\mathbf{0}$ is again a sink, but the images are quite different, showing a combination of rotation mixed with decay.

```
subplot(1,2,1), plot(0,0,'.'), hold on, plot(c)
J = [-1 1; -1 -1]; L.op = op(J);
for k = 1:16
  L.lbc = [u0(k); v0(k)]; [u,v] = L\0; arrowplot(u,v)
end
subplot(1,2,2), plot(0,0,'.'), hold on, plot(c)
J = [-1 2.5; 0 -1/2]; L.op = op(J);
for k = 1:16
  L.lbc = [u0(k); v0(k)]; [u,v] = L\0; arrowplot(u,v)
end
```

Fig. 15.2. Fixed points for the matrices (15.4)

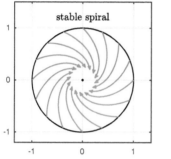 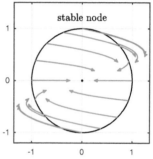

Note that in the left image there is no special direction along which trajectories eventually straighten out. Such a direction would correspond to an eigenvector, but for this matrix the eigenvectors are complex. The eigenvalues are $-1 + i$ and $-1 - i$, both in the left half-plane, which explains the decay toward the origin. In the right image, there are real eigenvectors again but they are far from orthogonal. The effect of this is that, although eventually all the trajectories decay to the origin, some of them grow for a while before decaying. This phenomenon is known as *transient growth*.

   All these plots correspond to the same simple case of a two-variable problem with a sink. This is only the beginning of the many configurations that can arise in linearized analysis of fixed points. If all the eigenvalues are in the open right half-plane, that is, with $\mathrm{Re}\,\lambda > 0$, then $\mathbf{y}_*$ is a **source** and the arrows are reversed. If some eigenvalues are in the left half-plane and the others are in the right half-plane, then $\mathbf{y}_*$ is a **saddle point**. Here are examples of saddle points corresponding to the matrices

$$\mathbf{J}_* = \begin{pmatrix} -1 & 0 \\ 0 & 1 \end{pmatrix}, \begin{pmatrix} -1 & 2 \\ 0 & 1 \end{pmatrix}. \tag{15.5}$$

The eigenvalues of both matrices are $\{-1, 1\}$.

```
subplot(1,2,1), plot(0,0,'.'), hold on, plot(c)
L = chebop(0,0.9); J = [-1 0; 0 1]; L.op = op(J);
for k = 1:16
  L.lbc = [u0(k); v0(k)]; [u,v] = L\0; arrowplot(u,v)
end
subplot(1,2,2), plot(0,0,'.'), hold on, plot(c)
J = [-1 2; 0 1]; L.op = op(J);
for k = 1:16
  L.lbc = [u0(k); v0(k)]; [u,v] = L\0; arrowplot(u,v)
end
```

Fig. 15.3. Fixed points for the matrices (15.5)

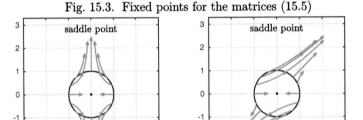

There is a general terminology and theory of behavior near fixed points that goes beyond these linearized approximations. We say that a fixed point of a system of the form (15.1) is **Lyapunov stable** if, for any neighborhood V of $\mathbf{y}_*$, there is a neighborhood $U \subseteq V$ such that every trajectory that starts in U remains in V for all t. This condition does not require decay, just boundedness. The fixed point is **asymptotically stable** if in addition U can be chosen such that every trajectory that starts in U converges to $\mathbf{y}_*$ as $t \to \infty$.[59] If $\mathbf{y}_*$ is not Lyapunov stable, it is **Lyapunov unstable**, implying that some (not necessarily all) trajectories starting near $\mathbf{y}_*$ diverge away as t increases. The following theorem, which we give without proof, summarizes some of the relationships between these general notions and the eigenvalues of $\mathbf{J}_*$.

Theorem 15.1. Stability and eigenvalues of the Jacobian (FIAsHI).
Let $\mathbf{y}_*$ be a fixed point of an autonomous ODE (15.1) where $\mathbf{f}$ is twice differentiable at $\mathbf{y}_*$, and let $\mathbf{J}_*$ be the associated Jacobian matrix. If all the eigenvalues λ of $\mathbf{J}_*$ satisfy $\mathrm{Re}\,\lambda < 0$, then $\mathbf{y}_*$ is asymptotically stable, and if at least one of them satisfies $\mathrm{Re}\,\lambda > 0$, then $\mathbf{y}_*$ is Lyapunov unstable.

Note that the theorem leaves open the situation in which all eigenvalues satisfy $\mathrm{Re}\,\lambda \leq 0$ but not all satisfy $\mathrm{Re}\,\lambda < 0$. In this case $\mathbf{y}_*$ is unstable if there is a defective multiple eigenvalue with $\mathrm{Re}\,\lambda = 0$ (i.e., associated with a Jordan block of size ≥ 2). If all eigenvalues with $\mathrm{Re}\,\lambda = 0$ are nondefective, then linear

---

[59]Despite this careful terminology, most of the time we will be more casual and just say a fixed point is stable if all nearby trajectories converge to it.

analysis is not enough to determine stability or asymptotic stability; it depends on the higher-order nonlinear behavior of $\mathbf{f}$.

Let us now consider three examples, systems of ODEs we looked at in Chapter 10. The first of these was the Lotka–Volterra equations (10.4)–(10.5),

$$u' = u - uv, \quad v' = -\tfrac{1}{5}v + uv,$$

whose behavior was plotted in Figs. 10.4–10.8 and again in Figs. 14.5–14.6. To calculate the fixed points we set $u' = 0$, implying $u = 0$ or $v = 1$, and $v' = 0$, implying $v = 0$ or $u = 1/5$. So the fixed points are $(u, v) = (0, 0)$ and $(1/5, 1)$. The Jacobian of the system at (u, v) is

$$\mathbf{J}(u, v) = \begin{pmatrix} 1 - v & -u \\ v & u - 1/5 \end{pmatrix},$$

implying

$$\mathbf{J}(0,0) = \begin{pmatrix} 1 & 0 \\ 0 & -1/5 \end{pmatrix}, \quad \mathbf{J}(1/5, 1) = \begin{pmatrix} 0 & -1/5 \\ 1 & 0 \end{pmatrix}.$$

The first matrix has eigenvalues 1 and $-1/5$, so $(0, 0)$ is a saddle point. The image on the right has eigenvalues $\pm i/\sqrt{5}$, both imaginary, so $(1/5, 1)$ is a center, a point of neutral stability. This explains the rotation of trajectories that is the conspicuous feature of Figs. 10.6–10.8.

The next example from Chapter 10 is the Lorenz equations (10.7),

$$u' = 10(v - u), \quad v' = u(28 - w) - v, \quad w' = uv - (8/3)w,$$

plotted in Figs. 10.9–10.11 and considered further in Chapters 13 and 14. To find fixed points we calculate that $u' = 0$ implies $v = u$, $v' = 0$ then implies $u = v = 0$ or $w = 27$, and $w' = 0$ implies $u = v = w = 0$ or $u = v = \pm\sqrt{8 \cdot 27/3} = \pm 6\sqrt{2}$. So there are three fixed points, and they are $(u, v, w) = (0, 0, 0)$ and $(\pm 6\sqrt{2}, \pm 6\sqrt{2}, 27)$. The Jacobian of the system at (u, v, w) is

$$\mathbf{J}(u, v, w) = \begin{pmatrix} -10 & 10 & 0 \\ 28 - w & -1 & -u \\ v & u & -8/3 \end{pmatrix},$$

implying

$$\mathbf{J}(0,0,0) = \begin{pmatrix} -10 & 10 & 0 \\ 28 & -1 & 0 \\ 0 & 0 & -8/3 \end{pmatrix}$$

and

$$\mathbf{J}(\pm 6\sqrt{2}, \pm 6\sqrt{2}, 27) = \begin{pmatrix} -10 & 10 & 0 \\ 1 & -1 & \mp 6\sqrt{2} \\ \pm 6\sqrt{2} & \pm 6\sqrt{2} & -8/3 \end{pmatrix}.$$

The eigenvalues of $J(0, 0, 0)$ are about -22.8, -2.7, and 11.8, so this is an unstable saddle point. The other fixed points are the more interesting ones, with eigenvalues about -13.9 and $0.9 \pm 10.2i$. Thus these fixed points are unstable too, mildly so, but because of the large imaginary term they have a big rotational component, as we know well from the Lorenz trajectories of Figs. 10.11 and 13.1.

The other main example of Chapter 10 is the system of equations (10.10) of an SIR model from epidemiology, which with the parameter choices $\beta = 2$ and $\gamma = 1$ takes the form

$$S' = -2SI, \quad I' = (2S - 1)I, \quad R' = I.$$

Behaviors were explored in Figs. 10.13–10.14. For a fixed point analysis we first set $R' = 0$, implying $I = 0$. This then implies $R' = S' = 0$, so we see that every choice of R and S gives a fixed point, so long as $I = 0$. The Jacobian matrix is

$$\mathbf{J}(S, I, R) = \begin{pmatrix} -2I & -2S & 0 \\ 2I & 2S - 1 & 0 \\ 0 & 1 & 0 \end{pmatrix},$$

which at a fixed point becomes

$$\mathbf{J}(S, I, R) = \begin{pmatrix} 0 & -2S & 0 \\ 0 & 2S - 1 & 0 \\ 0 & 1 & 0 \end{pmatrix},$$

Since this matrix is block lower-triangular, with an upper-left 2×2 block that is itself upper-triangular, we see that the eigenvalues are 0, 0, and $2S - 1$. The latter number has immediate significance: if $S > 1/2$, the matrix has a positive eigenvalue and the system is unstable, ready to begin an epidemic as soon as any patient gets infected.

APPLICATION: TRANSITION TO TURBULENCE IN A PIPE

Of all the fixed points in the mathematical sciences, perhaps none has received more attention, or caused more confusion, than laminar fluid flow in a pipe.[60] (Laminar means smooth and steady.) This discussion is adapted from Trefethen, Trefethen, Reddy, and Driscoll, "Hydrodynamic stability without eigenvalues," *Science,* 1993.

The problem was made famous by Osborne Reynolds in 1883. Imagine a long circular pipe with a fluid such as water flowing through it. The flow is governed by the set of time-dependent PDEs known as the Navier–Stokes equations, determining the evolution of the velocity field $\mathbf{v}(\mathbf{x}, t)$, and an analytical

---

[60]There are competitors, though the equations are not so clear-cut, in climate science. Whenever you hear the phrase "tipping point," you can be sure that there is a question of stability of a fixed point at hand. One tipping point of great concern involves the melting of the ice in the Arctic: as ice melts, the earth reflects less light out to space, and the ice melts faster. See D. Paillard, "The timing of Pleistocene glaciations from a simple multiple-state climate model," *Nature* 391 (1998), pp. 378–381.

solution corresponding to laminar flow can be written down easily: $\mathbf{v}$ is a time-independent field pointing along the pipe, corresponding to a steady flow with a velocity that is maximal at the centerline and decreases quadratically to zero at the wall. This solution is a fixed point of the equations, and it is mathematically stable. We have not discussed PDEs and their stability, but just as for ODEs, the idea is that any sufficiently small perturbation of the laminar flow velocity field in a pipe must eventually die away. So a mathematician would expect that laminar flow of water through a pipe should be possible at any speed.

The paradox is that, in practice, this is not what is observed. If the flow in a pipe is fast enough, it is invariably not laminar but turbulent — complicated, apparently chaotic, highly time-dependent. Clearly the mathematical solution, laminar flow, has something wrong with it in the laboratory. What is going on? How can a flow that is stable mathematically be unstable in practice?

The explanation is that although sufficiently small perturbations of the laminar velocity flow field must eventually decay, the threshold that defines "sufficiently small" is too small to be counted upon in practice. The mathematics of these high-speed flow problems is such that the minimal amplitude of perturbations that do *not* eventually decay is tiny. The slightest imperfection in the pipe or the smoothness of the inflow, or the slightest vibration of the laboratory, may be enough to kick the system into instability. Geometrically, we say that the *basin of attraction of the laminar state is very narrow*. This makes the laminar state often effectively unobservable in practice.

A simple ODE model explains how an extremely narrow basin of attraction can come about in a set of equations that seems far from extreme. Let $R > 0$ be a parameter, a caricature of the Reynolds number, the nondimensional centerline velocity of the laminar flow. Let u and v be two dependent variables, caricatures of the field of velocity perturbations of the laminar flow, satisfying the equations

$$u' = -R^{-1}u + v - v\sqrt{u^2 + v^2}, \quad v' = -2R^{-1}v + u\sqrt{u^2 + v^2}. \tag{15.6}$$

Rewriting (15.6) in matrix form reveals the structure more plainly:

$$\begin{pmatrix} u \\ v \end{pmatrix}' = \begin{pmatrix} -R^{-1} & 1 \\ 0 & -2R^{-1} \end{pmatrix} \begin{pmatrix} u \\ v \end{pmatrix} + \sqrt{u^2 + v^2} \begin{pmatrix} 0 & -1 \\ 1 & 0 \end{pmatrix} \begin{pmatrix} u \\ v \end{pmatrix}. \tag{15.7}$$

The term on the left is linear, and the term on the right is quadratic (if u and v are doubled, it multiplies by 4). As always, it is the linear term that governs behavior for sufficiently small u and v. Since the matrix is triangular, its eigenvalues are the diagonal entries, $-R^{-1}$ and $-2R^{-1}$, and since these numbers are negative, $(0,0)$ is a sink.

On the left below is an image of the linear part of the problem for $R = 10$ showing this sink, very much like the second panel of Figure 15.2. Something physically important is revealed in this image: a great deal of transient growth before the eventual decay. (In the fluid mechanics problems this effect is sometimes called "lift-up," in which vorticity aligned with a shear flow excites a growth in local velocity anomalies.) On the right is an image of the nonlinear problem for the same value $R = 10$. What happens here is that the quadratic term catches hold of the linear amplification and moves it onto a new track entirely. Though the initial conditions in this nonlinear experiment start at a distance of only 0.02 from the fixed point, most of the trajectories spiral up to size $O(1)$ rather than decaying to the center. For this model, this is the caricature of transition to turbulence.

```
th = (pi/8)*(1:16) + .0001; u0 = cos(th); v0 = sin(th);
subplot(1,2,1), plot(0,0,'.'), hold on, plot(.02*c)
N = chebop(0,18); R = 10;
N.op = @(t,u,v) [diff(u) + u/R - v; diff(v) + 2*v/R];
for k = 1:16
  N.lbc = [.02*u0(k); .02*v0(k)]; [u,v] = N\0; arrowplot(u,v)
end
subplot(1,2,2), plot(0,0,'.'), hold on, plot(.02*c)
N = chebop(0,30);
N.op = @(t,u,v) [diff(u) + u/R - v + v*sqrt(u^2+v^2)
                 diff(v) + 2*v/R - u*sqrt(u^2+v^2)];
for k = 1:16
  N.lbc = [.02*u0(k); .02*v0(k)]; [u,v] = N\0; arrowplot(u,v)
end
```

Fig. 15.4. Stable node with narrow basin of attraction

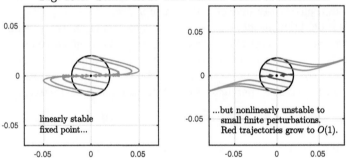

Zooming out the second plot shows where the red trajectories are heading.

Fig. 15.5. Same dynamics shown on a larger scale

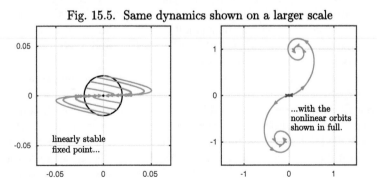

Let us draw a plot to visualize this behavior in another way. For the same equations (15.7) with $R = 10$, Figure 15.6 shows $(u^2 + v^2)^{1/2}$ as a function of t for six trajectories emanating from initial points $(u, v) = (0, v_0)$ with $v_0 = 0, 001, 0.0025, 0.005, 0.01, 0.02, 0.04$. The three initial conditions of lowest amplitude lead to trajectories that eventually decay to zero, but the other three, shown in red, increase to $O(1)$.

```
N = chebop(0,60);
N.op = @(t,u,v) [diff(u) + u/R - v + v*sqrt(u^2+v^2)
                 diff(v) + 2*v/R - u*sqrt(u^2+v^2)];
for v0 = [.001 .0025 .005 .01 .02 .04]
  N.lbc = [0; v0]; [u,v] = N\0;
  big = (norm([u(end) v(end)])>.2);
  if big, semilogy(sqrt(u.^2+v.^2))
  else semilogy(sqrt(u.^2+v.^2)), end, hold on
end
```

Fig. 15.6. ODE model (15.7) of transition to turbulence

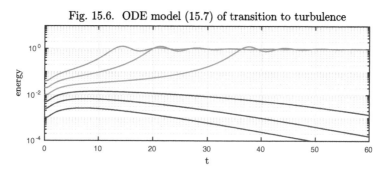

Unlike turbulence, the model (15.7) is non-chaotic, and indeed it could not possibly be chaotic since it is an autonomous first-order system with just two variables. Similar models with three variables instead of two, however, combine the narrow basin of attraction of the laminar state with chaotic long-time trajectories. See Baggett, Driscoll, and Trefethen, "A mostly linear model of transition to turbulence," *Physics of Fluids*, 1995.

HISTORY. The general theory of stability of ODEs was developed by Aleksandr Mikhailovich Lyapunov, a student of Chebyshev, who was one of the outstanding Russian mathematicians of the era before the 1917 revolution. Lyapunov's interest in questions of stability began with fluid and solid mechanics and was set forth in his great work of 1892, *The General Problem of the Stability of Motion*. His academic descendants include Smirnov, Sobolev, Kantorovich, Ladyzhenskaya, and other major figures of 20th century Russian mathematics.

OUR FAVORITE REFERENCE. The idea of a tipping point was made famous by Malcolm Gladwell's bestseller *The Tipping Point: How Little Things Can Make a Big Difference*, which first appeared in 2000. Gladwell emphasizes tipping points related to the mathematics of epidemiology — which, as he vividly shows, applies to many more areas than just epidemiology.

SUMMARY OF CHAPTER 15. *The starting point of analysis of an autonomous system of ODEs* $\mathbf{y}' = \mathbf{f}(\mathbf{y})$ *is determination and classification of its fixed points* $\mathbf{y}_*$, *defined by the condition* $\mathbf{f}(\mathbf{y}_*) = \mathbf{0}$. *For* $\mathbf{y} \approx \mathbf{y}_*$, *the difference* $\delta\mathbf{y}(t) = \mathbf{y}(t) - \mathbf{y}_*$ *evolves approximately according to the linear equation* $(\delta\mathbf{y})' = \mathbf{J}_*(\delta\mathbf{y})$, *where* $\mathbf{J}_* = (\partial\mathbf{f}/\partial\mathbf{y})(\mathbf{y}_*)$ *is the Jacobian matrix at* $\mathbf{y}_*$. *A fixed point is stable if all the eigenvalues of* $\mathbf{J}_*$ *lie in the left half of the complex plane and unstable if at least one eigenvalue is in the right half-plane.*

Exercise 15.1. *Unstable or stable?* Classify the fixed point $y = y' = y'' = 0$ for the ODEs *(a)* $y'' + 5y' + 4y = 0$, *(b)* $y''' + 6y'' + 11y' + 6y = 0$.

Exercise 15.2. *A system with four fixed points.* Consider the system $u' = \frac{1}{3}(u - v)(1 - u - v)$, $v' = u(2 - v)$. *(a)* Give a formula for the Jacobian matrix $\mathbf{J}$ as a function of u and v. *(b)* Determine the fixed points and evaluate the Jacobian at these points. *(c)* Find the eigenvalues analytically, and classify the nature of each fixed point.

Exercise 15.3. *Eulerian wobble.* Determine the fixed points of (10.9) and analyze their stability.

Exercise 15.4. *Fixed points are unattainable.* Let $\mathbf{y}'(t) = \mathbf{f}(\mathbf{y})$ be an autonomous ODE satisfying the continuity hypotheses of Theorems 11.2 or Theorem 11.3, and suppose $\mathbf{y}_*$ is a fixed point. Let $\mathbf{y}(t)$ be the solution for $t > 0$ with initial value $\mathbf{y}(0)$. Prove that if $\mathbf{y}(0) \neq \mathbf{y}_*$, then $\mathbf{y}(t) \neq \mathbf{y}_*$ for all t.

Exercise 15.5. *A cyclic system of three ODEs* (adapted from Guckenheimer and Holmes, "Structurally stable heteroclinic cycles," *Mathematical Proceedings of the Cambridge Philosophical Society*, 1988). Consider the system of ODEs $u' = u(1 - u^2 - bv^2 - cw^2)$, $v' = v(1 - v^2 - bw^2 - cu^2)$, $w' = w(1 - w^2 - bu^2 - cv^2)$, where b and c are parameters. *(a)* Plot the solution $u(t)$ for $t \in [0, 800]$ with $b = 0.55$, $c = 1.5$ and initial conditions $u(0) = 0.5$, $v(0) = w(0) = 0.49$. Make similar plots of $v(t)$ and $w(t)$, and also of the whole trajectory in u-v-w space, and comment on these shapes. *(b)* What are the four fixed points of this system that the plots just drawn come close to? For large t, the trajectory moves approximately in a cycle from one fixed point, to another, to a third, and then back again. (It is approximating a *heteroclinic cycle*.) Which fixed point is the trajectory near at $t = 800$? *(c)* Find the eigenvalues of the appropriate matrix at one of these fixed points. What does this tell us about the structure of this fixed point? How does that fit with the observed trajectory?

Exercise 15.6. *Oregonator.* Exercise 10.2 presented the nonlinear equations known as the Oregonator. Here, continue with the parameters as presented in that exercise. *(a)* The origin $u = v = w = 0$ is a fixed point. Determine the relevant eigenvalues and classify the linearized behavior of the system there. *(b)* There is another fixed point with $u = w > 0$. Find it, determine its eigenvalues, and classify it.

16. Multiple solutions of nonlinear BVPs

In the subject of linear algebra, existence and uniqueness are straightforward. A scalar linear equation $ay = b$ has a unique solution for any b if $a \neq 0$, whereas if $a = 0$, it either has infinitely many solutions (if $b = 0$) or no solution at all (if $b \neq 0$). For a system of n linear equations $\mathbf{Ay} = \mathbf{b}$, where $\mathbf{A}$ is an $n \times n$ matrix, the situation is a generalization of the same alternative. If $\mathbf{A}$ is nonsingular, there is a unique solution for any $\mathbf{b}$, whereas if $\mathbf{A}$ is singular, there are infinitely many solutions if $\mathbf{b} \in \mathrm{range}(\mathbf{A})$ and no solutions at all if $\mathbf{b} \notin \mathrm{range}(\mathbf{A})$.

Nonlinear algebraic problems, by contrast, can do almost anything. Consider first a nonlinear equation involving a scalar real variable y, which without loss of generality we can write with a zero right-hand side as $f(y) = 0$. If $f(y) = \exp(y)$ there is no solution; if $f(y) = y + \exp(y)$, there is one solution; and if $f(y) = \mathrm{round}(y)$, there are infinitely many solutions, namely all the numbers in the interval $(-0.5, 0.5)$, together with perhaps -0.5 or 0.5 depending on exactly how you define the "round" function. More important, it may happen that there are multiple solutions that are separated from one another. These may be finite in number, as with $f(y) = y^2 - 1$, whose solutions are $y = \pm 1$, or they may be infinite in number, as with $f(y) = \sin(\pi y)$, whose solutions are all the integers. The function $f(y) = \sin(\pi y) + 0.01y^2$ illustrates another possibility: that a problem may have quite a few isolated solutions without having infinitely many.

```
f = chebfun(@(y) sin(pi*y)+0.01*y.^2,[-15 15]);
plot(f), hold on, r = roots(f); plot(r,f(r))
```

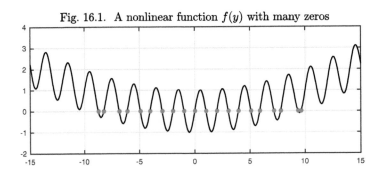

Fig. 16.1. A nonlinear function $f(y)$ with many zeros

All this is for a scalar equation $f(y) = 0$. For a nonlinear system of equations $\mathbf{f}(\mathbf{y}) = \mathbf{0}$, further possibilities arise.

Now let us look at differential as opposed to algebraic equations. What can we say about the possibility of nonuniqueness, that is, of problems with multiple solutions?

For linear ODEs, we have already made the main observations. Theorems 2.1–2.4 asserted uniqueness of solutions to first-order scalar linear IVPs, and these results carry over to IVP linear systems and equations of higher order. For linear BVPs, we saw in Chapter 6 that the key matter is whether or not a problem has an *eigenfunction*. If not, there is a unique solution. If so, there are either no solutions or a continuum of solutions.[61]

For nonlinear ODE IVPs, uniqueness is again usually not a problem. Theorem 11.1 asserted existence and uniqueness for any problem $y'(t) = f(t, y)$ if f is continuous with respect to t and Lipschitz continuous with respect to y, and Theorem 11.2 made the analogous statement for systems of IVPs. For uniqueness to fail for an IVP, f must lack these continuity properties, as in the example $y' = y^{1/2}$ of equation (3.16) or the further examples discussed in Chapter 11.

When it comes to nonlinear ODE BVPs, however, anything is possible. We saw illustrations of nonlinear nonuniqueness with equation (5.10) and Exercise 9.2, and the BVPs associated with the nonlinear pendulum of Chapter 9 also have nonunique solutions, though we did not mention that there. Phenomena of this kind are the subject of this and the next two chapters.

To make a start, consider the linear BVP

$$y'' = -y, \quad x \in [0, 1], \ y(0) = y(1) = 1. \tag{16.1}$$

This problem has no eigenfunction, so there is a unique solution.

```
N = chebop(0,1); N.op = @(x,y) diff(y,2) + y;
N.lbc = 1; N.rbc = 1;
y = N\0; plot(y)
```

---

[61]For example, $y'' + y = 0$ with boundary condition $y(0) = 0$ has the general solution $y(x) = A\sin(x)$. On any interval $[0, L]$ where L is not an integer multiple of π, there is a unique solution for any b when the second boundary condition $y(L) = b$ is specified. If L is an integer multiple of π, on the other hand, there are infinitely many solutions if $b = 0$ and no solutions if $b \neq 0$.

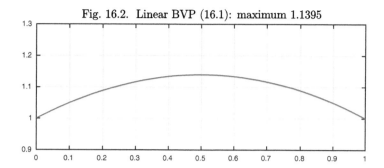

Fig. 16.2. Linear BVP (16.1): maximum 1.1395

Now consider the nonlinear variant in which the right-hand side of (16.1) is replaced by its cube,

$$y'' = -y^3, \quad x \in [0,1], \; y(0) = y(1) = 1. \tag{16.2}$$

(A quintic as opposed to cubic "nonlinear spring law" appeared in eq. (4.8).) If we give this problem to Chebfun, a solution is produced that looks approximately like the last one, but about 10% larger.

```
N.op = @(x,y) diff(y,2) + y^3; y1 = N\0; plot(y1)
```

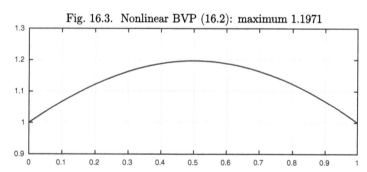

Fig. 16.3. Nonlinear BVP (16.2): maximum 1.1971

However, this is not the only solution to (16.2). First let us present another solution; then we shall explain how we got it.

```
x = chebfun('x',[0 1]); N.init = 1-25*(x-x^2); y2 = N\0; plot(y2)
```

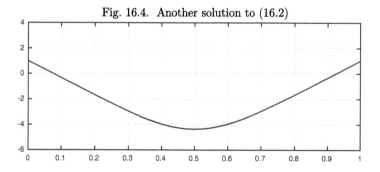

Fig. 16.4. Another solution to (16.2)

The last two figures show that there exist at least two distinct solutions to
(16.2). Now this is not a book of numerical analysis, but a word must be said
at this point about algorithms. In every area of computational mathematics, to
solve nonlinear problems, it is usually necessary to use some kind of iteration,
in which the solution is approached via a sequence of linear problems. The prototypical iteration is Newton's method, and Chebfun uses a version of Newton's
method to solve nonlinear BVPs.[62]

If a problem has more than one solution, which one will an iteration like
Newton's method converge to? The first thing to be said is that, sometimes, it
may not converge at all, and there is a large subject of nonlinear numerical optimization that aims to improve matters in this respect. When it does converge,
however, the solution it converges to is often one that is close to the *initial guess*
employed by the iteration. Every Newton iteration starts from some initial guess
or other, even if it is the zero function. In the case of Chebfun, if the user does
not specify an initial guess explicitly, then the iteration starts from a simple
polynomial in the variable x constructed to match the boundary conditions,
and this is what Chebfun did to obtain the solution plotted in Figure 16.3.

To get the second solution of (16.2), we overrode the default by specifying
a different initial guess in the field N.init. This function, $1 - 25(x - x^2)$, was
chosen because it has approximately the right shape. There are few guaran-
tees in this business, but Chebfun duly converged to the solution plotted in
Figure 16.4. Here we superimpose the initial guess on the plot.

```
hold on, plot(N.init,'--')
```

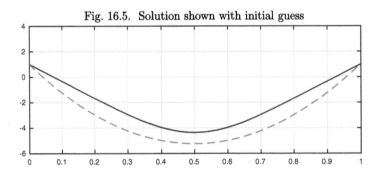

Fig. 16.5. Solution shown with initial guess

As an autonomous scalar equation of second order, (16.2) can be examined
in the y-y' phase plane. Here is an image showing the phase plane trajectories
of the two solutions just computed.

```
y1p = diff(y1); plot(y1([0 1]),y1p([0 1]),'.'), hold on
y2p = diff(y2); plot(y2([0 1]),y2p([0 1]),'.')
arrowplot(y1,y1p), arrowplot(y2,y2p)
```

---

[62]When applied like this to find functions as opposed to just numbers, Newton iteration is
also called *Newton–Kantorovich iteration*.

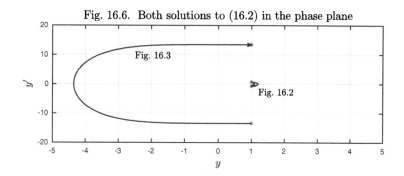

Fig. 16.6. Both solutions to (16.2) in the phase plane

Each solution makes a half-circuit clockwise around the origin, one on the right starting at $(y, y') = (1, 0.7258)$, and the other on the left starting at $(y, y') = (1, -13.4074)$. By considering this picture we may be tempted to conjecture that, in fact, (16.2) has infinitely many additional solutions besides these: at least two that wind around exactly once, two that wind around 1 1/2 times, and so on (Exercise 16.3). As the winding numbers increase, so do the amplitudes. For example, here is the next solution in the sequence, which we obtain by starting with the initial guess $y(x) = 5 \sin(2\pi x)$. In the phase plane, this corresponds to a large oval winding around one full revolution clockwise, beginning at $(y, y') = (1, 38.8855)$ (not shown).

```
N.init = 5*sin(2*pi*x); plot(N.init,'--'), hold on
y3 = N\0; plot(y3); y3p = diff(y3);
```

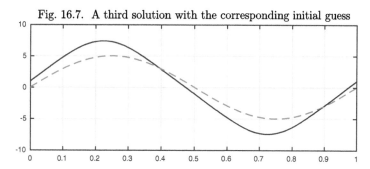

Fig. 16.7. A third solution with the corresponding initial guess

Whereas nonlinear BVPs can be rather delicate, nonlinear IVPs are relatively straightforward. With this in mind, it is interesting to solve (16.2) as an initial-value problem, fixing the left-hand value at $y(0) = 1$ and taking various choices $y'(0) = a$ in the range $[-50, 50]$ for the left-hand derivative value:

$$y'' = -y^3, \quad x \in [0, 1], \quad y(0) = 1, \quad y'(0) = a. \tag{16.3}$$

```
N.rbc = [];
for a = -50:5:50
  N.lbc = [1;a]; y = N\0; plot(y), hold on
end
```

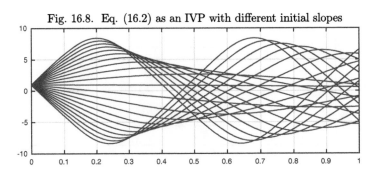

Fig. 16.8. Eq. (16.2) as an IVP with different initial slopes

If we study this image carefully, we can see that there are five choices of initial slope $y'(0) = a$ that lead to the condition $y(1) = 1$ being satisfied at the right. Regarding $y(1)$ as a function of a, let us plot this function over the given range $a \in [-50, 50]$.

```
fa = @(a) chebop(@(x,y) diff(y,2)+y^3,[0,1],[1;a],[])\0;
f = chebfun(@(a) feval(fa(a),1),[-50,50],120); plot(f)
```

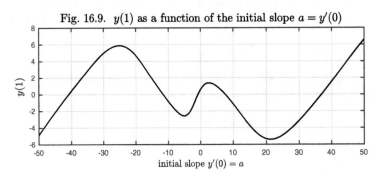

Fig. 16.9. $y(1)$ as a function of the initial slope $a = y'(0)$

Solutions to the BVP (16.2) correspond to points where this curve takes the value 1.

```
r = roots(f-1); hold on, plot(r,f(r),'.')
```

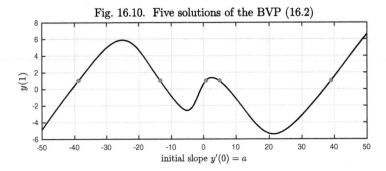

Fig. 16.10. Five solutions of the BVP (16.2)

Five solutions appear in this range,

```
r'
```

```
ans =
  -38.8855  -13.4074   0.7258   4.8424   38.8855
```

and we have seen three of them already,

```
[y1p(0) y2p(0) y3p(0)]
```

```
ans =
    0.7258  -13.4074   38.8855
```

In numerical analysis, the technique of varying a slope at one end of an interval so as to satisfy a boundary condition at the other end is known as the *shooting method*.

Let us turn to a more celebrated example of nonuniqueness, one involving just two solutions rather than an infinite set, the *Bratu equation*:

$$y'' + 3\exp(y) = 0, \quad x \in [0,1], \ y(0) = y(1) = 0. \tag{16.4}$$

Here we show two solutions on a single plot, one resulting from Chebfun's default initial guess (the zero function) and the other from the alternative initial guess $8(x - x^2)$.

```
N = chebop(0,1); N.op = @(x,y) diff(y,2) + 3*exp(y);
N.lbc = 0; N.rbc = 0; y1 = N\0; plot(y1)
hold on, x = chebfun('x',[0 1]); N.init = 8*(x-x.^2);
y2 = N\0; plot(y2)
```

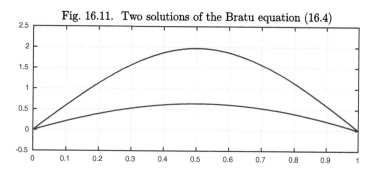

Fig. 16.11. Two solutions of the Bratu equation (16.4)

These are the only two solutions to this problem, as we can explain (though not quite rigorously prove without some more work) by the same method of shooting as before.

```
N.rbc = [];
for a = -8:2:16
  N.lbc = [0;a]; y = N\0; plot(y), hold on
end
```

Fig. 16.12. The Bratu eq. as an IVP with different initial slopes

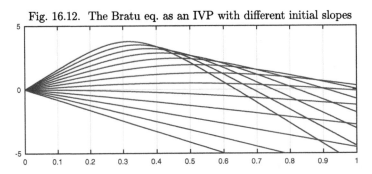

In Chapter 18 we shall consider the behavior of equation (16.4) as a parameter is varied, namely the coefficient that here takes the value 3.

We close this chapter with a final pair of examples of nonlinear BVPs with multiple solutions. In each case, shooting is a good method to explore the variety of solutions, at least when the coefficient multiplying the highest derivative is not too small. Another method of investigation for such problems is *path-following*, to be considered in Chapter 18. Besides these approaches, a further technique is the idea of *deflation* (Exercise 16.4).

First we consider the inhomogeneous equation

$$\varepsilon y'' + y + y^2 = 1, \quad x \in [-1, 1], \ y(\pm 1) = 0. \tag{16.5}$$

For $\varepsilon = 0.2$ this problem has four solutions: two symmetric and two asymmetric. Higher values of ε would have just two symmetric solutions; the asymmetric ones emerge in a pitchfork bifurcation (see next chapter) at a critical value of ε.

```
N = chebop(-1,1); N.lbc = 0; N.rbc = 0;
N.op = @(x,y) 0.2*diff(y,2) + y + y^2; x = chebfun('x');
N.init = x.^2-1; y1 = N\1; plot(y1), hold on
N.init = 1-x.^2; y2 = N\1; plot(y2)
N.init =  sin(pi*x); y3 = N\1; plot(y3)
N.init = -sin(pi*x); y4 = N\1; plot(y4)
```

Fig. 16.13. Four solutions of (16.5) with $\varepsilon = 0.2$

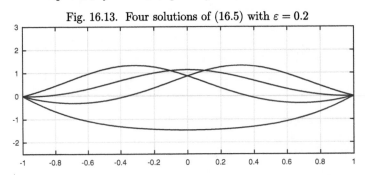

Equation (16.5) is a constant-coefficient variant of an equation known as the *Carrier equation*,

$$\varepsilon y'' + 2(1 - x^2)y + y^2 = 1, \quad x \in [-1, 1], \ y(\pm 1) = 0. \tag{16.6}$$

For $\varepsilon = 0.2$ this also has four solutions, of similar structure.

```
N = chebop(-1,1); N.lbc = 0; N.rbc = 0;
N.op = @(x,y) 0.2*diff(y,2) + 2*(1-x^2)*y + y^2;
N.init = x.^2-1; y1 = N\1; plot(y1), hold on
N.init = 1-x.^2; y2 = N\1; plot(y2)
N.init =  sin(pi*x); y3 = N\1; plot(y3)
N.init = -sin(pi*x); y4 = N\1; plot(y4)
```

Fig. 16.14. Four solutions of Carrier eq. (16.6) with $\varepsilon = 0.2$

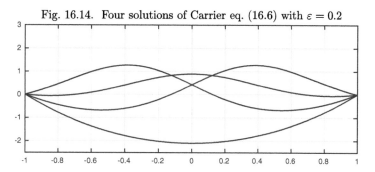

APPLICATION: SENDING A SPACECRAFT TO A DESTINATION

There may be several ways to get a spacecraft from A to B, even in a specified time interval. For example, suppose the sun is fixed at the origin in the x-y plane and a spacecraft starts at position $(-2,1)$. Starting from the initial velocity $(0.7, 0.7)$, here is the orbit up to the time $T = 6$. We have solved this as a second-order IVP in two variables x and y defining the position of the spacecraft.

```
T = 6; N = chebop(0,T); x0 = -2; y0 = 1; u0 = 0.7; v0 = 0.7;
N.op = @(t,x,y) [diff(x,2) + x/(x^2+y^2)^1.5; ...
                 diff(y,2) + y/(x^2+y^2)^1.5];
N.lbc = @(x,y) [x-x0; y-y0; diff(x)-u0; diff(y)-v0];
[x1,y1] = N\0; plot(0,0,'.'), hold on, h1 = arrowplot(x1,y1);
```

Fig. 16.15. A spacecraft trajectory starting at $(x,y) = (-2,1)$

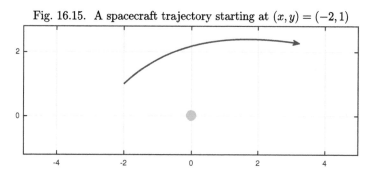

Of course, actual spacecraft are not simply launched into free flight from an initial position and velocity; they have rockets and make adjustments along the way. We are considering a simplified problem.

Now suppose our goal is to choose the initial conditions so that the spacecraft will be at position $(2, 1)$ at time T. This is a problem of the kind mentioned in the first footnote of Chapter 5: a BVP in t rather than x. If we start from the initial guess of a straight line orbit from $(-2, 1)$ to $(2, 1)$, Chebfun finds a solution.

```
xT = 2; yT = 1; N.lbc = @(x,y) [x-x0; y-y0]; N.rbc = [xT; yT];
t = chebfun('t',[0 T]); N.init = [-2+2*t/3; 1+0*t];
[x2,y2] = N\0; arrowplot(x2,y2)
```

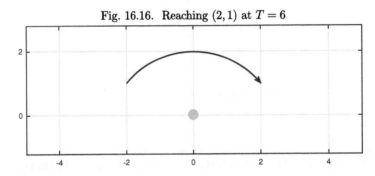

Fig. 16.16. Reaching $(2, 1)$ at $T = 6$

Here are the corresponding initial velocities.

```
u20 = deriv(x2,0); v20 = deriv(y2,0); disp([u20 v20])
```

```
    0.4460     0.5665
```

There is another solution, however, following a longer orbit the other way around. Its average speed will be greater, and it will pass closer to the sun. Here is this second solution plotted as a dashed line, obtained by starting from another initial guess.

```
N.init = [-2+2*t/3; 1-2*sin(pi*t/T)];
[x3,y3] = N\0; arrowplot(x3,y3,LS,'--')
```

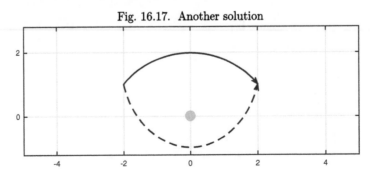

Fig. 16.17. Another solution

The vector of initial velocities now points down instead of up.

```
u30 = deriv(x3,0); v30 = deriv(y3,0); disp([u30 v30])
    0.1597    -0.7098
```

Both the solutions we have just found are arcs of ellipses, as the reader may confirm by extending the orbits to a later time. A good choice is $T = 27.4$.

This 2-body problem belongs to Newtonian mechanics, and it would have given little difficulty to scholars of earlier centuries. It is well known that any orbit will be an ellipse or a hyperbola, or a parabola in the borderline case. In the present example we got ellipses rather than hyperbolas because the number T was sufficiently large. If the spacecraft needs to get from A to B faster, for example in $T = 2$ time units, then the simplest solution is a nearly straight trajectory that begins pointed almost at B, like firing a bullet. This time the spacecraft has more than enough kinetic energy to escape the sun's gravitational field, and the orbit is an arc of a hyperbola rather than an ellipse.

```
T = 2; N.domain = [0 T];
N.lbc = @(x,y) [x-x0; y-y0]; N.rbc = [xT; yT];
t = chebfun('t',[0 T]); N.init = [-2+2*t; 1+0*t];
plot(0,0,'.'), hold on, [x4,y4] = N\0; arrowplot(x4,y4)
```

Fig. 16.18. Faster hyperbolic trajectory: $T = 2$

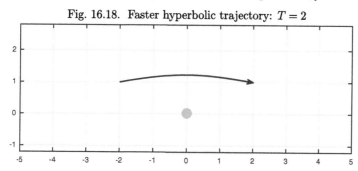

Again there is a second solution, also a hyperbola, that passes the other way around.

```
N.init = [-2+2*t; 1-1.5*sin(pi*t/T)];
[x5,y5] = N\0; arrowplot(x5,y5,LS,'--')
```

Fig. 16.19. Another fast trajectory: $T = 2$

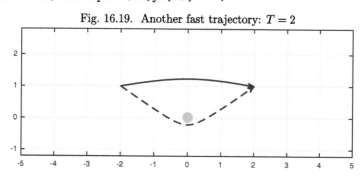

The initial velocities are much greater than before. In space travel, a speedy journey may cost a lot of energy!

```
u40 = deriv(x4,0); v40 = deriv(y4,0); disp([u40 v40])
u50 = deriv(x5,0); v50 = deriv(y5,0); disp([u50 v50])

    1.8848     0.3469
    1.6315    -1.1912
```

As we mentioned, the calculations above are classical. When a third body is introduced, however, everything changes and only numerical computations are available. For example, suppose that instead of one sun at $(0,0)$ we have two fixed stars, one at $(0,0)$ and the other at $(0,1)$. All your experience with elliptical orbits is now irrelevant. To see a little of the complexity, let us consider solutions up to time $T = 12$ beginning with $x'(0) = 0.8$ with $y'(0) = 0.549$ and $y'(0) = 0.4$. We see the beginnings of two orbits that will remain bounded but are certainly not ellipses.

```
T = 12; N = chebop(0,T); u0 = .8;
N.op = @(t,x,y) ...
   [diff(x,2) + x/(x^2+y^2)^1.5 + x/(x^2+(y-1)^2)^1.5; ...
    diff(y,2) + y/(x^2+y^2)^1.5 + (y-1)/(x^2+(y-1)^2)^1.5];
N.lbc = @(x,y) [x-x0; y-y0; diff(x)-u0; diff(y)-0.549];
[x6,y6] = N\0; subplot(1,2,1)
plot([0 0],[0 1],'.'), hold on, arrowplot(x6,y6);
N.lbc = @(x,y) [x-x0; y-y0; diff(x)-u0; diff(y)-0.40];
[x7,y7] = N\0; subplot(1,2,2)
plot([0 0],[0 1],'.'), hold on, arrowplot(x7,y7);
```

Fig. 16.20. Orbits about two fixed suns

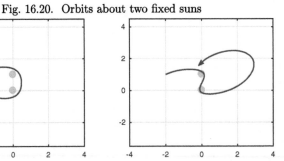

Here are the same orbits extended to time $T = 140$. On the left we see apparent periodicity. This is not typical; it results from the particular choice $v'(0) = 0.549$.

```
N.domain = [0 140];
N.lbc = @(x,y) [x-x0; y-y0; diff(x)-u0; diff(y)-0.549];
[x6long,y6long] = N\0; subplot(1,2,1)
arrowplot(x6long,y6long), hold on, plot([0 0],[0 1],'.')
```

```
N.lbc = @(x,y) [x-x0; y-y0; diff(x)-u0; diff(y)-0.40];
[x7long,y7long] = N\0; subplot(1,2,2)
arrowplot(x7long,y7long), hold on, plot([0 0],[0 1],'.')
```

Fig. 16.21. More orbits about two suns

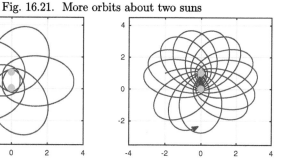

Still more complicated orbits can be found by exploring values $v'(0)$ such as 0.456, 0.455, and 0.454.

No solar system, of course, has two stars fixed motionless in space. However, our two-star model still has relevance to real problems. First, we could build a system just like this involving marbles rolling on a surface with two suitably shaped drains in a fixed position (there are demonstrations along these lines at some science museums). Second, there are many binary star systems that differ from this only in that the two stars are in orbit around each other, which just adds a few more terms to the equations. Third, a single star like our sun may have planets orbiting around it, and spacecraft trajectories are often chosen to swing close to some of the planets to get to their destination fast with less cost in fuel. The plot of the 2016 movie *The Martian* turns on such an unexpected choice of orbit.

HISTORY. We do not know who first focused on the phenomenon that a nonlinear BVP can have multiple solutions, but certainly one of earliest and most consequential examples of this kind concerns the buckling of columns. Euler published his great paper on this subject in 1759 (in French), "On the strength of columns." He writes, "And so we see that, however small the force F acting horizontally, it must always produce a certain deflection, which is proportional to F itself. But it is not the same when the force acts vertically, or if the column must sustain a load from above. At first it seems that such a force, no matter how great, could not bend the column: for there is no reason why it should bend in one direction rather than another. But the least inequality in the parts of the column, or the least stress which it feels from any side, will soon furnish a sufficient reason for it to bend in a particular direction."

OUR FAVORITE REFERENCE. Many features of our world, from the fundamental laws of physics to the pattern of stripes on a tiger, originated in a process of *symmetry breaking*, in which a choice is made among a multiplicity of potential solutions. For a popular account of such effects see Stewart and Golubitsky, *Fearful Symmetry: Is God a Geometer?*, first published in 1993.

SUMMARY OF CHAPTER 16. *Nonlinear ODE BVPs can have no solutions, one solution, finitely many solutions, or infinitely many solutions. Some strategies for investigating multiple solutions include (a) phase plane analysis, (b) shooting, (c) path-following, and (d) deflation. In general, finding all solutions of a nonlinear BVP is difficult.*

Exercise 16.1. *Fisher equation.* The function $y(x)$ satisfies $y'' + y - y^2 = 0$ for $x \in [-1, 1]$ with $y(-1) = 1$, $y(1) = 0$. *(a)* If $y(0) \approx 0.6$, what is $y(0.5)$? Plot the solution. *(b)* If $y(0) \approx -2.5$, what is $y(0.5)$? Plot the solution. *(c)* Sketch both of the orbits just described in the phase plane.

Exercise 16.2. *Bounce pass.* A ball is thrown from player A to player B, 5 meters away, starting and finishing at height 1 meter. This is an idealized ball that travels as a point mass with no air resistance or rotation and bounces perfectly with equal angles and speeds of impact and rebound. The pass is a slow one: it takes a full 3 seconds to get from A to B. *(a)* Assuming the ball does not bounce, sketch its trajectory. You do not need to write any differential equations. *(b)* Assuming the ball bounces once, sketch all of its possible trajectories. Again you do not need to write any differential equations. *(c)* Now consider all possible solutions to this BVP, with any number of bounces. Assume it takes 0.45 seconds for a point mass to fall from a height of 1 meter. Exactly how many solutions are there all together? Sketch them.

Exercise 16.3. *Multiple solutions of cubic oscillator.* Figure 16.6 shows phase plane plots of two of the five solutions of (16.2) indicated in Figure 16.10. Expand the plot to include all five solutions. How do you think the conjectures stated after Figure 16.6 about solutions with various winding numbers should be corrected?

Exercise 16.4. *Deflation.* *(a)* Equation (16.2) can be written $N(y) = 0$, where N is a nonlinear operator applying to functions on $[0, 1]$ with boundary values equal to 1. Compute the solution to (16.2) shown in Figure 16.3, and call this function Y. Now consider the new nonlinear operator $M(y) = N(y)(1 + \|y - Y\|^{-1})$, where $\|\cdot\|$ is the 2-norm. Note that $M(y) = 0$ for $y \neq Y$ if and only if $N(y) = 0$. Use Chebfun to solve $M(y) = 0$ numerically. Which solution from Figure 16.10 do you get? *(b)* This process is automated by the Chebfun `deflate` command. Show that you get the same solution with `deflate(N,Y,1,1)`. Which solution do you get with `deflate(N,Y,2,0)`? (For information on deflation, see Farrell, Birkisson, and Funke, "Deflation techniques for finding distinct solutions of nonlinear partial differential equations," *SIAM Journal on Scientific Computing* 37 (2015), pp. A2026–A2045.)

17. Bifurcation

As parameters vary, the solutions of an ODE may change in structural properties. This is the subject of bifurcation theory.

For a prototypical example, consider a marble resting on a surface whose height as a function of horizontal position y is

$$h(y) = -cy^2, \qquad (17.1)$$

where c is a constant. For any value of c, the marble is in equilibrium at the fixed point $y = 0$: there is no net force on it. But it is clear that the equilibrium will be stable if $c < 0$, neutrally stable if $c = 0$, and unstable if $c > 0$.[63] The critical value $c = 0$ is the **bifurcation point** at which the behavior switches from one class to the other.

```
y = chebfun('y',[-1.3 1.3]);
marble = .14i + .12*exp(pi*1i*(0:60)/30);
for k = 1:3
  c = -.4+.2*k; surface = -c*y^2;
  subplot(1,3,k), plot(surface), hold on
  fill(real(marble),imag(marble),[0 0 0])
end
```

---

[63] As mentioned in the first footnote of Chapter 15, there is some inconsistency between formal and more casual uses of terms related to stability. Our use of "stable" and "unstable" here matches the formal definitions given in that chapter. We did not define "neutrally stable," which here corresponds to a case that is unstable, but with unstable trajectories growing just algebraically, not exponentially.

$c = -0.2$, stable $c = 0.0$, neutrally stable $c = 0.2$, unstable

Let us examine the ODE implicit in these pictures. We make the physics as elementary as possible, regarding the marble simply as a point mass moving along a surface in a gravitational field with constant 1. (Thus this marble has no internal angular momentum.) Since the slope of the surface at position y is $h'(y) = -2cy$, the ODE for its position $y(t)$ as a function of time t is

$$y'' = 2cy. \tag{17.2}$$

Following the pattern of Chapter 15, we plot some typical trajectories in a neighborhood of the fixed point $(0,0)$ in the (y, y') phase plane.

```
th = (pi/6)*(1:12)+.000001; u0 = cos(th); v0 = sin(th);
cc = chebfun('exp(1i*pi*x)'); L = chebop(0,2.5);
for j = 1:3
  subplot(1,3,j), plot(0,0,'.'), hold on, plot(cc)
  c = -.4+.2*j; L.op = @(t,y) diff(y,2) - 2*c*y;
  for k = 1:12
    L.lbc = [u0(k); v0(k)] + 1e-4*[1;1];
    y = L\0; arrowplot(y,diff(y))
  end
end
```

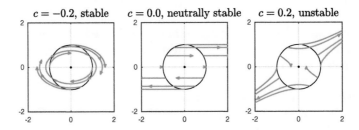

The three images show a center, a degenerate node, and a saddle point, corresponding to $c = -0.2$, 0, and 0.2. The Jacobian matrices are

$$\mathbf{J}_* = \begin{pmatrix} 0 & 1 \\ -0.4 & 0 \end{pmatrix}, \begin{pmatrix} 0 & 1 \\ 0 & 0 \end{pmatrix}, \begin{pmatrix} 0 & 1 \\ 0.4 & 0 \end{pmatrix},$$

with eigenvalues

$$\{\lambda_1, \lambda_2\} = \{di, -di\}, \ \{0, 0\}, \ \{d, -d\}, \quad d = \sqrt{0.4}.$$

As an example of the interpretation of these results, what is the physics of the third problem of Figure 17.1, the unstable configuration with the marble at the top of a hill? From the phase plot we can see the answer. Almost any nonzero initial position in the phase plane will lead to divergence to infinity in a northeasterly or southwesterly direction: to be precise, in the direction of a positive or negative multiple of the eigenvector $(1, \sqrt{0.4})$ of $\mathbf{J}_*$. The exception is the special situation in which the marble begins with position (y, y') exactly equal to a multiple of the other eigenvector, $(1, -\sqrt{0.4})$. In this case the marble is moving up the hill with just the right amount of energy to reach the top with velocity zero at $t = \infty$. (In general, the set of initial points that converge to a fixed point of a dynamical system is called the **stable manifold** of that point.) Of course, this is a physically unstable situation, which would be undone by the slightest perturbation.

For problems depending on a parameter, it is common to draw a **bifurcation diagram** indicating the dependence of some measure of a fixed point — an equilibrium — on the parameter. For the marble on the surface, the bifurcation diagram is very simple.

```
plot([-2 0],[0 0],'-',[2 0],[0 0],'--')
```

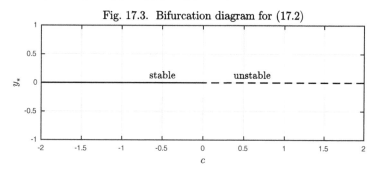

Fig. 17.3. Bifurcation diagram for (17.2)

For each value of c there is a single fixed point y_*, and the diagram plots the dependence of y_* on c. For this very simple problem, the dependence is trivial since the fixed point is $y_* = 0$ for all c. For $c < 0$ the equilibrium is stable, and the curve is shown solid. For $c > 0$ it is unstable, and the curve is shown dashed. In general, dashed curves in bifurcation diagrams correspond to unstable steady states of a system, which one would not ordinarily expect to observe in an experiment.

There is an interesting way to trace parts of a bifurcation diagram dynamically: set up a time-dependent problem in which the parameter of interest varies slowly in time, slowly enough that at each t, the behavior is approximately that of a constant-coefficient system. (In quantum physics this would be called an *adiabatic transition* from one parameter value to another.) For example, suppose we modify (17.2) to the equation

$$y'' = 2c(t)y, \quad c(t) = -2 + t/150. \tag{17.3}$$

Here is the solution with $y(0) = 0.02$, $y'(0) = 0$.

```
L = chebop(0,600); L.lbc = [0.02;0]; L.maxnorm = 0.9;
L.op = @(t,y) diff(y,2) - 2*(-2+t/150)*y;
y = L\0; plot(y)
```

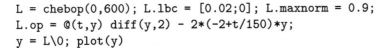

Fig. 17.4. Solution of (17.3) with slowly varying parameter c

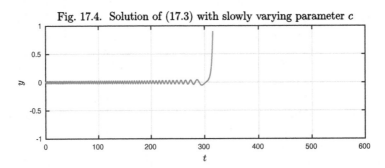

For $t < 300$ we see quasi-steady oscillation around $y = 0$, with frequency decreasing to 0 as t approaches 300. After this, the character of the problem changes and an exponential explosion begins. There is no steady state; the orbit is diverging to ∞.

By varying features of the marble problem, we can begin to explore the rich world of bifurcation theory. A good way to start is to introduce a quartic term in (17.1),

$$h(y) = -cy^2 + y^4. \tag{17.4}$$

Now the surfaces look like this.

```
y = chebfun('y',[-1.4 1.4]);
for k = 1:3
  c = -2+k; surface = -c*y^2 + y^4;
  subplot(1,3,k), plot(surface), hold on
  fill(real(marble),imag(marble),[0 0 0])
end
```

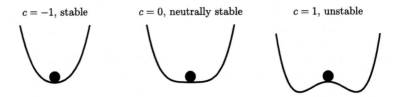

$c = -1$, stable $c = 0$, neutrally stable $c = 1$, unstable

The slope is $h'(y) = -2cy + 4y^3$, and (17.2) becomes

$$y'' = 2cy - 4y^3. \tag{17.5}$$

Here are some trajectories in the (y, y') phase plane.

```
N = chebop(0,2.5);
for j = 1:3
  subplot(1,3,j), plot(0,0,'.'), hold on
  c = -2+j; N.op = @(t,y) diff(y,2) - 2*c*y + 4*y^3;
  if c>0, plot(sqrt(c/2)*[-1 1],[0 0],'.'), end
  for k = 1:12
    N.lbc = [u0(k); v0(k)];
    y = N\0; arrowplot(y,diff(y))
  end
end
```

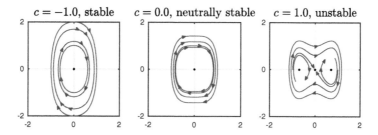

The bifurcation diagram for this problem is drawn below. This is called a **pitchfork bifurcation**, or more fully a **supercritical pitchfork bifurcation**. For $c > 0$, we se that the marble has stable rest positions at $x = \pm\sqrt{c/2}$.

```
plot([-2 0],[0 0],'-',[2 0],[0 0],'--')
ystar = chebfun('y'); c = 2*ystar^2; hold on, plot(c,ystar)
```

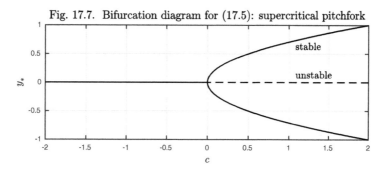

Fig. 17.7. Bifurcation diagram for (17.5): supercritical pitchfork

Let us again consider a variable coefficient problem with a slowly changing coefficient $c(t)$,

$$y'' = 2c(t)y - 4y^3, \quad c(t) = -2 + t/150. \tag{17.6}$$

This time we see a continuous transition from oscillation about 0 to oscillation about a nonzero value, beautifully matching one branch of the bifurcation diagram.

```
N = chebop(0,600); N.lbc = [0.02;0];
N.op = @(t,y) diff(y,2) - 2*(-2+t/150)*y + 4*y^3;
y = N\0; plot(y)
```

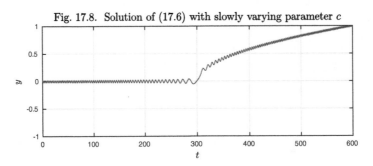

Fig. 17.8. Solution of (17.6) with slowly varying parameter c

The solution settles on the upper rather than the lower branch for no particular reason, a phenomenon known as *symmetry breaking* (discussed further in Chapters 18 and 22). If we alter the initial conditions, it might as easily find the lower branch. Here is an example of that behavior, where the only difference is that the initial amplitude $y(0)$ has been increased from 0.02 to 0.05.

```
N.lbc = [0.05;0]; y = N\0; plot(y)
```

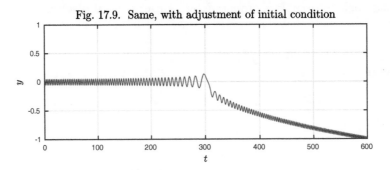

Fig. 17.9. Same, with adjustment of initial condition

In the curves above, the departure from the steady state has been seeded by a nonzero initial condition. Another approach is to start from a zero condition but introduce perturbations along the way. Here we carry out such an experiment, with the perturbation consisting of 0.003 times a smooth random function $f(t)$ of the kind described in Chapter 12,

$$y'' = 2c(t)y - 4y^3 + 0.003f(t), \quad c(t) = -2 + t/150. \tag{17.7}$$

The details differ, but the overall behavior is as before, with the trajectory again happening to find the lower branch of the bifurcation diagram.

```
N.lbc = [0;0]; rng(2), rhs = .003*randnfun(1,[0 600],'big');
y = N\rhs; plot(y)
```

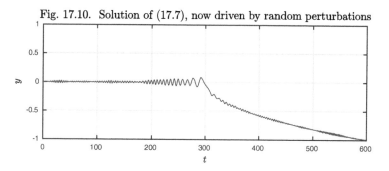

Fig. 17.10. Solution of (17.7), now driven by random perturbations

A conspicuous feature of the last three plots is persistent oscillations, an effect we saw in Chapter 8 in the discussion of resonance. To construct problems that are not so influenced by past history, we can introduce a damping term in the ODE. Specifically, from now on we shall add the term $-0.2y'$, so that (17.5), for example, becomes

$$y'' = 2cy - 4y^3 - 0.2y'. \tag{17.8}$$

The trajectories in the phase plane change their shapes. Now they always spiral into fixed points, just as the marble in Figure 17.5 will eventually come to rest if there is friction.

```
N = chebop(0,5);
th = (pi/2)*(1:4)+.000001; u0 = cos(th); v0 = sin(th);
for j = 1:3
  subplot(1,3,j), plot(0,0,'.'), hold on
  c = -2+j; N.op = @(t,y) diff(y,2) - 2*c*y + 4*y^3 + .2*diff(y);
  if c>0, plot(sqrt(c/2)*[-1 1],[0 0],'.'), end
  for k = 1:4
    N.lbc = [u0(k); v0(k)];
    y = N\0; arrowplot(y,diff(y))
  end
end
```

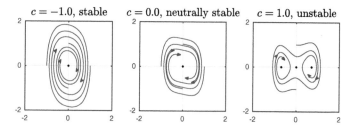

Here is a trajectory for the damped time-dependent problem

$$y'' = 2c(t)y - 4y^3 - 0.2y' + 0.003f(t), \quad c(t) = -2 + t/150, \tag{17.9}$$

with the same random forcing function $0.003f(t)$ as before.

```
N = chebop(0,600); N.lbc = [0;0];
N.op = @(t,y) diff(y,2) - 2*(-2+t/150)*y + 4*y^3 + .2*diff(y);
y = N\rhs; plot(y)
```

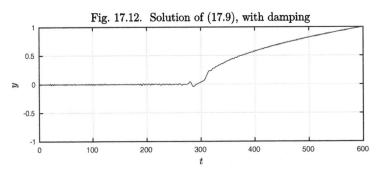

Fig. 17.12. Solution of (17.9), with damping

*   *   *

Let us review what we have done so far in this chapter. We have looked at two dynamical systems: first the quadratic problem (17.1)–(17.2), then the quartic problem (17.4)–(17.5). For each one we displayed four figures showing the physical interpretation by a marble on a surface, the phase plane, a bifurcation diagram, and a trajectory for a problem with slowly varying $c(t)$. In the second case we actually showed four such trajectories: two for different initial conditions, then one driven by a small random forcing term $0.003f(t)$, then a fourth of the same kind but with damping included in the equation.

We are now going to follow the same pattern for one final kind of bifurcation: a **subcritical pitchfork bifurcation**. The simplest starting point of this discussion could be equations (17.4) and (17.8) again, but with a sign change on the quartic term:

$$h(y) = -cy^2 - y^4 \qquad (17.10)$$

and

$$y'' = 2cy + 4y^3 - 0.2y'. \qquad (17.11)$$

This gives a new marble diagram,

```
y = chebfun('y',[-1.4 1.4]);
for k = 1:3
  c = -2+k; surface = -c*y^2 - y^4;
  subplot(1,3,k), plot(surface), hold on
  fill(real(marble),imag(marble),[0 0 0])
end
```

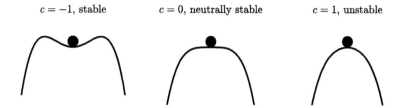

and a new bifurcation diagram,

```
plot([-2 0],[0 0],'-',[2 0],[0 0],'--')
ystar = chebfun('y'); c = -2*ystar^2;
hold on, plot(c,ystar,'--')
```

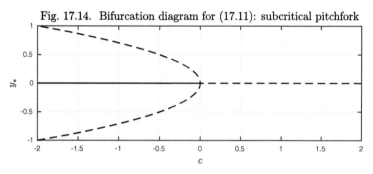

Fig. 17.14. Bifurcation diagram for (17.11): subcritical pitchfork

However, let us immediately modify the problem further to make it more realistic, and more interesting, by adding a stabilizing y^6 term:

$$h(y) = -cy^2 - y^4 + y^6 \qquad (17.12)$$

and

$$y'' = 2cy + 4y^3 - 6y^5 - 0.2y'. \qquad (17.13)$$

Now the marble diagram looks like this.

```
y = chebfun('y',[-1.4 1.4]);
for k = 1:3
  c = -.4+.1*k; surface = -c*y^2 - y^4 + y^6;
  subplot(1,3,k), plot(surface), hold on
  fill(real(marble),.5*imag(marble),[0 0 0])
end
```

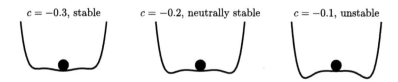

The bifurcation diagram becomes more complicated.

```
plot([-2 0],[0 0],[2 0],[0 0],'--')
ystar = chebfun('y',[-1 1]/sqrt(3)); c = -2*ystar^2 + 3*ystar^4;
hold on, plot(c,ystar,'--')
ystar = chebfun('y',[1/sqrt(3) 1.1]); c = -2*ystar^2 + 3*ystar^4;
plot(c,[ystar,-ystar])
```

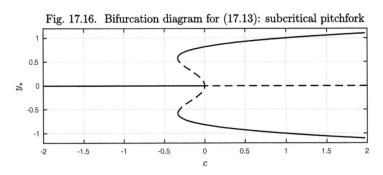

Fig. 17.16. Bifurcation diagram for (17.13): subcritical pitchfork

New dynamical possibilities are implied by this figure. One implication is that if c increases slowly through $c = 0$, one may expect a sudden *jump transition* to an amplitude $y \approx \pm\sqrt{2/3}$. A simulation confirms this prediction.

```
N.lbc = [0;0];
N.op = @(t,y) diff(y,2)-2*(-2+t/150)*y-4*y^3+6*y^5+.2*diff(y);
y = N\rhs; plot(y)
```

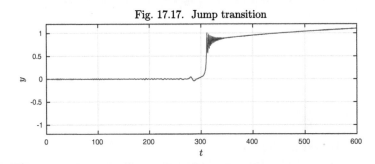

Fig. 17.17. Jump transition

Another implication is that if we now let c *decrease* through 0, we may observe the effect known as **hysteresis**, in which the jump back to the initial state occurs at a parameter value different from the initial one.

```
y0 = y(600); yp0 = deriv(y,600); N.lbc = [y0;yp0];
N.op = @(t,y) diff(y,2)-2*(2-t/150)*y-4*y^3+6*y^5+.2*diff(y);
y = N\rhs; hold on, treverse = chebfun('600-t',[0 600]);
plot(treverse,y')
```

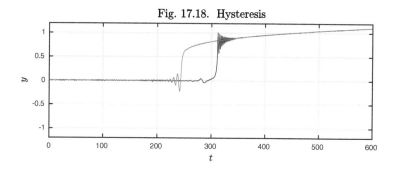

Fig. 17.18. Hysteresis

APPLICATION: FITZHUGH–NAGUMO EQUATIONS OF NEURAL SIGNALS

One of the great achievements of 20th century science was the model of propagation of neural signals by Alan Hodgkin and Andrew Huxley in 1952, which won them the 1963 Nobel Prize for Physiology or Medicine. In the words of J. D. Murray in his book *Mathematical Biology I* (Springer, 2002), from which this discussion is adapted, "The theory of neuron firing and propagation of nerve action potentials is one of the major successes of real mathematical biology."

Hodgkin and Huxley worked on the neuron of the giant squid, expressing the current out of the axon of the neuron in terms of the oscillations of an activator–inhibitor system. The full description requires a PDE, but the model is interesting even when reduced to an ODE by ignoring variation along the length of the axon. FitzHugh and Nagumo subsequently simplified the equations even further to a two-variable ODE system now known as the *FitzHugh–Nagumo equations*,

$$v' = v - \frac{1}{3}v^3 - w + I, \quad w' = 0.08(v - 0.8w + 0.7). \tag{17.14}$$

Here $v(t)$ represents the electric potential across the membrane of the neuron, which is experimentally accessible. The $w(t)$ component is an approximation of the current through the membrane due to movement of ions. Finally, I is a current applied to stimulate the cell experimentally. This will be our bifurcation parameter.

In view of the plus and minus signs in (17.14), we can say that v is self-activating but inhibited by w. Conversely, w is activated by v but otherwise decays (down to the level $w = 0.7/0.8$). This a bit like the interaction of rabbits and foxes in the Lotka–Volterra model, but with different details. While v and w tend to grow and decrease in opposition to one another, they are also given some inhomogeneous growth. If I, the external forcing for v, is too small, then v does not recover fast enough to excite the system. However, when I passes a threshold I_1, the neuron begins to fire, with v reaching peaks and troughs repeatedly. If I continues to increase, it passes another threshold I_2

past which w is pushed into a higher steady state that again shuts down the
activation of v.

We can see all three of these behaviors by allowing I to grow slowly in time,
with a small random perturbation included to make the system noisy. We plot
just the component w; the behavior of v is similar.

```
N = chebop([0 1000]); t = chebfun('t',[0 1000]);
I = t/500 + .01*randnfun(2,[0 1000],'big');
N.op = @(t,v,w) [ diff(v)-(v-v^3/3-w)
                  diff(w)-0.08*(v-0.8*w+0.7) ];
N.lbc = @(v,w) [v;w];
[v,w] = N\[I; 0*I]; plot(w)
```

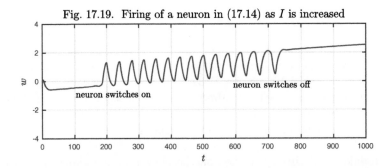

Fig. 17.19. Firing of a neuron in (17.14) as I is increased

This image reveals that there must be a pair of bifurcations as the parameter I is
increased. At $t \approx 180$, with $I \approx 0.36$, the oscillation switches on, and at $t \approx 700$,
with $I \approx 1.4$, it switches off again. Bifurcations like this where an oscillation
turns on or off are known as **Hopf bifurcations**, and they are characterized
by a pair of eigenvalues of the Jacobian matrix crossing the imaginary axis to
move into or out of the right half of the complex plane.[64]

We can confirm these guesses as follows. A fixed point v_*, w_* of (17.14) is
characterized by the conditions

$$v_* - \frac{1}{3}v_*^3 - w_* + I = 0, \quad v_* - 0.8w_* + 0.7 = 0,$$

and eliminating w_* with the aid of the second equation gives

$$I = -v_* + \frac{v_*^3}{3} + \frac{v_* + 0.7}{0.8}. \tag{17.15}$$

By inverting this equation we get a plot v_* as a function of I.

```
v = chebfun('v',[-2,2]); I = -v + v^3/3 + (v+.7)/.8;
vstar = inv(I); plot(vstar)
```

---

[64]There are many examples of Hopf bifurcation in our lives, such as that annoying vibration
that sets in when your car passes a particular speed.

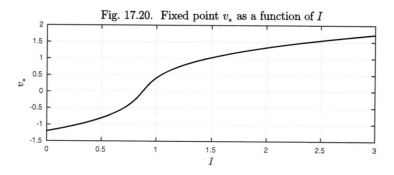

Fig. 17.20. Fixed point v_* as a function of I

By differentiating the two equations of (17.14) with respect to v_* and w_* we find the corresponding Jacobian matrix, which depends only on v_* since w enters the equations linearly:

$$\mathbf{J}_* = \begin{pmatrix} 1 - v_*^2 & -1 \\ 0.08 & -0.064 \end{pmatrix}. \qquad (17.16)$$

We now plot the maximal real part of the eigenvalues of $\mathbf{J}_*$, the *spectral abscissa* (introduced in Chapter 14), as a function of I.

```
J = @(v) [1-v^2 -1; .08 -.064];
abscissa = chebfun(@(I) max(real(eig(J(vstar(I))))),[0 3], ...
    'splitting','on');
plot(abscissa,'m'), hold on
Ibifurc = roots(abscissa); plot(Ibifurc,0*Ibifurc,'.')
```

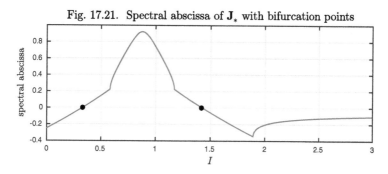

Fig. 17.21. Spectral abscissa of $\mathbf{J}_*$ with bifurcation points

The two bifurcation points are shown as black dots. They match our earlier estimates nicely.

```
Ibifurc

Ibifurc =
    0.3313
    1.4187
```

You may wonder why the plot of the spectral abscissa is not smooth, but breaks into four regions separated by discontinuities of the derivative. Actually, this effect appeared already in Figure 14.7. The discontinuities correspond to transitions between regimes where the dominant eigenvalues of $\mathbf{J}_*$ are a complex conjugate pair (the second and the fourth parts of the curve) and regimes where there is a single dominant real eigenvalue (the first and third). As predicted, when the spectral abscissa passes through zero for this problem, it is with a pair of complex conjugate eigenvalues, signaling a Hopf bifurcation:

```
eig(J(vstar(Ibifurc(1))))
```

```
ans =
   -0.0000 + 0.2755i
   -0.0000 - 0.2755i
```

The magnitude of the imaginary part of these eigenvalues, 0.2755, gives the frequency of the linearized oscillation. This corresponds to a period of $2\pi/0.2755 \approx$ 22.8, slightly less than the period observed in Figure 17.19.

Here are plots of trajectories in the v-w plane for $I = 0.31$, below the bifurcation, and $I = 0.34$, above.

```
dom = [0 75]; N = chebop(dom);
N.op = @(t,v,w) [ diff(v)-(v-v^3/3-w)
                  diff(w)-0.08*(v-0.8*w+0.7) ];
I = chebfun('0.31+0*t',dom); vs = vstar(0.31); ws = (vs+.7)/.8;
subplot(1,2,1), plot(vs,ws,'.'), hold on
N.lbc = @(v,w) [v-vs;w-ws-.2];
[v,w] = N\[I; 0*I]; arrowplot(v,w)
I = chebfun('0.34+0*t',dom); vs = vstar(0.34); ws = (vs+.7)/.8;
subplot(1,2,2), plot(vs,ws,'.'), hold on
N.lbc = @(v,w) [v-vs;w-ws-.2];
[v,w] = N\[I; 0*I]; arrowplot(v,w)
```

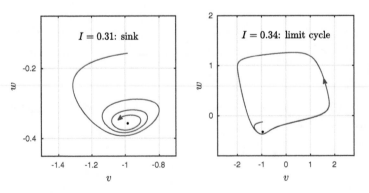

The equations above are simple enough that the calculation could be done analytically. The trace of $\mathbf{J}_*$, the sum of its diagonal entries, is $0.936 - v_*^2$, and this will be equal to the sum of the eigenvalues. When the eigenvalues form a conjugate pair, both have the same real part, and thus the Hopf bifurcation will occur when the trace passes through zero, that is, $v_* = \pm\sqrt{0.936}$. Thus by (17.15), the two bifurcation points correspond to the parameter values

$$I_c = \pm a + \frac{\pm a^3}{3} + \frac{\pm a + 0.7}{0.8}, \quad a = \sqrt{0.936}.$$

HISTORY. The observation that a system may change stability when a parameter passes through a critical value was well known to 19th century applied mathematicians such as Helmholtz, Kelvin, and Rayleigh. The technical use of the term "bifurcation" may be due to Poincaré in 1885. Further foundations of the mathematical theory of bifurcations were laid by Andronov and Pontryagin in the Soviet Union in the 1930s.

OUR FAVORITE REFERENCE. For a marvelously rich discussion of all kinds of bifurcation effects see Seydel, *Practical Bifurcation and Stability Analysis*, 3rd ed., Springer, 2009. The original edition appeared in 1994.

SUMMARY OF CHAPTER 17. *Bifurcation refers to the change of the qualitative nature of a solution to a nonlinear problem as a parameter varies through a critical value. Typically what changes at the critical value is the stability structure of a fixed point of the system. For example, if an eigenvalue crosses into the right half-plane, then a stable solution may become unstable, so that trajectories jump instead to other solutions. If it is a complex conjugate pair of eigenvalues that crosses into the right half-plane, we have a Hopf bifurcation, leading to the onset of oscillations.*

Exercise 17.1. Van der Pol equation. Consider the fixed point $y = y' = 0$ of the van der Pol equation $y'' + y - \mu(1 - y^2)y' = 0$, as in (9.6). *(a)* Determine the Jacobian matrix and its eigenvalues analytically, and show that there is a Hopf bifurcation as μ passes from negative to positive. *(b)* A different bifurcation takes place as μ passes through -2 or 2. Explain.

Exercise 17.2. FitzHugh–Nagumo experiment and noise. Rerun the experiment of Figure 17.19 without the random perturbation term. What is the change in the output? Can you explain why?

Exercise 17.3. Slowly-varying logistic map. This book deals with continuous-time processes, also known as *flows*, defined by equations like $y' = f(y)$. Every topic we consider has an analogue for discrete-time processes, also known as *maps*, defined by equations like $y_{n+1} = f(y_n)$. Execute the code

```
r = linspace(2,4,npts); y = 0*r; y(1) = .5;
for j = 1:npts-1, y(j+1) = r(j)*y(j)*(1-y(j)); end
plot(r,y,'.','markersize',3)
```

for $\texttt{npts} = 10^2, 10^3, \ldots, 10^7$ and show the plots that result. Write down five careful sentences describing what you think these plots reveal in the light of the discussion of this chapter. Make specific reference to relevant figure numbers.

Exercise 17.4. *Bifurcation diagram for the nonlinear pendulum.* Consider the nonlinear pendulum equation (9.6), $y'' = -\sin(y)$, on the interval $t \in [0, d]$ with boundary conditions $y(0) = y(d) = 0$. *(a)* Making reference to the phase plane diagram, explain why for $d \leq \pi$ this problem has a unique solution and describe that solution. *(b)* Explain why there is a bifurcation at $d = \pi$ and describe the two new solutions that appear for $d > \pi$. *(c)* Explain why there is another bifurcation at $d = 2\pi$ and describe the two new solutions that appear there. Meanwhile what has happened to the three solutions already present? *(d)* Exactly how many solutions will there be for $d = 100$, and what will they look like?

Exercise 17.5. *Subcritical pitchfork marble.* Consider the ODE (17.13) for a marble on a surface with $c = -0.2$ sketched in Figure 17.15, whose bifurcation diagram was shown in Figure 17.16. Consider the BVP for this problem $y(0) = y(T) = 0$, where $T > 0$ is a fixed constant. Assume in what follows that we are only interested in solutions with $y(t) \geq 0$ for all $t \in [0, T]$. *(a)* Describe physically, in terms of the marble rolling along the surface, three structurally different types of solutions that may exist for this problem (for appropriate values of T). *(b)* Draw a sketch of the phase plane and interpret your three solutions in this context.

Exercise 17.6. *Emergence of a limit cycle.* The system $u' = -v + u(\mu - u^2 - v^2)$, $v' = u + v(\mu - u^2 - v^2)$, where μ is a real parameter, has a fixed point $(u, v) = (0, 0)$. *(a)* Compute solutions for $t \in [0, 20]$ starting from $(u, v) = (2, 0)$ for $\mu = -1, -0.5, \ldots, 1$. Plot each curve in the (u, v) plane with axes equal. What dependence on μ do you observe? *(b)* Analyze the stability of the fixed point and discuss the bifurcation situation.

18. Continuation and path-following

As we have seen in the last chapter, a central idea in the study of ODEs is the investigation of the dependence of solutions on parameters. This is important both scientifically, since varying parameters may reveal the range of behaviors of a problem, and algorithmically, since solutions can often be calculated most reliably by varying a parameter incrementally from one range to another. In this chapter we pursue these ideas.

Dependence on parameters can be of interest for linear problems, as we shall see in our investigation of boundary and interior layers in Chapter 20. The heart of this subject, however, is nonlinear problems, where the varying of parameters may be essential to the computation of some solutions and to the elucidation of the structure of a problem.

As a starting example, suppose we are faced with the problem

$$\varepsilon y'' + y - y^2 = 0, \quad x \in [0,1], \ y(0) = 1, \ y(1) = 0 \qquad (18.1)$$

and seek a solution with $\varepsilon = 2^{-10}$. If we try calling Chebfun directly, it fails, as Newton iterations often do when started from an initial guess not close enough to a solution. Larger values of ε lead to ready convergence, however. Taking advantage of this effect, we can creep up on the solution we want, decreasing ε steadily in the process known as **continuation**.[65] The number ε is called the **continuation parameter**. The following code starts with $\varepsilon = 2^{-3}$ and reduces the value successively by factors of $\sqrt{2}$ until 2^{-10} is reached.

---

[65]Other terms include **embedding** and **homotopy** methods. Such ideas are important not just for ODEs (and PDEs), but also for finding solutions of nonlinear algebraic systems of equations.

```
N = chebop(0,1); N.lbc = 1; N.rbc = 0; epsvec = 2.^-(3:.5:10);
for ep = epsvec
  N.op = @(x,y) ep*diff(y,2) + y - y^2;
  y = N\0; plot(y), hold on, N.init = y;
end
```

Fig. 18.1. A family of solutions of (18.1) found by continuation in ε

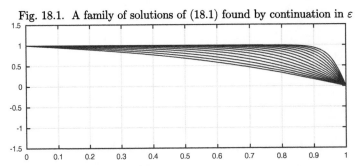

The key feature of this code segment is that for each value of ε after the first, an initial guess is specified in the N.init field corresponding to the converged solution from the previous value. Note that the solution obtained shows a boundary layer at $x = 1$; its width is $O(\varepsilon^{1/2})$ (see Exercise 18.2).

The family of solutions of (18.1) we have just plotted is not the only one. If we start from the initial guess $y(x) = 1 - x - 3e^x(x - x^2)$, another family emerges, which we plot in a new color. Again there is a boundary layer at $x = 1$. Images like these show that continuation may offer a powerful tool for investigating problems with multiple solutions.

```
x = chebfun('x',[0,1]); N.init = 1-x-3*exp(x)*(x-x^2);
for ep = epsvec
  N.op = @(x,y) ep*diff(y,2) - y^2 + y;
  y = N\0; plot(y), hold on, N.init = y;
end
```

Fig. 18.2. Another family of solutions of (18.1)

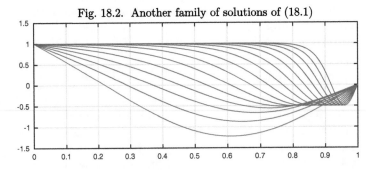

Next, let us turn to equation (16.5),

$$\varepsilon y'' + y + y^2 = 1, \quad x \in [-1,1], \; y(\pm 1) = 0. \tag{18.2}$$

Suppose we want a solution with $\varepsilon = 2^{-10}$. This time, a call to Chebfun is successful:

```
N = chebop(-1,1); N.lbc = 0; N.rbc = 0; ep = 2^-10;
N.op = @(x,y) ep*diff(y,2) + y + y^2;
y = N\1; plot(y)
```

Fig. 18.3. A solution of (18.2) with $\varepsilon = 2^{-10}$

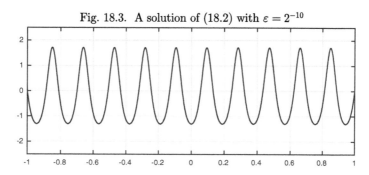

This solution is valid, but it is far from the simplest solution for this choice of ε. To find another, the following code segment uses continuation with $\varepsilon = 1/2, 1/4, \ldots, 1/1024$. Here we obtain solutions with boundary layers of width $O(\varepsilon^{1/2})$ at both ends.

```
N = chebop(-1,1); N.lbc = 0; N.rbc = 0; epsvec = 2.^-(1:10);
for ep = epsvec
  N.op = @(x,y) ep*diff(y,2) + y + y^2;
  y = N\1; plot(y), hold on, N.init = y;
end
```

Fig. 18.4. A family of solutions of (18.2) found by continuation in ε

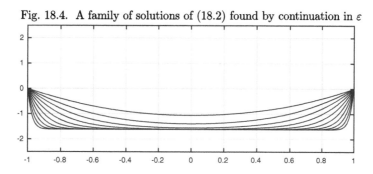

Using a continuation parameter may have a number of benefits, including these:

1. The computation may be faster because fewer Newton steps are needed.

2. Convergence may be achieved in cases where a cold start would fail.[66]

3. In problems with multiple solutions, continuation may help pick out the solution of interest.

---

[66]When we use an initial condition from a nearby problem to improve our results, this is called a *warm start*.

In the experiment we have just shown, benefit 3 has been the crucial one.

For a third example, let us look at the Bratu equation,

$$y'' + \lambda \exp(y) = 0, \quad x \in [0,1], \; y(0) = y(1) = 0. \tag{18.3}$$

In (16.4), λ took the value 3. Now, suppose we want it to range over the values $0, 0.25, \ldots, 3.5$. The continuation approach gives a simple family of curves.

```
N = chebop(0,1); N.lbc = 0; N.rbc = 0;
lamvec1 = 0:.25:3.5; mvec1 = [];
for lam = lamvec1
  N.op = @(x,y) diff(y,2) + lam*exp(y);
  y1 = N\0; plot(y1), hold on
  N.init = y1; mvec1 = [mvec1 y1(0.5)];
end
```

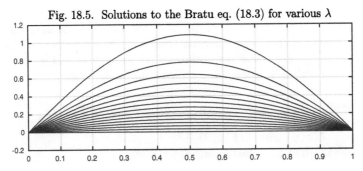

Fig. 18.5. Solutions to the Bratu eq. (18.3) for various λ

Starting from another initial guess, we can find the other branch of solutions, which we superimpose on the same plot with a new vertical scale.

```
N = chebop(0,1); N.lbc = 0; N.rbc = 0;
lamvec2 = 0.5:.25:3.5; mvec2 = [];
x = chebfun('x',[0 1]); N.init = 6*sin(pi*x);
for lam = lamvec2
  N.op = @(x,y) diff(y,2) + lam*exp(y);
  y2 = N\0; plot(y2)
  N.init = y2; mvec2 = [mvec2 y2(0.5)];
end
```

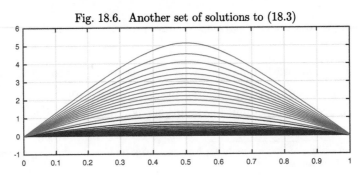

Fig. 18.6. Another set of solutions to (18.3)

At this point we have shown five examples of families of solutions to parameter-dependent nonlinear ODEs. In each case we superimposed collections of solutions on a single plot. There is another approach to such problems that is often fruitful, however, and that is to focus on a single scalar quantity that is characteristic of the solution of interest, an idea we have already explored in the last chapter on bifurcation.

For the Bratu problem, a natural scalar to measure is the maximum of $y(x)$, that is, $y(0.5)$. This quantity was stored at each step of the iterations above in the vectors `mvec1` and `mvec2`. Thus we can immediately plot $y(0.5)$ as a function of λ for the two families of solutions just computed, giving a bifurcation diagram for (18.3).

```
plot(lamvec1,mvec1,'.-'), hold on, plot(lamvec2,mvec2,'.-')
```

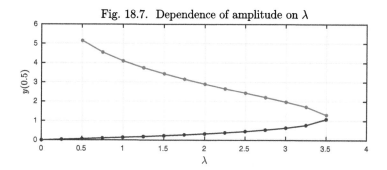

Fig. 18.7. Dependence of amplitude on λ

The point of interest is around $\lambda = 3.5$, where we have what is a called a **fold** or a **saddle-node bifurcation**, looking like a pitchfork without the central tine. To investigate the structure near such points, it is time to advance from *continuation* to **path-following**. The idea of path-following is that we will not just vary a parameter such as λ, but we will follow a path of solutions. For example, what happens to one of the solution branches in this plot as λ approaches 3.5? Clearly in some sense it bends around to turn back in the other direction, making $y(0.5)$ a double-valued function of λ. Let us show another plot, then explain what is going on.

```
H = chebop(0,1); H.op = @(x,y,lam) diff(y,2) + lam*exp(y);
H.lbc = @(y,lam) y; H.rbc = @(y,lam) y; lam0 = 0;
[y,lamvec,mvec,lamfun,mfun] = ...
    followpath(H,lam0,'measure',@(y) y(0.5),'maxstepno',17);
plot(lamfun,mfun), hold on, plot(lamvec, mvec,'.')
```

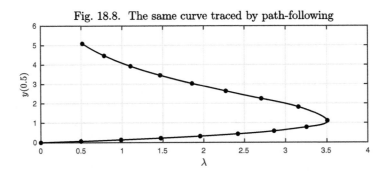

Fig. 18.8. The same curve traced by path-following

The plot shows a trajectory of solutions that passes around the turning point. Obviously more was involved in generating this plot than just varying λ. The data are the dots (not the curve, which is just a smooth interpolant), and they have been generated by a process called *pseudo-arclength continuation,* implemented in the Chebfun code `followpath`, whose details we shall not describe. The idea is to extrapolate from one dot to the next not just with respect to λ, but with respect to λ and also the solution y. A trajectory is in fact being followed in a high-dimensional space, though it is convenient to imagine that it is being followed in the two-dimensional space described by λ and the scalar measure $y(0.5)$.

The Bratu equation has just two solutions, but (18.2) has four or more, for $\varepsilon = 0.2$ at least, as shown in Figure 16.13. To get a sense of a more complicated bifurcation structure let us apply path-following to (18.2). We will use ε^{-1} as a parameter to track them, with $y'(1)$ as the scalar measure.

First, we compute the smoothest family of solutions, which arises from Chebfun's default initial guess.

```
H = chebop(-1,1); H.op = @(x,y,epi) diff(y,2)/epi +y+y^2-1;
H.lbc = @(y,ep) y; H.rbc = @(y,lam) y; epi0 = 0.01;
meas = @(y) feval(diff(y),1);
MSN = 'maxstepno'; DI = 'direction';
SM = 'stepmax'; ME = 'measure';
[y1,epi1,m1,epif1,mf1] = followpath(H,epi0,ME,meas,MSN,12,SM,1);
plot(y1)
```

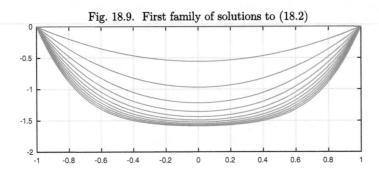

Fig. 18.9. First family of solutions to (18.2)

Here is the second symmetric family of solutions.

```
x = chebfun('x'); H.init = 5*(1-x^2); epi0 = 0.5;
[y2,epi2,m2,epif2,mf2] = followpath(H,epi0,ME,meas,MSN,27);
plot(y2)
```

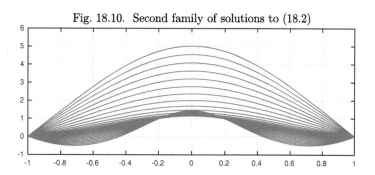

Fig. 18.10. Second family of solutions to (18.2)

Here is the first nonsymmetric family of solutions.

```
epi0 = 10; N.op = @(x,y) diff(y,2)/epi0 + y+y^2-1;
H.init = sin(pi*x);
[y3,epi3,m3,epif3,mf3] = followpath(H,epi0,ME,meas,MSN,13,DI,-1);
plot(y3)
```

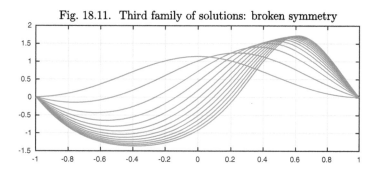

Fig. 18.11. Third family of solutions: broken symmetry

The second nonsymmetric family of solutions is the same, but with x replaced by $-x$.

```
H.init = -sin(pi*x);
[y4,epi4,m4,epif4,mf4] = followpath(H,epi0,ME,meas,MSN,13,DI,-1);
plot(y4)
```

Fig. 18.12. Fourth family of solutions: reflection of the third

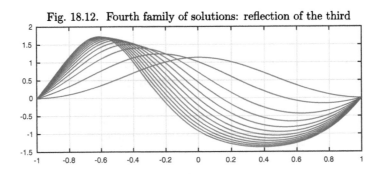

Let us now superimpose the ε-$y'(1)$ data from all four of these computations, retaining the same colors. We see an approximation to quite an interesting bifurcation diagram.

```
plot(epif1,mf1), hold on, plot(epi1,m1,'.')
plot(epif2,mf2), plot(epi2,m2,'.')
plot(epif3,mf3), plot(epi3,m3,'.')
plot(epif4,mf4), plot(epi4,m4,'.')
```

Fig. 18.13. Part of the bifurcation diagram for (18.2)

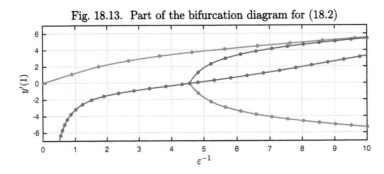

Each curve in the diagram has something to tell us. For $\varepsilon^{-1} = 0$, (18.2) reduces to the linear equation $y'' = 0$ with Dirichlet boundary conditions, with the unique solution $y = 0$. For any $\varepsilon > 0$, this solution evolves into the smooth mode captured by the green curves, always an even function of x. This solution satisfies $y(x) < 0$ for all $x \in (-1, 1)$.

The blue curve corresponds to a different even solution that exists for any $\varepsilon > 0$ but not for $\varepsilon = 0$; as $\varepsilon \to 0$, its amplitude diverges to infinity. This mode persists too for all values of ε.

The bifurcation diagram shows that something new happens when ε^{-1} rises above a bifurcation point at about 4.5, that is, when ε falls below about 0.2 (more precisely, about 0.2139). In a symmetry-breaking pitchfork bifurcation, just like what we saw in the final pages of the last chapter, the blue solution splits into three, two of which are no longer even functions of x.

As ε shrinks further, more and more solution branches appear. We shall not attempt to track them, but from Figure 18.3 we know they must exist.

APPLICATION: ARRHENIUS CHEMICAL REACTION

The phenomenon of spontaneous combustion or thermal runaway was mentioned in Chapter 3, and it can be modeled by the Bratu equation (18.3). Let us rewrite that equation with y replaced by T, indicating temperature,

$$T'' + \lambda \exp(T) = 0, \quad x \in [0,1], \ T(0) = T(1) = 0. \tag{18.4}$$

The function $T(x)$ represents the temperature distribution in a one-dimensional body with coordinate x. In (18.4), the body is undergoing a heat-generating chemical reaction whose reaction rate increases exponentially with T. The equation balances heat diffusion, the second derivative, against the reaction term, and a solution to the BVP corresponds to a steady-state temperature distribution. If λ is small enough, such a solution is possible, with heat leaving at the boundaries at $x = 0$ and 1 fast enough to balance the heat generation in the interior. For larger λ, the heat transfer at the boundaries is not fast enough. The medium keeps heating up until the temperature explodes to ∞ in a finite time, and there is no steady state. The physics of such processes was worked out by the Soviet physicist Frank-Kamenetskii in 1939.

Of course, this must be an idealized model if it predicts an infinite temperature. As a step towards more realistic chemistry, one may replace the exponential law in (18.4) by what is known as the *Arrhenius reaction rate*, which grows exponentially for smaller temperatures but then levels off. We will pick an explicit constant and write the equation in the form

$$T'' + \lambda \exp(T/(1 + 0.2T)) = 0, \quad x \in [0,1], \ T(0) = T(1) = 0. \tag{18.5}$$

Note that for small T, the exponential term grows exponentially as before, but as $T \to \infty$, this term is limited by the value $\exp(5)$.

An analysis of equations like (18.5) was presented by J. R. Parks of the Monsanto Chemical Company in "Criticality criteria for various configurations of a self-heating chemical as functions of activation energy and temperature of assembly," *Journal of Chemical Physics*, 1961. More details of the relevant mathematics can be found in Brown, Ibrahim, and Shivaji, "S-shaped bifurcation curves," *Nonlinear Analysis, Theory, Methods & Applications*, 1981. What we find for this equation is that the bounded reaction rate shuts off the explosion, allowing solutions for all λ. Moreover, the dependence on λ reveals an elegant *S-shaped bifurcation curve*, which we can track with `followpath`.

```
H = chebop(0,1); H.op = @(x,T,lam) diff(T,2) + lam*exp(T/(1+.2*T));
H.lbc = @(T,lam) T; H.rbc = @(T,lam) T; lam0 = 1;
[T,lamvec,mvec,lamfun,mfun] = ...
   followpath(H,lam0,'measure',@(T) T(0.5),'stepmax',2,'maxstepno',35);
semilogy(lamfun,mfun)
```

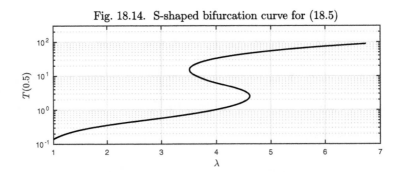

Fig. 18.14. S-shaped bifurcation curve for (18.5)

The curve shows that for most values of λ there is a single solution to (18.4). For λ approximately between 3.5 and 4.5, however, there are three solutions. For $\lambda = 4$, the amplitudes $T(0.5)$ will be approximately 1, 7, and 30, and we can use this information to find the solutions and plot them.

```
N = chebop(0,1); N.lbc = 0; N.rbc = 0;
lam = 4; N.op = @(x,T) diff(T,2) + lam*exp(T/(1+.2*T));
x = chebfun('x',[0 1]);
N.init =    sin(pi*x); T = N\0; plot(T), hold on
N.init =  7*sin(pi*x); T = N\0; plot(T)
N.init = 30*sin(pi*x); T = N\0; plot(T)
```

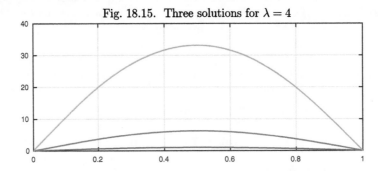

Fig. 18.15. Three solutions for $\lambda = 4$

HISTORY. Pseudo-arclength continuation is an idea closely associated with a software package, AUTO, written by Eusebius Doedel and growing out of his work with Herbert Keller at Caltech in the late 1970s. AUTO is written in Fortran and it has evolved and been used for research and applications now for four decades. A standard reference on continuation methods is Allgower and Georg, *Numerical Continuation Methods: An Introduction*, Springer, 2012.

OUR FAVORITE REFERENCE. A complicated bifurcation diagram is traced in extraordinary detail in S. J. Chapman and P. E. Farrell, Analysis of Carrier's problem, *SIAM Journal on Applied Mathematics* 77 (2017), pp. 924–950. Gradually reducing the value of ε in the Carrier equation (16.6), while also using the technique of deflation to discover new branches (see Exercise 16.4), the authors follow the curves connecting a pitchfork bifurcation at $\varepsilon \approx 0.2198$, a fold bifurcation at $\varepsilon \approx 0.0814$, another pitchfork bifurcation at $\varepsilon \approx 0.0551$, another fold bifurcation at $\varepsilon \approx 0.0295$, and so on in an infinite sequence of ever increasing multiplicity and complexity.

SUMMARY OF CHAPTER 18. *A powerful technique for the study of nonlinear problems is continuation, in which one moves incrementally from one solution to nearby solutions by varying a parameter. A refinement of this idea is path-following, in which a trajectory is followed involving not just a parameter but also the solution itself. These are fundamental tools of bifurcation analysis.*

Exercise 18.1. Allen–Cahn equation. One solution of the BVP $\varepsilon y'' + y - y^3 = 0$, $y(\pm 1) = 0$ is 0, but there is another one you will find by setting $\varepsilon = 0.1$ and starting from the initial guess $y(x) = 1 - x^2$. *(a)* Plot this solution and report its slope $y'(-1)$. *(b)* Plot the solution of the same structure and report $y'(-1)$ with $\varepsilon = 0.01$ and $\varepsilon = 0.001$. *(c)* In the other direction, what happens if you increase ε above 0.1? How far can you go and still find a nonzero solution? Based on your explorations, make a plot of $y'(-1)$ as a function of ε.

Exercise 18.2. Nonlinear boundary layer. In the text it is stated that the width of the boundary layer in Figure 18.1 is $O(\varepsilon^{1/2})$. Verify this numerically by determining, for each ε in the plot, the value δ such that $y(1 - \delta) = 0.5$. Make a table of $\delta(\varepsilon)$ and also the quotient $\delta(\varepsilon)/\varepsilon^{1/2}$, and plot $\delta(\varepsilon)$ against ε on a log-log scale.

Exercise 18.3. Deforming the S-shaped curve. *(a)* Rerun the example of Figure 18.14 with the coefficient 0.2 of (18.4) changed to 0.15 and 0.35. *(b)* To two digits of accuracy at least, what is the largest coefficient choice that gives a curve that is triple-valued for some values of λ?

Exercise 18.4. Hysteresis with the S-shaped curve. The subcritical pitchfork bifurcation of Figure 17.16 led to a jump transition and then hysteresis in Figure 17.18. Devise a similar experiment to generate a demonstration of hysteresis for the S-shaped bifurcation curve of Figure 18.14.

19. Periodic ODEs

Suppose we have an ODE defined for $t \in (-\infty, \infty)$ whose coefficients are 2π-periodic, or, in short, a **periodic ODE**. Will the solutions be 2π-periodic too?

Almost any experiment will show you that they don't *have* to be. For example, consider the problem

$$y' + (1 + \cos(t))y = 1, \quad y(0) = 0. \tag{19.1}$$

By Theorem 11.1, a unique solution exists for all t, negative and positive. This solution is not periodic, however, as we see by plotting it for $t \in [0, 10\pi]$.

```
L = chebop(0,10*pi);
L.op = @(t,y) diff(y) + (1+cos(t))*y; L.lbc = 0;
y = L\1; plot(y)
```

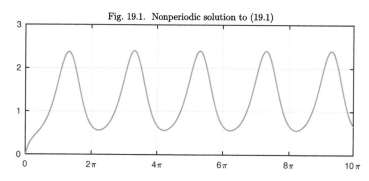

Fig. 19.1. Nonperiodic solution to (19.1)

Although this solution isn't periodic, it is very close to periodic after an initial phase. It would seem that there exists a truly periodic solution to this ODE that will oscillate between extremes of about 0.5 and 2.4. (From now on in this chapter, for simplicity, **periodic** usually means 2π-periodic.) Chebfun will find this solution if you specify the boundary condition `'periodic'`.

```
L = chebop(0,2*pi);
L.op = @(t,y) diff(y) + (1+cos(t))*y; L.bc = 'periodic';
y = L\1; plot(y)
```

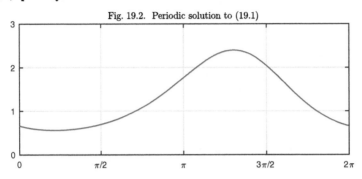

Fig. 19.2. Periodic solution to (19.1)

The minimum and maximum are as expected,

```
ymin = min(y), ymax = max(y)
ymin = 0.5625
ymax = 2.3974
```

and the value at $t = 0$ is a little bit above the minimum,

```
y0 = y(0)
y0 = 0.6601
```

If we solve the IVP on $[0, 10\pi]$ with this value specified as the initial condition, the periodic behavior is seen.

```
L = chebop(0,10*pi);
L.op = @(t,y) diff(y) + (1+cos(t))*y; L.lbc = y0;
y10pi = L\1; plot(y10pi)
```

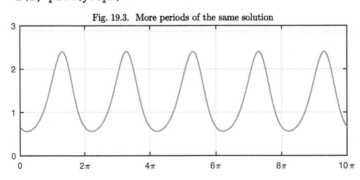

Fig. 19.3. More periods of the same solution

Encouraged by this experiment, let us try a second-order periodic equation,

$$y'' + (1 + \cos(t))y = 1, \quad y(0) = y'(0) = 0. \tag{19.2}$$

Again the first solution we find is nonperiodic.

```
L = chebop(0,10*pi);
L.op = @(t,y) diff(y,2) + (1+cos(t))*y; L.lbc = [4;0];
y = L\1; plot(y)
```

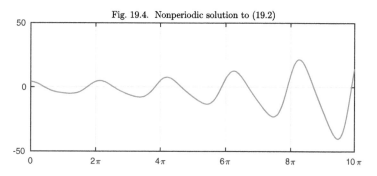

Fig. 19.4. Nonperiodic solution to (19.2)

This time, the curve is not settling down to a periodic form, but oscillating and growing exponentially. Nevertheless, again there exists a periodic solution.

```
L = chebop(0,2*pi);
L.op = @(t,y) diff(y,2) + (1+cos(t))*y; L.bc = 'periodic';
y = L\1; plot(y)
```

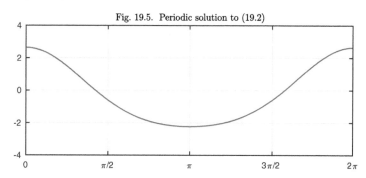

Fig. 19.5. Periodic solution to (19.2)

As before, we can recover periodic oscillations over $[0, 10\pi]$ if we set the initial conditions appropriately.

Nonlinear periodic ODEs often have periodic solutions too. For example, the equation

$$y'' + (1 + \cos(t))(y + (y/4)^3) = 1 \tag{19.3}$$

is a nonlinear variant of (19.2). Here we compute a periodic solution and immediately plot it on $[0, 10\pi]$.

```
L = chebop(0,2*pi);
L.op = @(t,y) diff(y,2) + (1+cos(t))*(y+(y/4)^3); L.bc = 'periodic';
y = L\1;
y10pi = chebfun(@(t) y(t),[0 10*pi],'trig'); plot(y10pi)
```

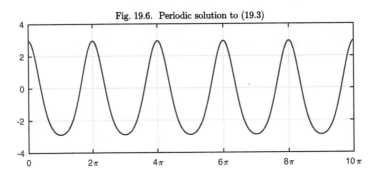

Fig. 19.6. Periodic solution to (19.3)

Of course, as usual, the behavior of nonlinear problems can vary greatly. If $(y/4)^3$ is changed to $(y/3)^3$ in (19.3), experiments indicate that there is no solution. For another example, in Chapter 1 we considered the van der Pol equation (1.2),

$$0.3y'' - (1 - y^2)y' + y = 0.$$

Like all autonomous equations, this ODE is not just 2π-periodic, but T-periodic for any period T. For any T, it has the T-periodic solution $y = 0$. For $T = 2\pi$, and for most other values of T, this is the only T-periodic solution. For the special value $T \approx 4.0725$, however, there is another nontrivial T-periodic solution corresponding to the limit cycle plotted in Chapter 1. In fact, this solution is one of an infinite family of distinct T-periodic solutions, since it could be shifted in t by any constant Δt.

Let us take stock of the situation. We have seen that a periodic ODE may or may not have periodic solutions, and that it will almost certainly have nonperiodic ones. The remainder of this chapter is organized around three questions for periodic ODEs:

1. Does there exist a periodic solution?

2. If so, is it unique?

3. What can we say about nonperiodic solutions?

These questions have rich histories going back to the 19th century, and as usual with ODEs, there are applications involving both time and space. For example, periodicity in time is associated with the dynamics of the solar system or of rotating or oscillating machinery, and periodicity in space is associated with propagation of sound and light waves in crystals. We will focus mainly on linear problems, with brief comments on nonlinear ones at the end. With regret, we shall mainly look just at questions (1) and (2), though the Application is of type (3).

Before turning to second-order periodic equations, the traditional focus in this subject area, let us consider the first-order case. Following the notation of Theorem 2.3, we start with the scalar linear problem

$$y' - a(t)y = g(t), \tag{19.4}$$

where a and g are assumed to be continuous and 2π-periodic. We can answer questions (1)–(2) above without much difficulty. First we note that by Theorem 10.1 there is a unique solution $y(t)$ of (19.4) associated with any initial condition $y(0) = y_0$. If $y(2\pi) \neq y(0)$, then by definition $y(t)$ is not 2π-periodic. If $y(2\pi) = y(0)$, on the other hand, then since the coefficients are periodic, the solution on $[2\pi, 4\pi]$ will be the same as on $[0, 2\pi]$, the solution on $[4\pi, 6\pi]$ will be the same as on $[2\pi, 4\pi]$, and so on, implying that the solution on all of $(-\infty, \infty)$ is 2π-periodic. Thus the question of 2π-periodicity reduces to the question of whether $y(2\pi) = y(0)$.

One special case of (19.4) is the situation where $a(t) = 0$,

$$y' = g(t). \tag{19.5}$$

Here the ODE reduces to an integral,

$$y(t) = y(0) + \int_0^t g(s)ds, \tag{19.6}$$

implying that the solution for any initial condition $y(0) = y_0$ will be periodic if and only if

$$\int_0^{2\pi} g(s)ds = 0. \tag{19.7}$$

Thus the answer to question (1) is that there is a periodic solution if and only if (19.7) holds, and the answer to (2) is that it is never unique since we could always add a constant.

The more substantial special case of (19.4) is the homogeneous case $g(t) = 0$,

$$y' - a(t)y = 0. \tag{19.8}$$

Here, following Theorem 2.2 (separation of variables), the solution is given by

$$y(t) = e^{h(t)}y(0), \tag{19.9}$$

where $h(t)$ is defined by

$$h(t) = \int_0^t a(s)ds. \tag{19.10}$$

In particular, we have

$$y(2\pi) = e^{h(2\pi)}y(0), \tag{19.11}$$

which implies that $y(2\pi) = y(0)$ if and only if

$$\left(1 - e^{h(2\pi)}\right)y(0) = 0.$$

This equation holds if and only if $y(0)$ is zero or $\exp(h(2\pi)) = 1$, that is,

$$h(2\pi) = 2\pi i \times \text{integer}. \tag{19.12}$$

If (19.12) holds, (19.8) is said to be **critical**; otherwise it is **noncritical**. Thus we see that if (19.8) is noncritical, then (19.8) has the unique periodic solution $y(t) = 0$: the answers to (1) and (2) are yes and yes. If it is critical, then any value $y(0)$ in (19.9) gives a 2π-periodic solution, so the answers are yes and no.

We shall now see that the behavior of the inhomogeneous problem (19.4) depends on the same condition (19.12) of criticality. By Theorem 2.3, the solution can be written

$$y(t) = e^{h(t)}y(0) + \int_0^t e^{h(t)-h(s)}g(s)ds, \tag{19.13}$$

where $h(t)$ is still defined by (19.10). Thus the value at $t = 2\pi$ is

$$y(2\pi) = e^{h(2\pi)}y(0) + \int_0^{2\pi} e^{h(2\pi)-h(s)}g(s)ds, \tag{19.14}$$

so the solution will be 2π-periodic if and only if

$$\left(1 - e^{h(2\pi)}\right)y(0) = \int_0^{2\pi} e^{h(2\pi)-h(s)}g(s)ds. \tag{19.15}$$

This leads to the following theorem encompassing the two special cases just considered.

Theorem 19.1. First-order scalar linear periodic ODEs (FLaShi).
Consider the equation

$$y' - a(t)y = g(t), \tag{19.16}$$

where $a(t)$ and $g(t)$ are continuous and 2π-periodic. If the equation is noncritical in the sense that (19.12) does not hold, then there exists a unique 2π-periodic solution y. If it is critical, then there exist infinitely many 2π-periodic solutions if the right-hand side of (19.15) is zero, and no 2π-periodic solutions if it is nonzero.

Proof. If the equation is noncritical, we may divide (19.15) by $1 - e^{h(2\pi)}$ to get

$$y(0) = \int_0^{2\pi} e^{h(2\pi)-h(s)}g(s)ds \bigg/ \left(1 - e^{h(2\pi)}\right),$$

producing a 2π-periodic solution (19.13) as claimed. Uniqueness follows since this condition on $y(0)$ determines $y(t)$ uniquely. If the equation is critical, then the left-hand side of (19.15) is zero regardless of the value of $y(0)$. If the right-hand side is zero, then each choice of $y(0)$ gives a distinct 2π-periodic solution, whereas if the right-hand side is nonzero, no choice of $y(0)$ gives a periodic solution. $\blacksquare$

The last few pages have considered scalar problems. For a system of equations, the pattern is similar. Extending Chapter 14, consider the equation

$$\mathbf{y}' - \mathbf{A}(t)\mathbf{y} = \mathbf{g}(t), \tag{19.17}$$

where $\mathbf{y}(t)$ for each t is an n-vector, $\mathbf{g}(t)$ is a given 2π-periodic continuous n-vector function of t, and $\mathbf{A}(t)$ is a given 2π-periodic continuous $n \times n$ matrix function of t. The general solution of (19.17) is

$$\mathbf{y}(t) = \mathbf{Y}(t)\mathbf{c} + \mathbf{Y}(t) \int_0^t \mathbf{Y}^{-1}(s)\mathbf{g}(s)ds \qquad (19.18)$$

for n-vectors $\mathbf{c}$, where $\mathbf{Y}(t)$ is the **fundamental matrix**, the $n \times n$ matrix function whose columns are the linearly independent solutions of the homogeneous problem $\mathbf{y}' - \mathbf{A}(t)\mathbf{y} = \mathbf{0}$, $\mathbf{y}^{(1)}(t), \ldots, \mathbf{y}^{(n)}(t)$ with $\mathbf{Y}(0) = \mathbf{I}$, the $n \times n$ identity. The values at $t = 0$ and $t = 2\pi$ are

$$\mathbf{y}(0) = \mathbf{c}$$

and

$$\mathbf{y}(2\pi) = \mathbf{Y}(2\pi)\mathbf{c} + \mathbf{Y}(2\pi) \int_0^{2\pi} \mathbf{Y}^{-1}(s)\mathbf{g}(s)ds,$$

so the solution will be 2π-periodic if and only if

$$(\mathbf{I} - \mathbf{Y}(2\pi))\,\mathbf{c} = \mathbf{Y}(2\pi) \int_0^{2\pi} \mathbf{Y}^{-1}(s)\mathbf{g}(s)ds. \qquad (19.19)$$

The criticality condition will be the condition that $\mathbf{I} - \mathbf{Y}(2\pi)$ is singular, or equivalently,

$$\mathbf{Y}(2\pi) \text{ has an eigenvalue equal to } 1. \qquad (19.20)$$

We say that (19.17) is **critical** if this condition holds and **noncritical** otherwise, i.e., all eigenvalues of $\mathbf{Y}(2\pi)$ are different from 1. Theorem 19.1 generalizes as follows.

Theorem 19.2. **First-order linear periodic systems of ODEs (FLashi).** *Consider the n-dimensional system*

$$\mathbf{y}' - \mathbf{A}(t)\mathbf{y} = \mathbf{g}(t), \qquad (19.21)$$

where $\mathbf{A}(t)$ and $\mathbf{g}(t)$ are continuous and 2π-periodic. If the equation is noncritical as defined by (19.20), then there exists a unique 2π-periodic solution $\mathbf{y}$. If it is critical, then there exist infinitely many 2π-periodic solutions if $\int_0^{2\pi} \mathbf{Y}^{-1}(s)\mathbf{g}(s)ds$ is in the range of the matrix $\mathbf{I} - (\mathbf{Y}(2\pi))^{-1}$, and no 2π-periodic solutions if it is not in this range.

Proof. If (19.21) is noncritical, we may multiply (19.19) on the left by $(\mathbf{I} - \mathbf{Y}(2\pi))^{-1}$ to get

$$\mathbf{c} = (\mathbf{I} - \mathbf{Y}(2\pi))^{-1}\mathbf{Y}(2\pi) \int_0^{2\pi} \mathbf{Y}^{-1}(s)\mathbf{g}(s)ds,$$

that is,

$$\mathbf{c} = ((\mathbf{Y}(2\pi))^{-1} - \mathbf{I})^{-1} \int_0^{2\pi} \mathbf{Y}^{-1}(s)\mathbf{g}(s)ds,$$

and this vector corresponds to a 2π-periodic solution (19.18) as claimed. Uniqueness follows since a given $\mathbf{c}$ corresponds to one and only one solution $\mathbf{y}(t) = \mathbf{Y}(t)\mathbf{c}$. If the equation is critical, then (19.19) is a singular system of equations, having infinitely many solutions if the right-hand side is in the range of $\mathbf{I} - \mathbf{Y}(2\pi)$ and no solutions if it is not in that range. For the right-hand side of (19.19) to be in the range of $\mathbf{I} - \mathbf{Y}(2\pi)$ is the same as for $\int_0^{2\pi} \mathbf{Y}^{-1}(s)\mathbf{g}(s)\,ds$ to be in the range of $(\mathbf{Y}(2\pi))^{-1} - \mathbf{I}$. ∎

Having written down these results for a first-order system of ODEs, let us immediately specialize them to the case that has had the most attention. **Hill's equation** is the scalar, homogeneous, second-order ODE

$$y'' + f(t)y = 0, \qquad (19.22)$$

where f is real and 2π-periodic.[67] Although one could introduce a nonzero right-hand side, the equation is conventionally considered in this homogeneous form. Note that there is no first-order term, so there is no damping. **Mathieu's equation** is the special case

$$y'' + (a + b\cos(t))y = 0, \qquad (19.23)$$

which is the simplest instance of Hill's equation in which the periodic coefficient is not simply a constant. It corresponds to taking the first nonconstant term in a Fourier series of f and is thus a natural first step in the study of (19.22). Again the equation is usually considered in this homogeneous form.

As always, (19.22) is equivalent to a first-order system of two variables via the identification $\mathbf{y} = (y_1, y_2)^T = (y, y')^T$, which transforms it to the equations

$$y_1' = y_2, \quad y_2' + f(t)y_1 = 0. \qquad (19.24)$$

For this system of ODEs, $\mathbf{Y}(t)$ takes the form

$$\mathbf{Y}(t) = \begin{pmatrix} u(t) & v(t) \\ u'(t) & v'(t) \end{pmatrix},$$

where u and v are the unique solutions of the IVPs

$$u'' + f(t)u = 0, \quad u(0) = 1, \; u'(0) = 0$$

and

$$v'' + f(t)v = 0, \quad v(0) = 0, \; v'(0) = 1.$$

If we write the vector $\mathbf{c}$ as $\mathbf{c} = (a, b)^T$, the solution (19.18) (here with $\mathbf{g} = \mathbf{0}$) becomes $y(t) = au(t) + bv(t)$. The solution will be 2π-periodic if and only if $y(2\pi) = y(0)$ and $y'(2\pi) = y'(0)$, that is,

$$\mathbf{D}\begin{pmatrix} a \\ b \end{pmatrix} = \begin{pmatrix} a \\ b \end{pmatrix},$$

---

[67] In the literature the period is often taken to be π instead of 2π.

with $\mathbf{D}$ defined by

$$\mathbf{D} = \begin{pmatrix} u(2\pi) & v(2\pi) \\ u'(2\pi) & v'(2\pi) \end{pmatrix}. \tag{19.25}$$

The criticality condition will be

$$\mathbf{D} \text{ has an eigenvalue equal to 1.} \tag{19.26}$$

By the usual reasoning we see that if $\mathbf{D}$ has no eigenvalue equal to 1, then (19.22) has a unique periodic solution, namely $y = 0$, corresponding to $a = b = 0$, whereas if $\mathbf{D}$ has an eigenvalue equal to 1, then (19.22) has infinitely many periodic solutions, corresponding to a nonzero eigenvector $(a, b)^T$.

We summarize these results in a theorem.

Theorem 19.3. Hill's equation (fLaSHi). *Consider the Hill equation*

$$y'' + f(t)y = 0, \tag{19.27}$$

where $f(t)$ is real, continuous, and 2π-periodic. If the equation is noncritical as defined by (19.25)–(19.26), then there exists a unique 2π-periodic solution y, namely $y(t) = 0$. If it is critical, then there exist infinitely many 2π-periodic solutions.

Equations (19.22)–(19.27) are homogeneous, meaning that in the generic case the only solution is the zero function. One reason such equations are interesting nonetheless is that we are effectively speaking here of eigenvalue problems. In the Mathieu equation (19.23), for example, $-a$ plays the role of an eigenvalue of the operator $y \mapsto y'' + b\cos(t)y$ with periodic boundary conditions. For $b = 0$, the nonzero eigenvalues are $-1, -4, -9, \ldots$, and each is a double eigenvalue because of the translational symmetry. For nonzero b the symmetry is broken and the eigenvalues become simple. This has dynamical consequences, a hint of which appears in Exercise 19.10.

We close this chapter with a few more remarks concerning periodic solutions of autonomous nonlinear ODEs, which are T-periodic for any T. For a second-order scalar problem of this type, or a system of two first-order equations, a phase plane analysis may quickly give an understanding of what periodic solutions may exist. For example, the phase plane portrait of the damped linear oscillator (8.4) makes it clear that $y = 0$ will be the unique T-periodic solution of this equation for any T. For another example, the phase plane of the nonlinear pendulum equation (9.7), $y'' = -\sin(y)$, explains why this problem has nonzero T-periodic solutions for all T in the range $(2\pi, \infty)$ (Exercise 19.5). Similarly, the Lotka–Volterra system (10.3) has nonzero T-periodic solutions for a range of values of T (Exercise 19.8). The van der Pol oscillator (1.2), with its unique limit cycle, has nonzero T-periodic solutions only when T takes exactly the right value, as mentioned below (19.3) (or an integer multiple of this value).

Suppose we have an autonomous problem like the van der Pol oscillator with a limit cycle, corresponding to a nonzero T-periodic solution for a particular value of T. As mentioned earlier, this solution will not be unique, since t can be shifted by any amount Δt, but one can make it unique, or make its multiplicity finite rather than infinite, by imposing one or more **anchor conditions**. For example, here is the van der Pol equation with the anchor condition $y(0) = 1$ and an unknown period T:

$$0.3y'' - (1 - y^2)y' + y = 0, \quad y(0) = 1, \quad y \ T\text{-periodic}. \tag{19.28}$$

From a phase diagram such as Figure 9.11, it is clear that there will be two solutions to this problem (for minimal T), depending on where in the oscillation the anchor condition is reached, and the two solutions will have $y'(0) > 0$ and $y'(0) < 0$.

Although (19.28) has the form of a T-periodic equation for unknown T, it can be converted to a 2π-periodic problem if we transform the independent variable to $s = 2\pi t/T \in [0, 2\pi]$:

$$0.3\frac{4\pi^2}{T^2}\frac{d^2y}{ds^2} - \frac{2\pi}{T}(1 - y^2)\frac{dy}{ds} + y = 0, \quad y \ 2\pi\text{-periodic with } y(0) = 1. \tag{19.29}$$

This is a 2π-periodic problem with an unknown parameter, but a trick that is sometimes used is to think of T not as a number but as a solution to the trivial differential equation

$$\frac{dT}{ds} = 0, \quad T \text{ is } 2\pi\text{-periodic}. \tag{19.30}$$

The unknown parameter has become an unknown constant value of one component of a solution of a system of ODEs, namely (19.29)–(19.30)! This formulation is not really simpler in any genuine way, but it has the advantage that one can now attempt to solve the problem simply by applying a software tool for solving nonlinear ODEs.

On p. 240 question 3 was raised concerning nonperiodic solutions of periodic ODEs. This is a very important subject which is dealt with by *Floquet theory*. For a scalar problem, the main result asserts that every solution can be written as a complex exponential $\exp(iax)$ for some a, real or complex, times a periodic function, a pattern readily seen in Figure 19.4. For systems of equations a becomes a matrix A. We shall not discuss this further except in the following application.

APPLICATION: BAND GAPS AND FORBIDDEN FREQUENCIES

The material world is made of atomic and molecular structures that are often periodic, at least on a microscopic scale, and electromagnetic waves propagate through these structures in distinctive ways. The resulting field of X-ray crystallography has been the basic tool by which structure of all kinds of molecules are determined, as recognized by Nobel Prizes to von Laue (1914), Bragg and Bragg (1915), Watson and Crick (1962), Hodgkin (1964), and others.[68] With

---

[68]William and Lawrence Bragg were father and son, and when the prize was announced, 25-year-old Lawrence was serving in the trenches in World War I. Incredibly, he remained in the trenches for a further year after winning the award. Nobel Prize winners get better treatment nowadays.

the advent of quantum mechanics it was seen that electrons too are associated with waves, whose distinctive modes of propagation though periodic structures determine whether a material is an insulator, a conductor, or a semiconductor.

Here we shall give an indication of a fundamental phenomenon of wave propagation in crystals that was investigated by Felix Bloch, another Nobel Prize winner, in the beginning of the quantum era. Let us return to the Schrödinger equation as given in (6.11), now (just for convenience) with periodic boundary conditions,

$$-y''/2 + V(x)y = \lambda y, \quad x \in [0, d], \ y(0) = y(d), \ y'(0) = y'(d). \qquad (19.31)$$

The important new feature is that we will take the potential function $V(x)$ to be periodic, consisting of a sequence of spikes with spacing 1,

$$V(x) = 60(\cos(\pi x))^{16}. \qquad (19.32)$$

(This is a variant of the *Kronig–Penney* model of a 1D crystal.) To keep the example simple we set $d = 8$, so V extends over just 8 periods. Here is a plot of the potential, in black, and the first 33 eigenfunctions, each one raised up a distance equal to its eigenvalue as in Chapter 6.

```
d = 8; L = chebop(0,d); L.bc = 'periodic';
V = chebfun('60*cos(pi*x)^16',[0 d],'trig');
L.op = @(x,y) -diff(y,2)/2 + V*y;
neigs = 33; [W,D] = eigs(L,neigs);
W = simplify(W,1e-4); e = sort(diag(D));
for k = 1:neigs, W(k) = e(k)+3*W(k); end, plot(W), hold on
plot(V)
```

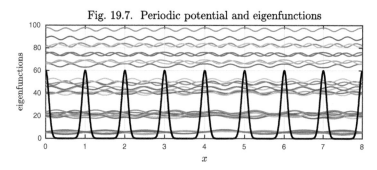
Fig. 19.7. Periodic potential and eigenfunctions

The striking thing about this plot is that the lower eigenfunctions are grouped into bands. At the bottom, hard to distinguish, are eight eigenfunctions with eigenvalue $\lambda \approx 5$. Then there are eight eigenfunctions less sharply focused with $\lambda \approx 20$ and another eight broadly distributed with $\lambda \approx 45$. The final nine eigenfunctions shown correspond to values λ greater than the maximum value of the potential $V(x)$. Here is a plot.

```
plot(e,'.')
```

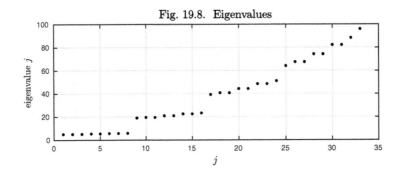

Fig. 19.8. Eigenvalues

The eigenvalues fall in groups of 8. If we had taken thousand or millions of periods, these would have fallen so close together as to produce effectively a continuum of eigenvalues, more or less like this:

```
for j = 0:3
  plot(j*d+[1 d],e(j*d+[1 d])), hold on
end
```

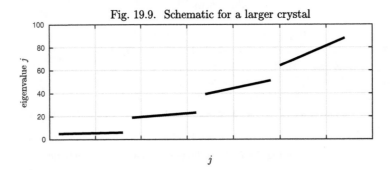

Fig. 19.9. Schematic for a larger crystal

The implications of this kind of structure for physics are enormous. A periodic medium may have *forbidden frequencies* at which no wave can propagate. To a condensed matter physicist, these represent an *energy gap* or *band gap* in the spectrum, and the gaps determine how electrons can propagate. Roughly speaking, a material is an insulator if it has an energy gap, a conductor if there is no gap, and a semiconductor if there is a gap but it is very small. One place to learn more is in the classic textbook *Introduction to Solid State Physics* by Kittel, first published in 1966, where it is pointed out that the difference in conductivity between an insulator and a conductor (a conductor of the usual sort, that is, not a superconductor) may be a factor as high as 10^{32}.

Where do band gaps come from? To understand this we can begin by recalling what the eigenfunctions of the Schrödinger problem would look like if the potential function $V(x)$ were constant rather than periodic. They would simply be sines and cosines, $\sin(kx)$ and $\cos(kx)$, for each value of the wave number k. In a structure with period L, however, interference effects occur when k is close to an integer multiple of π/L, corresponding to a wavelength close to one of the values $2L, 2L/2, 2L/3, \ldots$. The interfering waves may lead to reflection rather than propagation, and in X-ray crystallography this is known as as *Bragg reflection*.

To see the effect concretely, in our computed example, let us return to Figure 19.7 and zoom in on the highest eigenfunction of the first band, eigenfunction 8, and the lowest eigenfunction of the second band, eigenfunction 9.

```
plot(W(:,8:9)), hold on
for k = 8:9
  w = W{k}; plot(w); hold on
  plot([0 8],mean(w)*[1 1],'--');
end
plot(V)
```

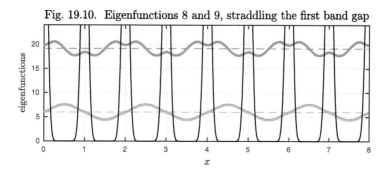

Fig. 19.10. Eigenfunctions 8 and 9, straddling the first band gap

Both eigenfunctions have the same wavelength, namely 2, and if the potential function were constant they would just be translates of one another corresponding to exactly the same eigenvalue. However, the periodic potential has broken the symmetry between the sines and the cosines. Eigenfunction 8 is concentrated between the spikes and is little affected by them, with an eigenvalue not so different from what it would be if the potential were zero. Eigenfunction 9, on the other hand, is concentrated within the spikes, making the potential weigh heavily so that the eigenvalue is much higher.

HISTORY. The study of periodic ODEs dates to the 1880s with the work of Hill, Floquet, and Mathieu. George William Hill (1838–1914), unusually for mathematicians of that era, was an American, and he was concerned with astronomical calculations related to the 3-body and 4-body problems. The general theory is due to Gaston Floquet (1847–1920) in "Sur les équations différentielles linéaires à coefficients périodiques" (you don't have to speak French to translate this one!), which appeared in *Annals of the École Normale Supérieure* 12 (1883), pp. 47–88. Physicists often give credit to Bloch.

OUR FAVORITE REFERENCE. An extensive treatment of periodic problems can be found in R. Grimshaw, *Nonlinear Ordinary Differential Equations*, CRC Press, 1991. This book includes a chapter on linear periodic problems, a chapter on periodic solutions of autonomous nonlinear problems, and further chapters on more advanced related topics.

> SUMMARY OF CHAPTER 19. *If the coefficients of an ODE are T-periodic for some T, then there may or may not exist T-periodic solutions. If the ODE is linear, there is an associated criticality condition. If the equation is noncritical, it has a unique solution, whereas if it is critical, it has no solutions or infinitely many solutions depending on the inhomogeneous forcing data.*

Exercise 19.1. Periodic solutions via shooting. Suppose we seek a 2π-periodic solution to $y' = -y^3 + \sin(t)$. *(a)* Produce a plot showing the solutions emanating from initial values $y(0) = -1.5, -1.3, \ldots, 1.3, 1.5$. Based on this plot, estimate by eye the value of $y(0)$ that gives a periodic solution. *(b)* Prove that if $y(0) \in [-1, 1]$, then $y(2\pi) \in [-1, 1]$. *(c)* Look up the Brouwer fixed point theorem and state it. Use it to prove that this ODE has a periodic solution. *(d)* Compute this solution with Chebfun using the `'periodic'` flag. You will need to provide an initial guess with roughly the form of the true solution. What is $y(0)$?

Exercise 19.2. An unstable variant. Now consider the equation of Exercise 19.1 with the other sign, $w' = w^3 + \sin(t)$. *(a)* Explain why shooting is much more difficult in this case with reference to a computer plot showing solutions emanating from several initial values $w(0)$. Instead of the whole interval $[0, 2\pi]$ you may use a shorter interval such as $[0, 0.5]$ or $[0, 1]$. *(b)* On the other hand, the plots suggest an easy way to reduce this problem to that of Exercise 19.1. Explain this reduction and use it to derive an analytic formula for w in terms of the solution y of Exercise 19.1.

Exercise 19.3. Criticality depends on the interval. *(a)* Explain how the theorems of this chapter allow for the possibility that a 2π-periodic linear ODE might have a unique 2π-periodic solution but not a unique 4π-periodic solution. *(b)* Find an example of this behavior.

Exercise 19.4. Two electrons and a nucleus. As in Exercise 13.5, consider the idealized problem of two electrons of mass 1 and charge -1 orbiting a nucleus of charge $+2$ fixed at the origin of the x-y plane. Let $z(t)$ be the position of one electron represented with the usual complex variable $z = x + iy$, and suppose the configuration is symmetric so that the other electron is at $\bar{z}(t)$. *(a)* Write down the ODE governing the evolution of $z(t)$ assuming an inverse-square electrostatic force law with constant 1. *(b)* Plot the trajectories $z(t)$, $t \in [0, 40]$ corresponding to the initial position $z(0) = ia$ and $z'(0) = 1$ for $a = 1$ and 2. *(c)* Find a value of a (to 3 digits of accuracy or more) that gives a periodic solution. (Use periodic boundary conditions in Chebfun or not, as you prefer.) What is the period?

Exercise 19.5. Nonlinear pendulum. Consider T-periodic solutions of the nonlinear pendulum equation $y'' = -\sin(y)$ satisfying $y(0) = 0$. Explain why there is one such solution for $T \in (0, 2\pi]$, three such solutions for $T \in (2\pi, 4\pi]$, five such solutions for $T \in (4\pi, 6\pi]$, and so on.

Exercise 19.6. Logistic equation with periodic harvesting. As a generalization of Exercise 3.15, consider the equation $y' = (1 - y/Y)y - \sin(t)^2$, where Y is a positive constant. *(a)* Solve the equation with Chebfun with $Y = 5$ for $t \in [0, 15]$ and make a plot of trajectories from initial values $y(0) = 0.5, 1, \ldots, 8$. *(b)* Use Chebfun to find the oscillatory periodic solution that the curves are approaching. Use the `mean` command to find the mean value of this solution. What would the mean be (figure this part out analytically) if $\sin(t)^2$ were replaced by its average value $1/2$? *(c)* Find and plot another periodic solution to this equation. Again compare the mean to what it would be if $\sin(t)^2$ were replaced by $1/2$.

Exercise 19.7. Periodic caffeine intake. Figure 2.8 showed the caffeine concentration in the bloodstream for a drinker enjoying three cups of coffee in a 24-hour period. Suppose the drinker has the same three cups at the same times every day. Compute the periodic solution, taking the time interval to be $[-2, 22]$. How does the maximum caffeine concentration for the periodic solution compare to that in Figure 2.8?

Exercise 19.8. Lotka–Volterra system. (a) In Chapter 10 the period T of the Lotka–Volterra system (10.6) was computed for initial populations $(u_0, v_0) = (1, 1)$ of rabbits and foxes, respectively. Now let u_0 vary from 0.2 to 4 and plot the dependence of T on u_0. (b) For $u_0 \to 0.2$, determine T analytically.

Exercise 19.9. Tokieda's teacup. Place a teacup on a table with the handle positioned in a direction we shall call north. Practice tapping gently on the rim with a spoon so that you hear a clean tone. Note that if you tap in the N, E, S, or W positions, you hear one tone, whereas if you tap in the NE, SE, SW, or NW positions, you hear a higher tone, often about one semitone higher (a factor of $2^{1/12}$). (There is a video of Tadashi Tokieda demonstrating this effect at `https://youtu.be/MfzNJE4CK_s`.) To explain this, we can imagine that the cup is a ring oscillating in certain eigenmodes. (a) First, to model a simple ring with no handle to break the symmetry, compute the first five eigenvalues and eigenfunctions of the differential operator y'' with periodic boundary conditions. Note that eigenvalues $2n$ and $2n + 1$ are equal for each $n \geq 1$ because of rotational symmetry. (b) Now add the handle — an extra mass at one point along the ring — by considering the differential operator $y''/m(x)$, where $m(x) = 1 + 0.6 \exp(-20(x - \pi)^2)$. Again compute the first five eigenvalues and eigenfunctions. Because of the added mass, all the frequencies will now be lower. Because of the broken symmetry, there will no longer be any degeneracies. It is modes 4 and 5 that we mainly hear when tapping the cup, corresponding to the ring alternately getting taller/thinner and shorter/fatter. Measure the ratio of frequency 5 to frequency 4 and discuss the result. Plot the eigenfunctions and explain why they are positioned where they are. (c) What connection do you see with the Application of this chapter? (The next exercise is also related.)

Exercise 19.10. Mathieu equation. Consider the Mathieu eigenvalue problem $y'' + b\cos(t)y = -\lambda y$ with periodic boundary conditions on $[0, 2\pi]$. For the rest of this exercise fix $b = 1$. (a) Determine the smallest six eigenvalues $\lambda_1 < \cdots < \lambda_6$ and plot the associated eigenfunctions. Comment on the relationships with the case $b = 0$. (b) Now solve $y'' + (a + b\cos(t))y = \exp(\sin(t))$ for $t \in [0, 100\pi]$ with initial data $y(0) = y'(0) = 0$ for four choices of a: the means of λ_2 and λ_3, λ_3 and λ_4, λ_4 and λ_5, and λ_5 and λ_6. Use `L.maxnorm = 0`. Plot the results and comment on the differences between these curves.

20. Boundary and interior layers

We have seen examples of boundary and interior layers already in Chapters 4, 7, and 18. This is a topic where the use of a tool like Chebfun is particularly compelling. With a computation or two, one quickly sees where layers lie and how their thickness depends on parameters.

To start the discussion, here is a reprise of the example of equation (5.3),

$$y'' = y, \quad x \in [0, 40], \; y(0) = y(40) = 1. \tag{20.1}$$

```
L = chebop(0,40); L.op = @(x,y) diff(y,2) - y; L.lbc = 1;
L.rbc = 1; y = L\0; plot(y)
```

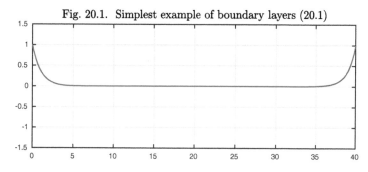

Fig. 20.1. Simplest example of boundary layers (20.1)

Just by looking at the image, one sees immediately at some level what is going on: the solution "wants to be zero" and more or less achieves this aim, apart from regions near the boundaries, where it goes through rapid transitions to satisfy the boundary conditions. What does it mean that it "wants to be zero"? This ODE is easy to analyze: the general solution is $A \exp(-x) + B \exp(x)$. This implies that all components grow exponentially either as x increases or as x decreases. Therefore, the only way y can deviate much from zero without deviating *hugely* from zero is for this to happen near a boundary.

Problems with boundary or interior layers usually contain a large or a small parameter. In (20.1), the parameter is the length of the interval, 40. To move to a more standardized formulation, let us transplant the equation to the interval $[-1, 1]$ with a small constant ε multiplying the highest-order derivative:

$$\varepsilon y'' = y, \quad x \in [-1, 1], \; y(-1) = y(1) = 1. \qquad (20.2)$$

The rescaling multiplies y'' by $(20)^2$, so the right choice if we wish to match (20.1) is $\varepsilon = (20)^{-2}$. As mentioned in Chapter 7, a problem like this with a small parameter multiplying the highest derivative is called a **singular perturbation problem**. Here is the solution to (20.2), looking the same as for (20.1).

```
L = chebop(-1,1); ep = (1/20)^2;
L.op = @(x,y) ep*diff(y,2) - y; L.lbc = 1; L.rbc = 1;
y = L\0; plot(y)
```

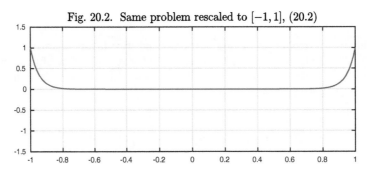

Fig. 20.2. Same problem rescaled to $[-1, 1]$, (20.2)

This example is so simple that we can quickly work out exact formulas. The general solution to the rescaled problem (20.2) is $A \exp(-\varepsilon^{-1/2}x) + B \exp(\varepsilon^{-1/2}x)$, or, as we may rewrite it with redefinitions of A and B,

$$y(x) = A \exp(-\varepsilon^{-1/2}(1+x)) + B \exp(-\varepsilon^{-1/2}(1-x)). \qquad (20.3)$$

The boundary conditions correspond to the equations

$$A + B \exp(-2\varepsilon^{-1/2}) = B + A \exp(-2\varepsilon^{-1/2}) = 1,$$

with solution

$$A = B = \frac{1 - \exp(-2\varepsilon^{-1/2})}{1 - \exp(-4\varepsilon^{-1/2})} = 1 + O(\exp(-2\varepsilon^{-1/2})).$$

Therefore (20.3) can be written

$$y(x) = \exp(-\varepsilon^{-1/2}(1+x)) + \exp(-\varepsilon^{-1/2}(1-x)) + O(\exp(-3\varepsilon^{-1/2})). \quad (20.4)$$

At $x = 0$, for example, we have

$$y(0) = 2\exp(-\varepsilon^{-1/2}) + O(\exp(-3\varepsilon^{-1/2})),$$

which for $\varepsilon = (20)^{-2}$ becomes

$$y(0) = 2\exp(-20) + O(\exp(-60)).$$

We confirm this result numerically:

```
y(0), 2*exp(-20)

ans = 4.1223e-09
ans = 4.1223e-09
```

Although this example is very simple, it illustrates a general idea. Consider the approximation (20.4), a sum of two terms. The first term consists of an approximation at the left boundary, and the second at the right. Together, they provide an accurate approximation to the solution throughout $[-1, 1]$. Such combinations are the business of **boundary layer analysis**, which constructs approximate solutions to all kinds of problems by combining different approximations in different regions. This is an advanced art, applicable for nonlinear as well as linear problems. In the remainder of this chapter, we will take some introductory steps into this subject for linear equations.

The starting point of boundary layer analysis is this principle:

1. *Outside a boundary or interior layer, terms involving ε are negligible.*

For example, for equation (20.2), outside any boundary or interior layers, we can expect

$$y = 0$$

to hold approximately. This equation applicable outside layers is called the **outer equation**.

If (20.2) is modified to include a further term, the outer equation will adjust accordingly. For example, suppose we consider

$$\varepsilon y'' = y + 2x, \quad x \in [-1, 1], \ y(-1) = y(1) = 1. \tag{20.5}$$

Now the outer equation is

$$y = -2x,$$

and the solution changes shape to look like $y = -2x$ away from $x = \pm 1$.

```
L.op = @(x,y) ep*diff(y,2) - y - 2*x;
y = L\0; plot(y)
```

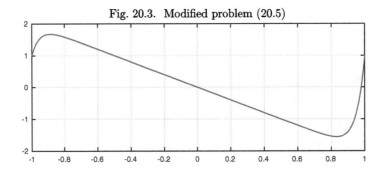

Fig. 20.3. Modified problem (20.5)

To proceed further with boundary layer analysis we add a pair of principles applicable inside a transition layer (i.e., a boundary or interior layer):

2. *Inside a layer, a low order derivative is negligible compared with a higher order one.*

3. *Inside a layer, a variable coefficient can be approximated by a constant, at least if it is locally nonzero.*

Let us see how these ideas work out in a slightly more complicated example, equation (7.8):

$$\varepsilon y'' + xy' + xy = 0, \quad x \in [-2, 2], \ y(-2) = -4, \ y(2) = 2. \tag{20.6}$$

With $\varepsilon = 0.001$, the solution shows an interior layer at $x = 0$, as we saw already in Figure 7.6.

```
L = chebop(-2,2); L.op = @(x,y) .001*diff(y,2) + x*diff(y) + x*y;
L.lbc = -4; L.rbc = 2; y = L\0; plot(y)
hold on
```

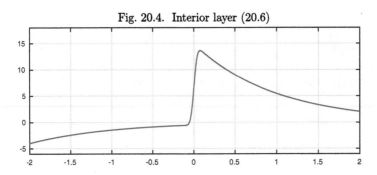

Fig. 20.4. Interior layer (20.6)

For a boundary layer analysis of this result, applying principle (1), we replace ε by zero in (20.6) and get the outer equation

$$xy' + xy = 0. \tag{20.7}$$

Thus we immediately have a prediction as to the behavior of a solution to (20.6). In every region, (i) y'' will be very large (of order ε^{-1}), or (ii) x will be close to zero, or (iii) $y(x)$ will approximate Ce^{-x} for some C.

From the picture it is clear that case (iii) applies for $|x| \gg 0$, with outer solutions $-4\exp(-(x+2))$ on the left and $2\exp(-(x-2))$ on the right. Here are thick dashed lines marking these approximations:

```
fleft = chebfun('-4*exp(-(x+2))',[-2,.2]); plot(fleft,'--');
fright = chebfun('2*exp(-(x-2))',[-.1,2]); plot(fright,'--')
```

Fig. 20.5. Outer solutions on left and right

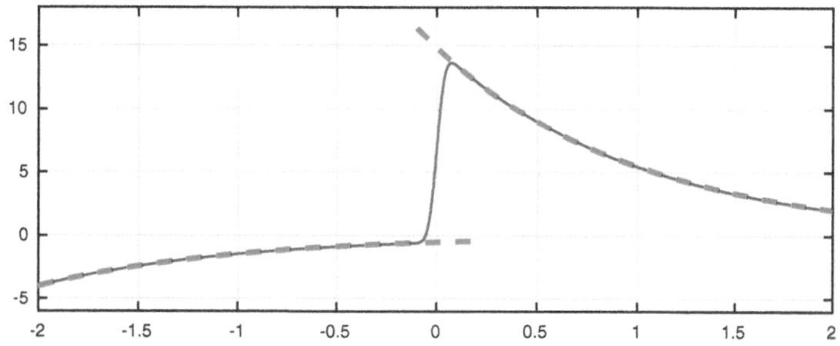

To explain the rest of the solution, we apply principle (2). In a transition layer, we can expect y'' to be much larger than y' and y' to be much larger than y. An approximation of (20.6) in a layer is accordingly

$$\varepsilon y'' + xy' = 0. \tag{20.8}$$

First, let us use this equation to see why there is no boundary layer at $x = 2$. Applying principle 3, we approximate (20.8) further by

$$\varepsilon y'' + 2y' = 0. \tag{20.9}$$

The general solution to this equation is $A + B\exp(-2\varepsilon^{-1}x)$, and the minus sign in the second of these terms implies that it decreases rather than increases with increasing x. Similarly, at $x = -2$,

$$\varepsilon y'' - 2y' = 0, \tag{20.10}$$

with general solution $A + B\exp(2\varepsilon^{-1}x)$, and again the sign is such that no boundary layer is possible.

Only $x = 0$ remains a candidate for a transition layer, matching the shape of the solution in the plot. Let us accordingly consider (20.8) for $x \approx 0$. Here we rescale variables to see what is happening. We define

$$s = x\varepsilon^{-1/2}, \quad u(s) = y(x),$$

which leads to

$$y''(x) = \varepsilon^{-1}u''(s), \quad y'(x) = \varepsilon^{-1/2}u'(s),$$

whereupon (20.8) becomes

$$u'' + su' = 0, \quad u(-\infty) = -4e^{-2}, \quad u(\infty) = 2e^2. \tag{20.11}$$

One solution of the ODE part of this equation is $u(s) = A$ for any constant A, and the other can be obtained by setting $w = u'$, yielding the equation $w' + sw = 0$. Separation of variables gives $w(s) = B\exp(-s^2/2)$ for a constant B, or after integration and redefinition of B, $u(s) = B\,\text{erf}(s/\sqrt{2})$, where erf is the error function. Thus we have

$$u(s) = A + B\,\text{erf}\left(\frac{s}{\sqrt{2}}\right), \quad A = e^2 - 2e^{-2}, \ B = e^2 + 2e^{-2}.$$

Here we superimpose on the plot a new dashed line corresponding to this approximation.

```
A = exp(2)-2*exp(-2); B = exp(2)+2*exp(-2);
ep = .001; s = @(x) x/sqrt(ep);
fmiddle = chebfun(@(x) A + B*erf(s(x)/sqrt(2)),[-.8 .8]);
plot(fmiddle,'--')
```

Fig. 20.6. Approximation to the transition layer

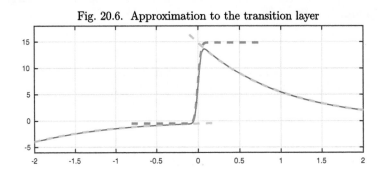

This completes our study of (20.6). Now let us look at the same equation, except with a sign change on the second derivative term:

$$-\varepsilon y'' + xy' + xy = 0, \quad x \in [-2, 2], \ y(-2) = -4, \ y(2) = 2. \tag{20.12}$$

The solution looks completely different. Instead of an interior layer, we have boundary layers at each end, but they are so thin as to be almost invisible in the plot.

```
L.op = @(x,y) -.001*diff(y,2) + x*diff(y) + x*y;
y = L\0; plot(y)
```

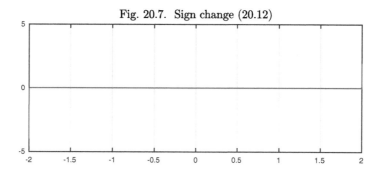

Fig. 20.7. Sign change (20.12)

An experienced eye immediately conjectures that the boundary layers are probably of width $O(\varepsilon)$ rather than $O(\varepsilon^{1/2})$, as a closeup at the left boundary confirms.

```
plot(y{-2,-1.98})
```

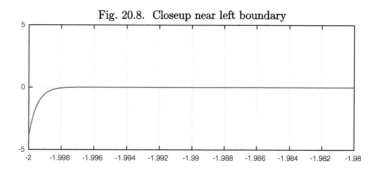

Fig. 20.8. Closeup near left boundary

The scaling of the widths of boundary and interior layers is of fundamental importance in applications. Let us illustrate this matter further with a constant-coefficient equation, an advection-diffusion problem:

$$\varepsilon y'' + y' + y = 0, \quad x \in [0,1], \; y(0) = y(1) = -1. \tag{20.13}$$

Here are the solutions for $\varepsilon = 0.1$, 0.02, and 0.004.

```
L = @(ep) chebop(@(x,y) ep*diff(y,2)+diff(y)+y,[0,1],'dirichlet');
y = @(ep) L(ep)\(-1);
for ep = [.1 .02 .004]
  plot(y(ep)), hold on
end
```

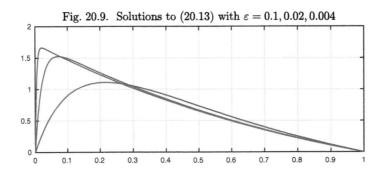

Fig. 20.9. Solutions to (20.13) with $\varepsilon = 0.1, 0.02, 0.004$

Let us informally define the width of a boundary layer to be the distance from 0 to the value of x at which the solution first reaches $y(x) = 0.5$ (compare Exercise 18.2). The widths for four values of ε show convincing $O(\varepsilon)$ dependence.

```
width = @(ep) min(roots(y(ep)-0.5));
for ep = 10.^(-1:-1:-4)
  disp([ep width(ep)]) ,
end
```

```
    epsilon    boundary layer width
    0.10000         0.0412988
    0.01000         0.0034865
    0.00100         0.0003443
    0.00010         0.0000344
```

Here is another variation on the theme of (20.6) and (20.12), with the left-hand boundary condition made positive to enhance the effect:

$$0.001y'' + xy' - y = 0, \quad x \in [-2, 2], \ y(-2) = 4, \ y(2) = 2. \qquad (20.14)$$

The transition here is called a *corner layer*.

```
L = chebop(-2,2); L.lbc = 4; L.rbc = 2;
L.op = @(x,y) .001*diff(y,2) + x*diff(y) - y;
y = L\0; plot(y)
```

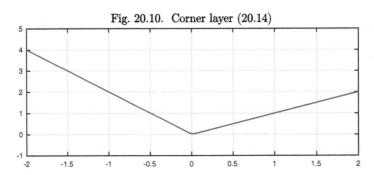

Fig. 20.10. Corner layer (20.14)

Almost anything is possible with interior and boundary layers, and we give this example as just another illustration.

APPLICATION: WHY IS NEW YORK HOTTER THAN SAN FRANCISCO?

New York is hot in July, around 9 degrees hotter than San Francisco (25°C vs. 16° are typical 24-hour averages). Yet in January, New York is 9 degrees colder than San Francisco (1° vs. 10°). What's going on? Why is the weather so much more moderate on the west coast of the USA than the east coast? We shall explain the effect in words first, then explore the mathematics and the connection with boundary layers.

The first key fact is that in the middle latitudes of Earth, prevailing winds blow from west to east. This means that San Francisco's weather comes from over the ocean, whereas New York's comes from over the land.

The second key fact is that ocean is liquid, and land is solid. When the summer sun beats down on the land, it heats up, but only down to a depth of a few meters, because the heat transfer is limited by conduction, which is slow. This lets the surface get very hot. Water, on the other hand, transfers heat by the much faster mechanism of convection — fluid motion. The stirring isn't enough to bring the summer heat down to the great depths, but it certainly brings it deeper than a few meters. The heat is spread over a much greater volume, so that the surface of the ocean never gets anywhere near as hot as the surface of the land, and San Franciscans can get by without air conditioning.

To model this effect mathematically, we shall be very rough, since the point is just to understand the main mechanism. Let us imagine that the earth is 100 meters deep, with a temperature T fixed at 13°C at the bottom (the average of the figures reported above for both New York and San Francisco). Our depth variable will be x, in units of meters, running from -100 to 0. At the earth's surface, let us imagine that heat flows in at the rate of 100 watts per square meter in July and flows out at the same rate in January, with a sinusoidal dependence on t in between,

$$\text{incoming heat in } W/m^2 = 100\exp(2\pi it),$$

where t is measured in years. (We use a complex exponential for the usual reason of convenience explained in Chapter 4; the physical temperature is the real part.) To get to an ODE, we start with a PDE, the heat equation,

$$\rho c \frac{\partial T}{\partial t} = \left(\frac{\text{year}}{\text{sec}}\right) k \frac{\partial^2 T}{\partial x^2}, \tag{20.15}$$

where ρ denotes density, c is heat capacity, and k is conductivity. (PDEs are considered systematically in Chapter 22.) We measure ρ in kilograms per cubic meter, c in joules per kilogram per degree, and k in watts per meter per degree. The quotient (year/sec), which is equal to about 3.1×10^7, is included to reconcile our choice of units of years for t and watts (joules per second) in the definition of k. With the not too unreasonable choices

$$\rho = 3000, \quad c = 2000,$$

(20.15) reduces to

$$\frac{\partial T}{\partial t} = 5.3k \frac{\partial^2 T}{\partial x^2}. \tag{20.16}$$

Meanwhile the boundary condition at $x = -100$ is

$$T(-100, t) = 13,$$

and our assumption concerning the heat influx gives the boundary condition at $x = 0$,

$$\frac{\partial T}{\partial x}(0, t) = 100k^{-1}\exp(2\pi it).$$

We now reduce the problem to an ODE by separating variables, assuming the solution takes the form

$$T(x, t) = 13 + e^{2\pi it}(y(x) - 13)$$

for some function y. The PDE (20.16) becomes

$$2\pi i(y - 13) = 5.3ky'', \tag{20.17}$$

and the boundary conditions become

$$y(-100) = 13, \quad y'(0) = 100k^{-1}. \tag{20.18}$$

We are ready to compute a solution. Taking $k = 3$ as a reasonable value of the conductivity, here is the temperature distribution we get from (20.17)–(20.18).

```
L = chebop(-100,0);
k = 3; L.op = @(y) 5.3*k*diff(y,2) -2i*pi*(y-13);
L.lbc = 13; L.rbc = @(y) diff(y)-100/k;
y = L\0; plot(real(y))
```

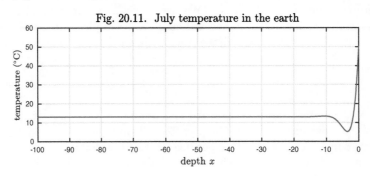

Fig. 20.11. July temperature in the earth

Note how hot it is in the boundary layer at the surface! New York's summers begin to make sense. Note also the dip below 13°C in the temperature at a depth of about 3 meters. This effect is genuine, reflecting a bit of wavelike behavior in the conduction of heat.[69]

As for mild San Francisco, we are not about to go into details of the physics of convection in the upper ocean. To get the general idea, however, let's imagine that ocean is like land, but with 100 times greater conductivity. The heat now reaches much deeper, giving a much more moderate surface temperature.

```
k = 300; L.op = @(y) 5.3*k*diff(y,2) -2i*pi*(y-13);
L.rbc = @(y) diff(y)-100/k;
y = L\0; plot(real(y))
```

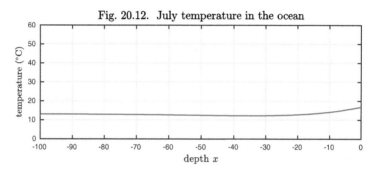

Fig. 20.12. July temperature in the ocean

The details of our models have hardly been precise, but the main message of Figs. 20.11 and 20.12 is genuine. New York is hotter than San Francisco in the summer because its weather is controlled by a thinner boundary layer.

HISTORY. Boundary-layer analysis began with an epochal contribution by the German fluid mechanician Ludwig Prandtl. An important feature of fluid mechanics is viscosity, that is, friction, but viscous effects are often insignificant away from solid boundaries. Prandtl realized that one could exploit this effect mathematically by dropping certain terms from the Navier–Stokes partial differential equations of fluid mechanics near a wall and dropping other terms away from the wall. These simplifications led to major advances in engineering, making it possible to solve problems that had previously been inaccessible. Prandtl presented these methods in 1904, and ever since then, boundary-layer analysis has been recognized as one of the fundamental tools of applied mathematics.

OUR FAVORITE REFERENCE. Generations of applied mathematics graduate students at MIT have learned asymptotics from the exceptionally rich book by Bender and Orszag, *Advanced Mathematical Methods for Scientists and Engineers,* McGraw-Hill, 1978.

---

[69]The thick stone walls of Italian villas exploit this effect to keep cool by day and warm by night. A thickness of $3m/20 = 15cm$ ought to be of the right order of magnitude, since days are about 20^2 times shorter than years and the effect in question involves a square root.

SUMMARY OF CHAPTER 20. *Singular perturbation problems, where a small parameter ε multiplies the highest derivative, typically have solutions featuring rapid transitions known as boundary or interior layers. The development of approximate solutions for such problems starts from three principles. (1) Outside a layer, terms involving ε are negligible. (2) Inside a layer, a low order derivative is negligible compared with a higher order one. (3) Inside a layer, a variable coefficient can be approximated by a constant, at least if it is locally nonzero.*

Exercise 20.1. *Corner layer.* (a) Plot the solution of $\varepsilon y'' + xy' - y = 0$, $y(-1) = 1$, $y(1) = 1$, $\varepsilon = 0.001$ (compare Figure 20.10). Which two terms are balanced to determine the outer solution, outside the transition region $x \approx 0$? Write down the outer equation and solve it to explain the behavior of y in this region. (b) Which two terms are balanced for $x \approx 0$? Write down the inner equation and show how it can capture the shape of $y(x)$ in this region. (c) Plot y again, but now on a semilogy scale and zooming in with `axis([-.1 .1 1e-4 1])`. On the same plot, superimpose curves corresponding to the other two terms of the ODE, $\varepsilon y''$ and xy'. For what range of values of x are the two terms that are balanced for the outer solution at least 10 times bigger than the omitted term? What is the answer to the same question for the inner solution?

Exercise 20.2. *Cusp.* (a) If we change the equation of the previous exercise by just one coefficient, $\varepsilon y'' + xy' - y/2 = 0$, the solution changes in an interesting way. Plot the solution for $\varepsilon = 10^{-3}$. Find the outer equation and explain the shape of the solution. (b) Use `tic` and `toc` to measure the computing time for this problem with $\varepsilon = 10^{-3}$, 10^{-4}, and 10^{-5}. The reason for the slow-down is that Chebfun is utilizing a Chebyshev grid of thousands of points, requiring the solution of a matrix problem of dimension in the thousands. Change the chebop domain to `L.domain = [-1 0 1]` and repeat the same timings; also plot the solution in the case $\varepsilon = 10^{-6}$. Now Chebfun has introduced a breakpoint at $x = 0$, so that separate Chebyshev grids are utilized on either side, and this makes the matrices smaller. (Although the user can introduce breakpoints like this at fixed locations, Chebfun does not offer adaptive gridding capabilities for ODE BVPs.)

Exercise 20.3. *Variable oscillations.* Solve $\varepsilon y'' + (x^2 - 1)y = 0$, $x \in [-2, 2]$ with $y(-2) = 1$ and $y(2) = 2$ for $\varepsilon = 10^{-5}$ and plot y. Explain the nature of this solution and derive an approximate formula for the wavelength of the oscillations in the oscillatory regions. (Compare Figure 7.5.) Note that, for this problem, principle 1 of our general method of boundary layer analysis does not apply because if the term involving ε is dropped, there is just one other term remaining, with nothing to balance it.

Exercise 20.4. *A double boundary layer.* (a) Solve $\varepsilon^3 y'' + x^3 y' + (x^3 - \varepsilon)y = 0$, $x \in [0, 1]$ with $y(0) = 2$ and $y(1) = 1$ for $\varepsilon = 0.005$ and plot the resulting solution. This problem has two boundary layers at $x = 0$, one of width $O(\varepsilon)$ and the other of width $O(\varepsilon^{1/2})$. Find a way to show this graphically based on solutions computed for various values of ε. (b) A good global approximation for y is $y(x) \approx 2\exp(-x/\varepsilon) + e[\exp(-\varepsilon/2x^2) + \exp(-x) - 1]$. What is the maximum error of this approximation for $\varepsilon = 10^{-1}$, 10^{-2}, and 10^{-3}?

Exercise 20.5. *Exponential ill-conditioning and pseudo-nonuniqueness.* (a) Solve $\varepsilon y'' - xy' + y = 1$, $x \in [-1, 1]$ with $y(-1) = 0$ and $y(1) = 0$ for $\varepsilon = 1/8, 1/16, 1/32, \ldots$

until you get a solution that looks completely unlike the others. Mathematically, this solution is not correct. However, it is a *pseudo-solution* in the sense that the residual $\varepsilon y'' - xy' + y - 1$ is very small. Confirm this by computing $\max_{x \in [-1,1]} |\varepsilon y'' - xy' + y - 1|$ for each of your values of ε. *(b)* Explain this effect by boundary layer analysis as follows. Find a formula for outer solutions to this problem and note that it matches the observed incorrect solution. Now find formulas for inner solutions corresponding to boundary layers at $x \approx \pm 1$ and note that these provide enough boundary conditions to match any choice of the outer solution. Thus, although the linear operator $\mathcal{L}$ that maps right-hand side functions to solutions of this BVP is mathematically nonsingular, hence has no null function, it has *pseudo-null functions* with exponentially small residual. This ODE BVP is exponentially ill-conditioned, and we may think of it as exponentially close to being underdetermined. (The reason this has happened is because of the sign change in the coefficient of y' in this equation at $x = 0$. This is related to the theories of *exponential dichotomy* and *pseudospectra*. See Chapters 10 and 11 of Trefethen and Embree, *Spectra and Pseudospectra*, Princeton, 2005.)

Exercise 20.6. Exponential ill-conditioning of the adjoint problem. Show that the adjoint of the operator $\mathcal{L}$ of Exercise 20.5 is $\mathcal{L}^*: v \mapsto \varepsilon v'' + xv' + 2v$ with boundary conditions $v(\pm 1) = 0$. Solve the problem $\mathcal{L}^* v = 1$ numerically for $\varepsilon = 1/8, 1/16, 1/32, \ldots$. What goes wrong now when when ε gets sufficiently small?

21. Into the complex plane

Most of the familiar mathematical functions are defined for complex arguments as well as real ones. For example, here are the Taylor series of two functions about the point $t_0 = 0$:

$$e^t = 1 + t + \frac{t^2}{2} + \frac{t^3}{3!} + \cdots, \quad \frac{1}{1+t^2} = 1 - t^2 + t^4 - t^6 + \cdots.$$

To define the value of a function when t is complex, we can use the same series, so long as t is close enough to t_0 for convergence.

We say that a function $y(t)$ is **analytic** at a point t_0 if it has a Taylor series at t_0 that converges to y in some neighborhood of t_0. If y is initially defined just for real values, then the neighborhood will be an interval (a, b) with $a < t_0 < b$. Once we've got a convergent power series, it can be used to define values in the complex plane too, and this is the process called **analytic continuation**. It is a basic fact of complex variables that every power series has a **radius of convergence** $r \in [0, \infty]$ with the property that the series converges for all real or complex numbers t with $|t - t_0| < r$ and diverges for all t with $|t - t_0| > r$. Thus a power series always converges inside a disk, the **disk of convergence**, which is the largest disk centered at t_0 inside which the function is analytic.

For $y(t) = e^t$, the disk of convergence has radius $r = \infty$, regardless of the choice of t_0, because the exponential function is analytic for all values of t. A function $y(t)$ that is analytic for all real and complex values of t is said to be **entire**. For $1/(1 + t^2)$ and $t_0 = 0$, we have $r = 1$, because the function has singularities at $t = \pm i$ (poles), where the value blows up to ∞. For $t_0 = 1$ with the same function, we would have $r = \sqrt{2}$.

It is a general idea of mathematics that one can learn things about a function by examining its singularities in the complex plane. For example, how would you explain to a student in a calculus class *why* the function $y(t) = 1/(1+t^2)$ has a Taylor series that converges just for $t \in (-1, 1)$? The answer is the presence of those singularities at $\pm i$, and if your student doesn't know about the complex plane, it is not clear how you could really give a satisfactory explanation.

Here is another example. The function $y(t) = \tanh(10t)$ makes a rapid transition from -1 to $+1$ near $t = 0$.

```
y = chebfun('tanh(10*t)'); plot(y)
```

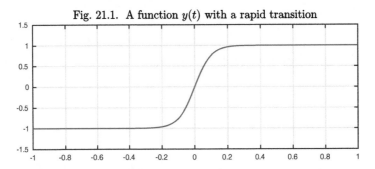

Fig. 21.1. A function $y(t)$ with a rapid transition

How does this transition come about? One way to understand it is to note that y has poles in the complex plane quite near to $t = 0$, at $\pm \pi i/20$, $\pm 3\pi i/20$, $\pm 5\pi i/20, \ldots$. As t increases along the real axis, y changes quickly as it passes these special points. A contour plot of $|y(t)|$ for t ranging over a rectangular region in the complex plane reveals the four poles of y closest to the origin.

```
x = linspace(-1.2,1.2,201); y = linspace(-0.5,0.5,101);
[xx,yy] = meshgrid(x,y); zz = xx + 1i*yy;
ff = tanh(10*zz); levels = [1 2 4];
contour(x,y,abs(ff),levels)
hold on, plot(pi*.05i*(-3:2:3),'.')
```

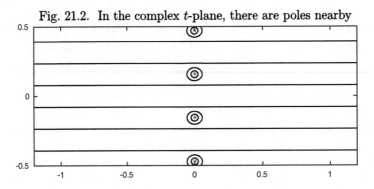

Fig. 21.2. In the complex t-plane, there are poles nearby

If the poles were ten times closer, y would make its transition ten times faster.

For another example, what can we make of the function

$$y(t) = -\log(1.1 + \cos(\pi t))? \qquad (21.1)$$

A plot reveals spikes near odd integer values of t.

```
f = chebfun('-log(1.1+cos(pi*t))',[-4 4]); plot(f)
```

Fig. 21.3. Another function $y(t)$ with regions of rapid transition

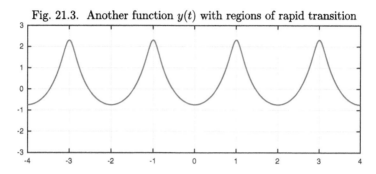

As before, these points of rapid change are associated with nearby singularities in the complex plane, which lie in pairs just above and below each odd integer.

```
x = linspace(-4,4,201); y = linspace(-1.5,1.5,101);
[xx,yy] = meshgrid(x,y); zz = xx + 1i*yy;
ff = -log(1.1+cos(pi*zz)); levels = 2.5:.5:7;
contour(x,y,abs(ff),levels)
hold on, plot(acos(1.1)/pi+(-3:2:3),'.')
plot(-acos(1.1)/pi+(-3:2:3),'.')
```

Fig. 21.4. Now the nearby complex singularities are branch points

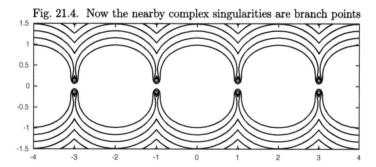

This contour plot requires more interpretation than the previous one. Before, each singularity t_s was a **pole**, with $y \sim C/(t - t_s)$ for some constant C. In this second contour plot, however, the two rows of singularities are not poles but **branch points**. A function with a branch point is not analytic and single-valued in any punctured neighborhood of the point, because if you continue it analytically all the way around, you reach a different value from the one you started with. To make a function y with branch points single-valued and analytic, it is customary to restrict the domain by introducing **branch cuts** connecting the branch points, along which y is not defined. Given a function with certain branch points, there is no unique set of branch cuts that the mathematics forces you to choose. Computer programming languages, however, generally take $\log(t)$ and $t^{1/2}$ to have branch lines extending along the negative real axis from 0 to $-\infty$, and this determines where the branch cuts lie for more complicated functions like (21.1). In the figure, the branch lines have ended up as vertical rays extending upward to ∞ from the branch points in the upper half-plane and downward to ∞ from the branch points in the lower half-plane.

Everything we have said in the last three pages about functions in general applies to the particular case of solutions of ODEs. Many of them make sense in the complex plane, and their behavior in the plane can both be interesting in its own right and also shed light on behavior, such as rapid transitions, on the real axis.

As the simplest possible example, consider the IVP

$$y' = y, \quad y(0) = 1. \tag{21.2}$$

The unique solution is e^t, an entire function in the complex t-plane, and thus for example at $t = i$ we have

$$y(i) = \exp(i) = \cos(1) + i\sin(1) \approx 0.5403 + 0.8415i.$$

We can interpret (21.2) in the complex plane in two ways. One is to regard it as a differential equation that applies not just for real values of t but also complex ones. The value $y(i)$, for example, might be determined by integrating the ODE along the imaginary line segment extending from $t = 0$ to $t = i$. Chebfun doesn't work with complex intervals directly, but we can achieve the necessary effect by parametrizing the interval $[0, i]$ as is for $s \in [0, 1]$. The equation becomes

$$\frac{dy}{ds} = \frac{dt}{ds}\frac{dy}{dt} = iy, \tag{21.3}$$

or in Chebfun,

```
L = chebop(0,1); L.lbc = 1; L.op = @(s,y) diff(y) - 1i*y;
y = L\0; y(1)
```

```
ans = 0.5403 + 0.8415i
```

The other interpretation of (21.2) for complex t is that we may start from the solution $y(t)$ for real t, and then analytically continue it into the complex plane. This idea defines the same function as before, provided one uses the same branch cuts for the analytic continuation as for the ODE solution.

For example, here we solve (21.2) in the usual manner on the real interval $[0, 1]$, and then evaluate the result at the complex point $t = i$.

```
L = chebop(0,1); L.op = @(t,y) diff(y) - y; L.lbc = 1;
y = L\0; y(1i)
```

```
ans = 0.5403 + 0.8415i
```

Since Chebfun's solutions of ODEs are numerical rather than symbolic, it is entirely appropriate to wonder why this worked! The reason is that Chebfun's solution function y is actually a polynomial representation of $\exp(t)$ on $[0, 1]$, which also approximates the function in a larger region of the complex plane. So Chebfun has performed a numerical version of analytic continuation for us. As a rule, this trick works reasonably well for complex values of t close to the interval of definition, but not for values further out, and certainly not for values of t that lie further from the interval than some singularities of y.

Let us illustrate this by considering an example with a singularity. The nonlinear IVP

$$y' = -2ty^2, \quad t \in [-4, 4], \quad y(-4) = \frac{1}{17} \tag{21.4}$$

has the unique solution we examined at the start of the chapter,

$$y(t) = \frac{1}{1 + t^2},$$

with poles at $t = \pm i$. The solution looks as it should,

```
N = chebop(-4,4); N.lbc = 1/17; N.op = @(t,y) diff(y) + 2*t*y^2;
y = N\0; plot(y)
```

Fig. 21.5. Solution of an ODE passing near a complex singularity

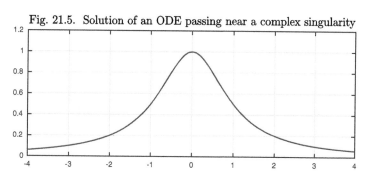

At $t = i/2$, the correct value of y is $4/3$, as Chebfun confirms:

```
y(1i/2)
```

```
ans = 1.3333 + 0.0000i
```

At $t = 3i/2$, however, on the far side of the pole at i, the correct value of y is $-4/5$, whereas Chebfun gets a huge incorrect value.

```
y(3i/2)
```

```
ans = 1.4284e+06 + 2.7297e+05i
```

One can never expect a simple evaluation like this to work, if the point of evaluation is further from the interval of computation than some of the singularities of the function.[70]

There is an alternative approach in Chebfun, however, that can often be used for numerical analytic continuation even beyond singularities, especially when the singularities are poles. The Chebfun command `aaa` approximates a function not by the usual Chebfun method involving polynomials, but by a rational function $r(t) = p(t)/q(t)$ of some adaptively determined type (n, n), which means that the numerator and denominator degrees are $\leq n$.[71] For example, the command

```
[r,pol] = aaa(y,'tol',1e-8);
```

constructs a rational approximation to y and evaluates its poles, which match those of y:

```
pol
```

```
pol =
   0.0000 + 1.0000i
   0.0000 - 1.0000i
```

This time, the value at $t = 3i/2$ comes out correct.

```
r(3i/2)
```

```
ans = -0.8000 + 0.0000i
```

Although rational approximations will usually not give precise information, especially since singularities of solutions to ODEs in the complex plane are usually more complicated than just poles, they are often good at giving a rough idea of the nature of such singularities near the domain of approximation. For example, in Chapter 13 we plotted one component of a solution to the Lorenz equations (13.1),

```
N = chebop(0,5); N.lbc = [-15; -15; 20];
N.op = @(t,u,v,w) [diff(u)-10*(v-u); ...
    diff(v)-u*(28-w)+v; diff(w)-u*v+(8/3)*w];
[u,v,w] = N\0; plot(u);
```

---

[70]This statement can be made mathematically precise with the use of *Bernstein ellipses*, ellipses in the complex t-plane whose foci are at the two endpoints of the interval of definition of the chebfun. A chebfun will normally give a degree of good approximation in the largest region of analyticity bounded by such an ellipse, as discussed in Chapter 8 of Trefethen, *Approximation Theory and Approximation Practice*, SIAM, 2013.

[71]See Nakatsukasa, Sète, and Trefethen, "The AAA algorithm for rational approximation," submitted manuscript, 2016.

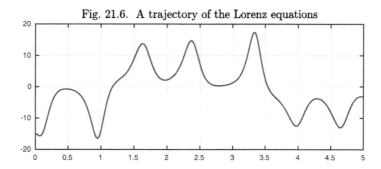

Fig. 21.6. A trajectory of the Lorenz equations

You might guess that these spikes are associated with nearby singularities in the complex plane, and here are the poles of the **aaa** rational approximation. Note that the sharpest spikes correspond to singularities closest to the real axis.

```
[r,pol] = aaa(u,'tol',1e-8); plot(pol,'.')
```

Fig. 21.7. Nearby complex singularities found by rational approximation

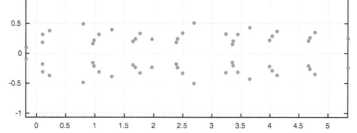

One should not imagine that the function plotted in Figure 21.6 truly has poles at all the points shown in Figure 21.7. Rather, it is likely that it has a singularity — probably not just a pole — near the point in each group that lies closest to the real axis. The rest of the dots are probably lining up along branch cuts.

Solutions to linear ODEs have no singularities unless the leading-order coefficient passes through 0 or the coefficients are singular, but solutions to nonlinear ODEs may have all kinds of singularities, which may be *movable* in the sense that they appear at locations dependent on initial data. A natural question for a mathematician is, are there nonlinear ODEs whose movable singularities are only poles, never branch points? It turns out that a full answer to this question is known in the case of second-order ODEs of the form $y'' = F(t, y, y')$, where F is a rational function. Paul Painlevé showed that all such equations possessing this property that the movable singularities are poles can be organized into 50 classes, 44 of which can be reduced to other known functions.[72] The remaining

---

[72]Painlevé was not your average mathematician. In 1917 and again in 1925, he served as Prime Minister of France, and he is buried in the Panthéon in Paris.

six classes are called the **Painlevé equations**, and their solutions are known as **Painlevé transcendents**. The **Painlevé I** equation is

$$y'' = 6y^2 + t, \tag{21.5}$$

and the **Painlevé II** equation is

$$y'' = 2y^3 + ty + \alpha, \tag{21.6}$$

where α is a parameter.

Let us take a look at (21.5), the Painlevé I equation. In Chapter 3, we saw that the first-order ODE $y' = y^2$ and various generalizations have solutions which blow up to ∞. The blowup points are simple poles. For (21.5), a second-order equation of a similar form, one gets double poles instead of simple poles. For example, here is a solution to (21.5) on the interval $[-15, 2.27]$ with "middle conditions" $y(0) = y'(0) = 0$. For $t < 0$, the solution is oscillatory and nonsingular, but for $t > 0$ the curve is approaching a double pole at $t \approx 2.6$.

```
N = chebop(0,2.27); N.op = @(t,y) diff(y,2)-6*y^2-t;
N.lbc = [0;0]; y = N\0; plot(y), hold on
N = chebop(-15,0); N.op = @(t,y) diff(y,2)-6*y^2-t;
N.rbc = [0;0]; y = N\0; plot(y)
```

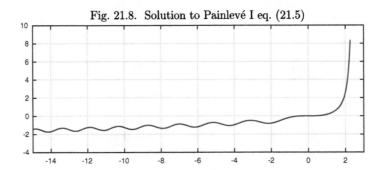

Fig. 21.8. Solution to Painlevé I eq. (21.5)

The reader of this chapter will suspect that if $y(t)$ oscillates like this on the negative t-axis, there must be singularities nearby in the left half of the complex t-plane. This is true, and in fact, there is an infinite array of double poles extending to ∞ in all directions.

The Painlevé I equation does have smooth solutions for certain boundary data, which we can isolate most easily by solving a BVP. Here is an example:

$$y'' = 6y^2 + t, \quad t \in [-24, 0], \ y(-24) = 2, \ y(0) = 0. \tag{21.7}$$

```
N = chebop(-24,0); N.op = @(t,y) diff(y,2) - 6*y^2 -t;
N.lbc = 2; N.rbc = 0; y = N\0; plot(y)
```

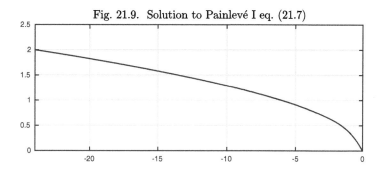

Fig. 21.9. Solution to Painlevé I eq. (21.7)

Because of the exponential sensitivities introduced by the nonlinear term, one is hardly likely to find such smooth solutions by solving an IVP. To illustrate this sensitivity, here we superimpose on the figure the solution to an IVP (or if you prefer a *final-value problem*) corresponding to the same solution just plotted, except that the boundary conditions are both specified at the right-hand boundary, with a small perturbation introduced in the derivative:

$$y'' = 6y^2 + t, \quad t \in [-24, 0], \ y(0) = 0, \ y'(0) = 0.999999\alpha. \qquad (21.8)$$

Here $\alpha \approx -0.451427$ is the value of $y'(0)$ corresponding to the solution of (21.7).

```
yp = diff(y); alpha = yp(0); N.lbc = [];
N.rbc = [0; 0.999999*alpha];
y = N\0; hold on, plot(y)
```

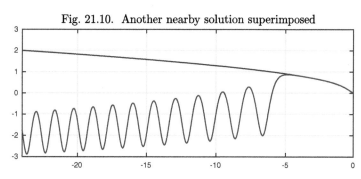

Fig. 21.10. Another nearby solution superimposed

The new solution matches the smooth one approximately for $t \in [-5, 0]$, but then diverges to an oscillatory form.

It is impossible to understand Painlevé equations very fully by looking just on the real axis, however, as is shown beautifully by the complex plane explorations of the paper by Fornberg and Weideman cited as our favorite reference below.

APPLICATION: JACOBI SINE FUNCTION

Let $m \in [0, 1)$ be a parameter and consider the nonlinear second-order initial-value problem

$$y'' = -(1 + m)y + 2my^3, \quad y(0) = 0, \ y'(0) = 1. \tag{21.9}$$

If m is zero, the equation is just $y'' = -y$ and the solution is $y(t) = \sin(t)$. As m increases, the nonlinearity becomes stronger. Here is what we find for $m = 0.998$ over the interval $t \in [0, 100]$.

```
N = chebop(0,100); N.lbc = [0;1];
m = 0.998; N.op = @(y) diff(y,2) + (1+m)*y - 2*m*y^3;
y = N\0; plot(y)
```

Fig. 21.11. Solution of (21.9): Jacobi sine function $\mathrm{sn}(t, 0.998)$

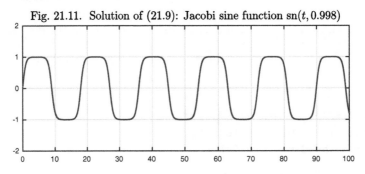

Like $\sin(t)$, this function oscillates between -1 and 1, but its shape is squarer. The period T is about three times longer than for $\sin(t)$, reflecting how much time this function spends lingering near ± 1:

```
[~,maxima] = max(y,'local'); T = maxima(3) - maxima(2)
```

```
T = 17.9814
```

Now $\sin(t)$ is completely smooth, analytic throughout the complex t-plane. The function $y(t)$, on the other hand, makes rapid transitions between -1 and 1, which will become more abrupt as m increases toward 1. We may accordingly guess that if this function is analytically continued into the complex plane, there will be singularities above and below the t-axis near $t = 0, T/2, T, \ldots$. A call to aaa confirms this prediction. In the next figure, the dots show the poles of the aaa rational approximant, and the vertical lines mark $\mathrm{Re}(t) = 0, T, \ldots, 6T$.

```
[r,pol] = aaa(y,'tol',1e-8);
plot([-10 110],[0 0]), hold on
for k = 0:6
  plot(k*T*[1 1],[-30 30])
end
plot(pol,'.')
```

Fig. 21.12. Poles near the real axis found by **aaa**

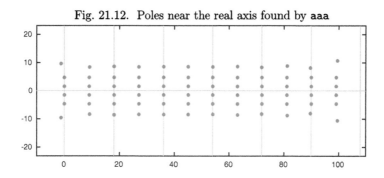

This is a striking configuration. In fact, the function y defined by (21.9) is *doubly periodic* in the complex t-plane, periodic not only in the real but also the imaginary direction. (The poles of the mathematically exact function keep going forever in a perfectly regular array, but **aaa** has just estimated some of the poles near $[0, 100]$.) It is the function known as the *Jacobi sine function* with parameter $m = 0.998$, written $\mathrm{sn}(t, 0.998)$. Although it is analytic for real values of t, it has poles for complex t, and they lie in an infinite doubly periodic array. Here is the period in the imaginary direction (close to π, but different):

```
imagpol = sort(abs(imag(pol)));
T2 = 2*min(abs(imag(pol)))


T2 = 3.1432
```

If we include horizontal lines in the plot too, we get an image marking fundamental domains of periodicity.

```
for k = -10:10
  plot([-10 110],k*T2*[1 1])
end
plot(pol,'.')
```

Fig. 21.13. Lines mark both real and imaginary periods

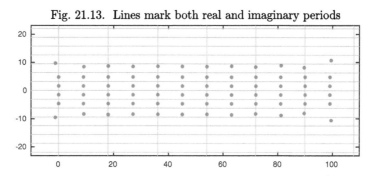

Here, arbitrarily, we verify the double periodicity by comparing $r(t)$ for $t = 5 - i$ and the same value plus T, iT_2, and $T + iT_2$. (See Exercise 21.8.)

```
t = 8-1i; r(t+[0; T; 1i*T2; T+1i*T2])
ans =
   1.0852 + 0.2778i
   1.0852 + 0.2778i
   1.0852 + 0.2778i
   1.0852 + 0.2778i
```

Doubly periodic functions, also known as *elliptic functions*, are among the core topics of complex analysis.

HISTORY. The idea of giving physical meaning to imaginary space or time has proved fruitful for quite a few problems of engineering and physics, from the design of transonic airplane wings to the explanation of the Big Bang. Stephen Hawking presented the latter idea in his 1988 blockbuster book *A Brief History of Time*. The elegant, singularity-free frame of reference in which to understand the universe, Hawking suggests, is one in which t runs in the imaginary direction. In that direction, he proposes, the universe's boundary conditions are periodic, so there are no boundaries and no singularities. It's only if you turn a right angle and do analytic continuation into the real-t direction — analytically continuing back to around $t = -14{,}000{,}000{,}000$ years, to be precise — that you encounter the mother of all singularities.

OUR FAVORITE REFERENCE. There is an excellent classic book by Einar Hille on *Ordinary Differential Equations in the Complex Domain*, but our favorite reference for this topic, with spectacular figures illustrating the functions in question, is Fornberg and Weideman, "A numerical methodology for the Painlevé equations," *Journal of Computational Physics*, 2011.

SUMMARY OF CHAPTER 21. *Many ODEs make sense for complex as well as real arguments. Solutions $y(t)$ for complex t can be defined by applying the ODE in the complex plane, or by analytic continuation from solutions for real t. If $y(t)$ changes rapidly as t varies through certain real values, there are usually one or more singularities of y nearby in the complex t-plane. Typically such singularities will be branch points, requiring associated branch cuts, but in the case of Painlevé equations the only movable singularities (i.e., lying at data-dependent locations) are poles.*

Exercise 21.1. *Painlevé I change of variables.* Suppose $y(t)$ is a solution to (21.5). Show that another solution is $\omega^3 y(\omega t)$, where $\omega = \exp(2\pi i/5)$.

Exercise 21.2. *Multiple solutions to Painlevé BVP.* Compute and plot another solution to (21.7) by starting from the initial guess $y(t) = -\exp(-10(t+1)^2)$. What is its minimum value?

Exercise 21.3. *Some singularities are just pseudo-singularities.* (a) Repeat the calculation of Figure 20.4 for the ODE of (20.6), $\varepsilon y'' + xy' + xy = 0$ with $\varepsilon = 0.001$. Then plot the poles of the AAA approximants of the solution y, as in Figures 21.7 and 21.12, for tol $= 10^{-4}$, 10^{-6}, and 10^{-8}. You will see that the poles of these approximations vary with the tolerance. They are not approaching any actual singularities of the true solution y, because y, despite its steep interior layer near $x = 0$, cannot have any singularities since the equation is linear with analytic coefficients and a nonzero leading-order coefficient. *(b)* In such a case y, though analytic as a function of x, must increase rapidly in magnitude as x leaves the real axis. (One can prove this via *Cauchy's estimate*.) To confirm this, examine values of x along the imaginary axis. First, make the substitution $x = is$ as in (21.3) and write down the form that the ODE takes when transformed to the s variable. *(c)* Now solve (20.6) numerically for $x \in [0, 0.2i]$, that is, $s \in [0, 0.2]$, taking as initial data the appropriately transformed values $y(0)$ and $y'(0)$ from the solution of *(a)*. Make a semilogy plot of $|y(x)|$ against $|x|$. How big is $|y(0.2i)|$?

Exercise 21.4. *Bypassing blowup.* As we have discussed at several points in the book, positive solutions to $y' = y^2$ blow up to ∞ in finite time. The situation changes, however, if y is even very slightly complex. *(a)* Draw a quiver plot of $y' = y^2$ in the complex y-plane and describe the shape of the complex trajectories in this plot. *(b)* Solve $y' = y^2 + f$ with $y(0) = 1$ for $t \in [0, 1]$, where f is the complex random function generated by `rng(1)`, `f = 0.01*randnfun([0 1],'big','complex')`. Plot the solution with `axis equal`. (For analysis of such problems see Herzog and Mattingly, "Noise-induced stabilization of planar flows I", *Electronic Journal of Probability, 2015*.)

Exercise 21.5. *Jacobi sine function.* A chebfun `y2` representing the Jacobi sine function as plotted in Figure 21.11 could be constructed directly from the MATLAB function `ellipj(t,0.998)`. Do this and plot `abs(y-y2)` to give an indication of accuracy of this Chebfun ODE solution.

22. Time-dependent PDEs

Many ODE BVPs that arise in applications are related to time-dependent PDEs. In the simplest case the solution $y(x)$ of the BVP is a **time-independent** or **steady solution** of the PDE, that is, a solution $y(x, t)$ of the PDE that is independent of t. Often a solution of a PDE may converge to time-independent form as $t \to \infty$.

Laplace and heat equations. The archetypal pair of equations related in this way are the Laplace equation, an ODE BVP when restricted to one space dimension, and the heat equation, a PDE IBVP (*initial boundary-value problem*). Specifically, the **1D Laplace equation** is the equation $y'' = 0$, that is, $d^2y/dx^2 = 0$. In this chapter, since time derivatives will also come into play, we will write this in the notation $y_{xx} = 0$, where y_{xx} is an abbreviation for $\partial^2 y/\partial x^2$. For example, here is the 1D Laplace equation with homogeneous Dirichlet boundary conditions on $[-\pi, \pi]$:

$$y_{xx} = 0, \quad x \in [-\pi, \pi], \ y(\pm\pi) = 0. \tag{22.1}$$

We hardly need a computer to see that the solution is $y(x) = 0$.

Now let us consider how (22.1) may arise in describing steady solutions of the **1D heat equation**, $u_t = u_{xx}$. Here is an **initial boundary-value problem (IBVP)** for this equation with a particular choice of initial data, a pulse centered at $x = 1$:

$$u_t = u_{xx}, \quad x \in [-\pi, \pi], \ u(\pm\pi, t) = 0, \ u(x, 0) = \exp(-50(x - 1)^4). \tag{22.2}$$

Physically, the zero solution just mentioned represents the effect that eventually, all the heat described by (22.2) will flow out the ends of the interval, where the

temperature is held at zero. A plot of the initial condition together with the
solution at times $t = 0.01$, 0.1, and 1 shows the beginning of this process.[73]
In this and other figures of this chapter displaying PDE solutions at various
times t, we plot the curves in orange, with the initial curve in brown.

```
u0 = chebfun('exp(-50*(x-1)^4)',[-pi,pi]);
pdefun = @(t,x,u) diff(u,2);
bc.left = @(t,u) u; bc.right = @(t,u) u;
opts = pdeset('plot','off');
t = [0 .01 .1 1]'; [t,u] = pde15s(pdefun,t,u0,bc,opts);
plot(u), hold on, plot(u0)
```

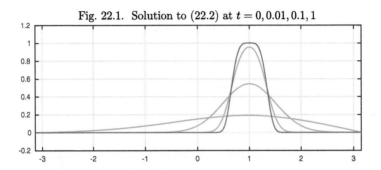

Fig. 22.1. Solution to (22.2) at $t = 0, 0.01, 0.1, 1$

It is apparent in this figure that, until the last curve, the boundaries have
had little effect. We can confirm this by integrating the curves to determine the
total heat at each time, which doesn't diminish much until $t = 1$.

```
disp([t sum(u)'])
```

t	heat
0	0.6817
0.0100	0.6817
0.1000	0.6817
1.0000	0.5874

As t increases further, the left boundary begins to be important as well as the
right one, as is clear from these images for $t = 1$ (again) and $2, 4, 8, 16$.

```
u = u(:,end);
t = [1 2 4 8 16]'; [t,u] = pde15s(pdefun,t,u,bc,opts);
plot(u), hold on, plot(u(:,1))
```

---

[73] As the experiments of this chapter show, Chebfun can be very effective in solving certain
PDEs. PDEs are not Chebfun's main focus, however, and its syntax is not as simple nor its
capabilities as comprehensive for PDEs as for ODEs.

Fig. 22.2. Solution continued to $t = 1, 2, 4, 8, 16$

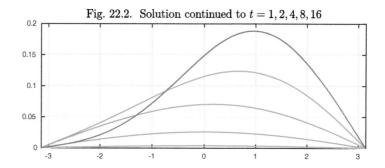

Note how the pulse is now moving to the center, approaching its asymptotic form $C\exp(-t/4)\cos(x/2)$, as determined originally by Joseph Fourier around 1807. The integrals confirm that the total heat content is now diminishing speedily, with 98% of the heat gone by $t = 16$.

```
disp([t sum(u)' 0.76*exp(-t/4)])
```

t	heat	0.76*exp(-t/4)
1	0.5874	0.5919
2	0.4590	0.4610
4	0.2786	0.2796
8	0.1025	0.1029
16	0.0139	0.0139

The Laplace and heat equations may be the archetypes, but these simple linear equations give only a hint of the rich relationship between time-dependent PDEs and associated ODE BVPs. We will now look at some further examples illustrating the phenomena of stability, instability, and symmetry-breaking bifurcation.

Stability and instability. Let us add an exponential term to (22.1) and (22.2) to make them into ODE and PDE versions of the nonlinear *Bratu equation*, considered in Chapters 16 and 18. Here is (16.4) again, with the constant on the nonlinear term adjusted to compensate for the change in domain from $[0, 1]$ to $[-\pi, \pi]$.

$$y_{xx} + \frac{3e^y}{4\pi^2} = 0, \quad x \in [-\pi, \pi], \; y(\pm\pi) = 0. \tag{22.3}$$

As shown in Chapter 16, there are two solutions to this ODE BVP. We plot one of them as a dashed line, the one we shall find is unstable.

```
N = chebop(-pi,pi); N.op = @(x,y) diff(y,2) + (.75/pi^2)*exp(y);
N.lbc = 0; N.rbc = 0;
y1 = N\0; plot(y1), hold on
x = chebfun('x',[-pi pi]); N.init = .2*(pi^2-x^2);
y2 = N\0; plot(y2,'--')
```

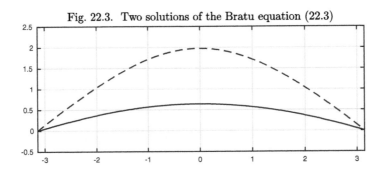

Fig. 22.3. Two solutions of the Bratu equation (22.3)

Now let us embed the problem in a time-dependent PDE with initial condition $u(x,0) = u_0(x)$,

$$u_t = u_{xx} + \frac{3e^u}{4\pi^2}, \quad x \in [-\pi, \pi], \ u(\pm\pi, t) = 0, \ u(x,0) = u_0(x). \qquad (22.4)$$

First of all, suppose we take $u_0(x) = 0$. Then as $t \to \infty$, the solution increases and approaches a steady state, the lower solution of (22.3) just plotted.

```
u0 = 0*x; pdefun = @(t,x,u) diff(u,2)+(.75/pi^2)*exp(u);
t = (0:2:12)'; [t,u] = pde15s(pdefun,t,u0,bc,opts);
plot(u), hold on, plot(u0), plot(y1), plot(y2,'--')
```

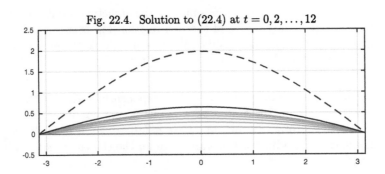

Fig. 22.4. Solution to (22.4) at $t = 0, 2, \ldots, 12$

Many other initial conditions also lead to the same steady state, which is a stable solution of this PDE. For example, in this plot we choose u_0 to have a few wiggles and include extra values $t = 0.05, 0.2$ to show how transient their influence is.

```
u0 = sin(x)+.3*sin(3*x)+.1*sin(13*x); t = [0 0.05 0.2 2:12]';
[t,u] = pde15s(pdefun,t,u0,bc,opts);
plot(u), hold on, plot(u0), plot(y1), plot(y2,'--')
```

Fig. 22.5. Solution to (22.4) at $t = 0, .05, .2$ and $2, 4, \ldots, 20$

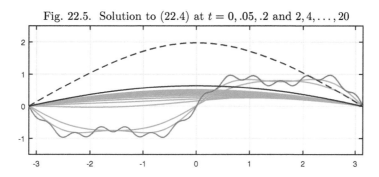

As another example, next we take u_0 to be 0.9 times the *upper* solution of the BVP (22.3). Despite that starting point, the PDE converges to the other, lower solution. The upper solution of the BVP is an unstable solution of the PDE.

```
u0 = 0.9*y2; t = (0:4:32)'; [t,u] = pde15s(pdefun,t,u0,bc,opts);
plot(u), hold on, plot(u0), plot(y1), plot(y2,'--')
```

Fig. 22.6. Solution to (22.4) at $t = 0, 4, \ldots, 32$

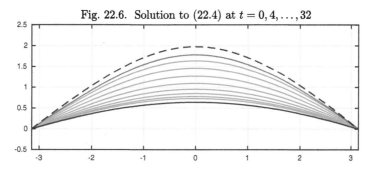

If we take u_0 to be a little larger than the upper solution of the BVP, the same instability is manifested as divergence to ∞ in finite time, at $t \approx 6.914$ for this particular initial condition.

```
u0 = 1.1*y2; t = [0 4 6 6.5 6.8 6.9 6.913]';
[t,u] = pde15s(pdefun,t,u0,bc,opts);
plot(u), hold on, plot(u0), plot(y1), plot(y2,'--')
```

Fig. 22.7. Solution to (22.4) at $t = 0, 4, 6, 6.5, 6.8, 6.9, 6.913$

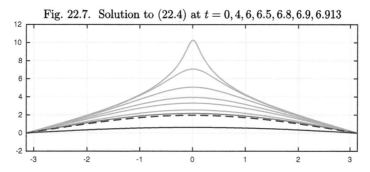

As we have discussed at many points in this book, phenomena of stability and instability are of pervasive importance in the mathematical sciences. Generally speaking, a stable solution is likely to be observable in an experiment and an unstable one is not. Also, generally speaking, a stable solution is likely to emerge as a steady state of a time-dependent process and an unstable one is not. Still, a study of unstable solutions may be important to a full understanding of a problem, and they can often be determined by solving time-independent BVPs.

Symmetry-breaking bifurcation. We have seen in Chapters 16–18 that the number of solutions of an ODE BVP may change as a parameter varies. Often when new solutions appear, this corresponds to a loss of stability of an old solution, and the new solutions are less symmetric than the original one.[74]

To illustrate this effect, let us look at the time-dependent **Allen–Cahn equation**,

$$u_t = \varepsilon u_{xx} + u - u^3, \quad x \in [-1,1], \ u(\pm 1, t) = 0, \ u(x, 0) = u_0(x). \qquad (22.5)$$

For $\varepsilon > \varepsilon_1 \approx 0.406$, the unique steady solution of this problem is $u \equiv 0$, as we illustrate here with $\varepsilon = 0.6$. The associated ODE BVP, which appeared in Exercise 18.1, is

$$\varepsilon y_{xx} + y - y^3 = 0, \quad x \in [-1,1], \ y(\pm 1) = 0, \qquad (22.6)$$

and we show its (zero) solution superimposed on the plot.

```
x = chebfun('x'); ep = 0.5; pdefun = @(t,x,u) ep*diff(u,2)+u-u.^3;
u0 = 0.5*cos(pi*x/2)+.7*sin(pi*x); t = (.5:.5:4)';
[t,u] = pde15s(pdefun,t,u0,bc,opts);
plot(u), hold on, plot(u0), y1 = 0*x; plot(y1)
```

Fig. 22.8. Convergence to 0 for Allen–Cahn eq. (22.5) with $\varepsilon = 0.6$

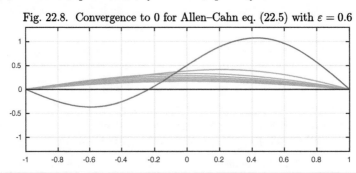

Reducing ε to 0.15, on the other hand, illustrates a different situation. Here, the zero solution is still valid, but it is unstable. With the same initial condition as before, the curve approaches a positive form as $t \to \infty$. By symmetry, if the initial condition were negated, the steady solution as $t \to \infty$ would be negated too.

---

[74]Symmetry-breaking bifurcations are at the root of *phase transitions* in physics. Physicists believe that some particularly important phase transitions occurred soon after the Big Bang, when a single unified force separated into the different fundamental forces recognized today such as the electromagnetic and weak forces.

```
ep = 0.15; pdefun = @(t,x,u) ep*diff(u,2)+u-u.^3;
[t,u] = pde15s(pdefun,t,u0,bc,opts);
plot(u), hold on, plot(u0)
N = chebop(-1,1); N.lbc = 0; N.rbc = 0;
N.op = @(x,y) ep*diff(y,2) + y - y^3; N.init = u0;
y2 = N\0; y3 = -y2; plot(y1,'--'), plot([y2 y3])
```

Fig. 22.9. New solutions and broken symmetry with $\varepsilon = 0.15$

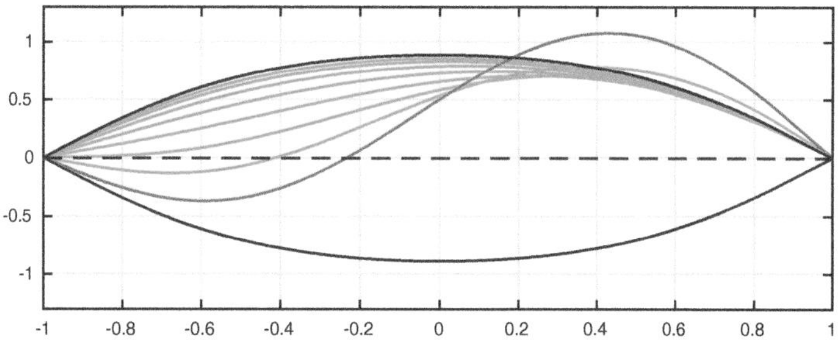

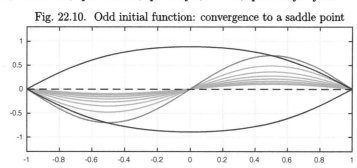

What if one starts from an initial condition that is an odd function of x, hence equally close to the upper and lower solutions? For this value of ε, the solution quickly converges to zero.

```
u0 = .7*sin(pi*x); [t,u] = pde15s(pdefun,t,u0,bc,opts);
plot(u), hold on, plot(u0), plot(y1,'--'), plot([y2 y3])
```

Fig. 22.10. Odd initial function: convergence to a saddle point

The zero solution is not truly stable, however. It is a saddle point, and if it is perturbed by a function that is not odd, the perturbations will generally grow.

If ε is reduced further for this problem, below another bifurcation point $\varepsilon_2 \approx 0.1$, a further set of solutions appears.

```
ep = 0.02;
pdefun = @(t,x,u) ep*diff(u,2)+u-u.^3; u0 = .3*sin(pi*x);
[t,u] = pde15s(pdefun,t,u0,bc,opts);
plot(u), hold on, plot(u0)
N.op = @(x,y) ep*diff(y,2) + y - y^3;
N.init = cos(pi*x/2); y2 = N\0; y3 = -y2;
N.init = sin(pi*x); y4 = N\0; y5 = -y4;
plot(y1,'--'), plot([y2 y3]), plot([y4 y5],'--')
```

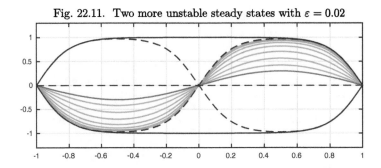

Fig. 22.11. Two more unstable steady states with $\varepsilon = 0.02$

We have marked the new solutions with dashed curves, because in fact these again are saddle points, not stable points. If the initial condition were not an odd function, the solution would eventually converge to one of the stable steady states of a single sign.

Time-harmonic solutions and resonance. Up to now we have looked at PDEs of first order in t. An ODE BVP may also be relevant to time-oscillatory solutions of a PDE that is of second order in t. (We considered such problems in Exercise 6.3 and in the Application of Chapter 20, "Why is New York hotter than San Francisco?") Suppose we have a linear PDE

$$u_{tt} = Lu + e^{i\omega t}f, \tag{22.7}$$

where L is a linear operator acting on functions of x, ω is frequency, and f is a function of x. A **time-harmonic** solution of (22.7) is a solution of the form

$$u(x,t) = e^{i\omega t}y(x) \tag{22.8}$$

for some function y. Inserting (22.8) in (22.7) gives

$$-\omega^2 u = Lu + e^{i\omega t}f,$$

or after dividing by $e^{i\omega t}$,

$$-\omega^2 y = Ly + f, \tag{22.9}$$

known as the **reduced equation** associated with (22.7). One of the fundamental techniques of mathematical physics is to solve reduced equations to find time-harmonic solutions of time-dependent equations.[75]

Further links between ODEs and PDEs. The difference between ODEs and PDEs is nothing more than the number of independent variables, so it is hardly surprising that connections between the two arise in many ways. In this chapter we have emphasized steady-state forms that a solution of a PDE may settle down to as $t \to \infty$. A related situation is that sometimes as $t \to \infty$ the solution of a PDE approaches not a fixed function but a *traveling wave*, a function

---

[75]In quantum mechanics, the technique is applied to the Schrödinger equation, which differs from (22.7) in being of first order in t. We saw this in the Application of Chapter 6, "Eigenstates of the Schrödinger equation."

$u(x,t) = y(x - ct)$ for some constant wave velocity c that in most cases is not known a priori. Here again ODEs play a natural role. Another way ODEs arise from PDEs is in *separation of variables,* and the time-harmonic solutions just looked at fall in this category. Separation of variables applies also in purely spatial problems, for example, if a radially symmetric elliptic PDE is factored into an ODE in r and an ODE in θ: this is the most familiar way in which one encounters the Bessel equation (Exercise 22.1). Another PDE-ODE link arises for problems that have *similarity solutions.* And if we move up one or more dimensions, it is worth noting that just as a PDE in one space dimension may reduce to an ODE in some limit, so a PDE in two or more space dimensions may reduce to a PDE in one dimension less. For example, steady solutions of the heat equation in a 2D spatial domain will be described by solutions of the Laplace equation, a PDE, in the same domain.

APPLICATION: SOLITONS AND THE KDV EQUATION

The simplest of all time-dependent PDEs is the *first-order 1D linear wave equation* (or *advection equation*),

$$u_t = -u_x, \tag{22.10}$$

whose solutions consist of an arbitrary wave form $y(x)$ traveling rightward at speed 1 without changing shape,

$$u(x,t) = y(x - t). \tag{22.11}$$

For example, here we start with a Gaussian of amplitude 50 centered at $x = -1$ and run to $t = 2$ using the Chebfun `spin` command ("stiff PDE integrator"). The wave slides along to $x = 1$ without changing shape.

```
dom = [-5,5]; x = chebfun('x',dom); u0 = 50*exp(-30*(x+1)^2);
S = spinop(dom,[0 2]); S.lin = @(u) -diff(u); S.init = u0;
u1 = spin(S,160,.01,'plot','off'); plot([u0 u1])
```

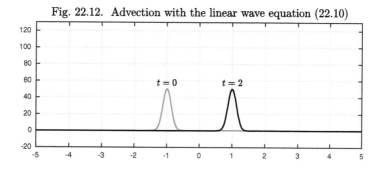

Fig. 22.12. Advection with the linear wave equation (22.10)

For a nonlinear equation, on the other hand, change of shape will be the rule. In this application we look at the most famous of all nonlinear wave equations, the *KdV* (*Korteweg–de Vries*) equation, which we write in the form

$$u_t = -0.03(u^2)_x - 0.01u_{xxx}. \qquad (22.12)$$

The equation blends first-order nonlinear *advection*, involving $(u^2)_x$ or equivalently $2uu_x$, with third-order linear *dispersion*, involving u_{xxx}. The constants 0.03 and 0.01 have no great significance and have been chosen to make the behavior approximately match that of $u_t = -u_x$ for our initial condition. In the next figure we solve (22.12) to $t = 2$ as before with spin, which is made for nonlinear problems like this.

```
S = spinop(dom,[0 2]); S.init = u0;
S.lin = @(u) -0.01*diff(u,3); S.nonlin = @(u) -0.03*diff(u.^2);
u1 = spin(S,160,.01,'plot','off'); plot([u0 u1])
```

Fig. 22.13. Nonlinear propagation with the KdV equation (22.12)

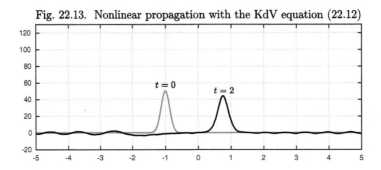

To first approximation, Figure 22.13 is like Figure 22.12. However, the peak is moving a little more slowly, and it is losing amplitude. Meanwhile a tail of dispersive oscillations is appearing behind. (The small oscillations ahead of the main pulse are due to the use of periodic boundary conditions in all spin simulations.) A complicated mix of effects like this is what one must expect to see, in general, with a nonlinear PDE.

But the KdV equation has special properties that this experiment does not reveal. It has special solutions, called *solitary waves* or *solitons*, that travel at fixed speed with exactly uniform shape. For any constant $c > 0$, the associated soliton profile is given by the formula

$$y(x) = 50c\,\mathrm{sech}(\sqrt{100c}\,(x+1)/2)^2, \qquad (22.13)$$

where $\mathrm{sech}(x) = 1/\cosh(x)$, the reciprocal of the hyperbolic cosine. Moreover, the speed at which the soliton moves is equal to c, which means that tall solitons move faster than short ones. Here we see this behavior with a simulation for $t \in [0,2]$ and $c = 1$. Note that the sech^2 function is much like a Gaussian, the difference in shape being too little to notice by eye.

```
c = 1; soliton1 = 50*c*sech(sqrt(100*c)*(x+1)/2)^2;
S.init = soliton1;
u1 = spin(S,160,.01,'plot','off'); plot([S.init u1])
```

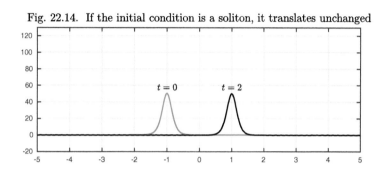

Fig. 22.14. If the initial condition is a soliton, it translates unchanged

Since we took $c = 1$, this soliton has traveled at speed 1. If we double the height, we double the speed.

```
c = 2; soliton2 = 50*c*sech(sqrt(100*c)*(x+2)/2)^2;
S.init = soliton2;
u1 = spin(S,160,.005,'plot','off'); plot([S.init u1])
```

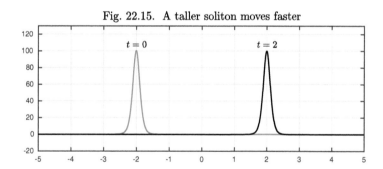

Fig. 22.15. A taller soliton moves faster

Another property of the KdV equation is truly extraordinary. *Solitons can pass through one another.* For example, if we start with a solution consisting of two well-separated solitons, the rear one taller than the front one, then the rear one will catch up, pull ahead, and eventually return to the same shape and speed it had before. Here is an illustration.

```
S.init = soliton1 + soliton2;
u1 = spin(S,160,.005,'plot','off'); plot([S.init u1])
```

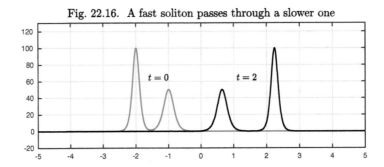

Fig. 22.16. A fast soliton passes through a slower one

Note the locations of the peaks in this figure for the curve at $t = 2$. The speeds have returned to essentially their initial values 2 and 1, but the tall soliton is a bit further along than $x = 2$, and the short soliton is not as far along as $x = 1$. This is because a shift of each soliton is introduced during the time of their interaction around $t = 1$. The details of these nonlinear interactions are subtle and fascinating, as the reader can easily explore with further computations. A waterfall plot gives the idea.

```
spin(S,160,.005,'plot','waterfall');
```

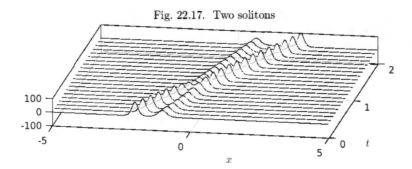

Fig. 22.17. Two solitons

A soliton is an example of a traveling wave, which we defined earlier as a solution of a time-dependent PDE of the form

$$u(x,t) = y(x - ct) \tag{22.14}$$

for some function $y(x)$. Of course we know that in the case of the KdV equation, the formula for y must be (22.13), but let us suppose we do not know this. Inserting (22.14) in (22.12) gives $-cy_x = -0.03(y^2)_x - 0.01y_{xxx}$, that is,

$$y_{xxx} = 100cy_x - 3(y^2)_x.$$

This looks like a nonlinear third-order ODE. However, all three terms are differentiated, so we can integrate it once to get the second-order equation

$$y_{xx} = 100cy - 3y^2 + C$$

for some constant C. Now let us use this ODE to find the shape of a traveling wave solution. If we assume that y and its derivatives approach 0 as $|x| \to \infty$, then we have $C = 0$, and the equation becomes

$$y_{xx} = 100cy - 3y^2. \tag{22.15}$$

This could be dealt with analytically, or one could try various things on the computer. For example, suppose we regard (22.15) as an IVP on the interval $x \in [-2, 2]$, with $c = 1$. With initial conditions $y(-2) = 0$ and $y'(-2) = 10^{-4}$ we get a soliton of just the expected amplitude 50. The horizontal location has no particular significance; it would be different with a different value of $y'(-2)$.

```
N = chebop(-2,2); N.op = @(y) diff(y,2) - 100*y + 3*y^2;
N.lbc = [0; 0.0001];
y = N\0; plot(y)
```

Fig. 22.18. Soliton travelling wave profile determined from an ODE

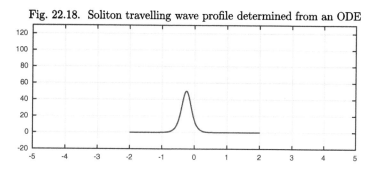

We have not mentioned the scientific uses of the KdV equation. These began with water waves, and the story is often told of John Scott Russell's chase on horseback of a solitary wave in the Union Canal in Scotland in 1834. Two centuries later, the important applications are in optics. Light pulses traveling through optical fibers experience nonlinear effects combined with dispersion, and the KdV equation and its relatives are fundamental nowadays in optical technology.

HISTORY. There are few equations with more impact in the history of mathematics than the KdV equation. The understanding of solitons and their interactions came in the 1960s and led to sensational new discoveries related to so-called completely integrable dynamical systems; some of the key names were Zabusky, Kruskal, and Lax. The technical details are exhilarating, and so are the wider implications, for it was work around the KdV equation that led to some of our deepest understanding of the significance of nonlinearity. All this was sparked by computers. Though the KdV equation goes back to the 19th century, the great advances began with a 1955 paper by Fermi, Pasta, and Ulam, who worked on the Maniac I computer at Los Alamos.

OUR FAVORITE REFERENCE. *The PDE Coffee Table Book* was a group project at Oxford in the late 1990s coordinated by Trefethen together with Kristine Embree. The idea was to present 100 PDEs in the simplest possible

terms, each getting exactly a two-page spread with just the right information
about mathematics, applications, and history, and always with a colorful computed illustration. Alas, the project halted when it was only 34% complete, but
that 34% is worth checking out: see *The (Unfinished) PDE Coffee Table Book*,
https://people.maths.ox.ac.uk/trefethen/pdectb.html.

SUMMARY OF CHAPTER 22. *Many ODE BVPs are related to associated
time-dependent PDEs in one space dimension. The ODEs may arise as
limits $t \to \infty$ in which solutions approach a steady state, a steady oscillation, or a traveling wave. ODEs may also arise from purely spatial PDEs
by the process of separation of variables.*

Exercise 22.1. Bessel equation for a circular drum. A 2D membrane with a fixed
boundary Γ oscillates according to the wave equation $u_{tt} = \Delta u$, where Δ is the Laplacian operator, $\Delta u = u_{xx} + u_{yy}$. This is a PDE in two space variables and time. *(a)* Assume that u takes the form $u(x, y, t) = \exp(i\omega t)v(x, y)$ for a fixed frequency ω and
function v. Show that this assumption reduces the equation to a PDE eigenvalue equation in two space variables. *(b)* Now assume that Γ is the unit circle and that v takes
the polar coordinates form $v(r, \theta) = \exp(ik\theta)y(r)$ for a fixed integer wave number k.
Using the polar coordinates representation of the Laplacian, $\Delta v = v_{rr} + r^{-1}v_r + r^{-2}v_{\theta\theta}$,
show that this reduces the problem to an ODE eigenvalue problem involving Bessel's
equation.

Exercise 22.2. Asymptotic behavior of advection-diffusion problem. *(a)* Execute
chebgui and run the demo labeled "Advection-diffusion equation 2" under the tab
Demos/PDE-scalar. The IBVP here is $u_t = 0.3u_{xx} + 10u_x$ for $x \in [-1, 1]$ with initial condition $u(x, 0) = \exp(-10x^4/(1 - x^2))$ and boundary conditions $u(\pm 1) = 0$.
Describe in words how the solution behaves as $t \to \infty$. *(b)* This behavior can be analyzed by looking for solutions of this equation of the form $u(x, t) = e^{\lambda t}y(x)$, where y
is a fixed function of x. Write down the formulas showing that y and λ are solutions
of an eigenvalue problem. Determine y and λ, either analytically or numerically, for
the value of λ corresponding to the slowest decay of $u(x, t)$ as $t \to \infty$. Show that y
has a shape corresponding to the observations of part *(a)*. *(c)* By pressing the "Export solution" button in Chebgui and then typing **max(u(:,end))**, find the value of
$\max_{x \in [-1, 1]} u(x, 0.25)$ (since the final time of this simulation is $t = 0.25$). Combine
this figure with the result of part *(b)* to estimate $\max_{x \in [-1, 1]} u(x, 5)$ to an accuracy of
within 1%. *(d)* The asymptotic rate of decay is different if the advection term $10u_x$ is
removed from the equation. (Physically, heat transfer is faster with convection than
just conduction — the oceanic effect that we found makes San Francisco cooler than
New York in the summer.) Estimate $\max_{x \in [-1, 1]} u(x, 5)$ in this case.

Exercise 22.3. Metastability of Allen–Cahn equation. *(a)* Execute **chebgui** or **pde15s**,
as you prefer, for the Allen–Cahn equation $u_t = 0.05u_{xx} + u = u^3$ for $x \in [-5, 5]$
and $t \in [0, 50]$ with boundary conditions $u(-5) = u(5) = -1$ and initial condition
$u(x, 0) = -1 + 2\exp(-x^2)$. Show how the initial function quickly changes to a "stalagmite" form that looks like a steady state. *(b)* Now run the calculation for $t \in [0, 1000]$
and show that the apparent steady state was not truly steady, only metastable. Estimate the time at which the stalagmite is extinguished — say, the time t at which
$\max_{x \in [-5, 5]} u(x, t)$ becomes negative. How does this critical time change if the diffusion coefficient 0.5 is increased to 0.6 or 0.7? (With values of the diffusion coefficient

much less than 0.5 the time soon becomes nearly infinite in practice — too long to be measured by a Chebfun computation — though it is always finite in principle.) *(c)* Write down the ODE in the variable y for a time-independent solution of the Allen–Cahn equation. One solution of the ODE is $y(x) = -1$. The waveform observed for $t = 50$ in part *(a)* is a "pseudo-solution": it nearly satisfies the ODE, though not exactly. Insert this solution in the ODE to quantify "nearly."

Appendix A. Chebfun and its ODE algorithms

This is not a book of numerical analysis, yet its heart is numerical explorations. Here we outline Chebfun's ODE algorithms, with references to papers giving further details listed at the end, and mention some of the people who developed them.

Functions. The Chebfun project began at Oxford in 2002 with Trefethen and his DPhil student Zachary Battles [3,19]. The starting idea, which remains the project's central vision, is to utilize Chebyshev interpolants and expansions to enable "numerical computing with functions." Specifically, Chebfun overloads MATLAB commands for discrete vectors to analogues for continuous functions, aiming to deliver speedy results that are accurate to close to machine precision.

In Chebfun, each function (or piece of a function, for piecewise representations) is represented by a polynomial whose domain is a real interval, $[-1, 1]$ by default. Polynomials are manipulated via Chebyshev series and coefficients defined by the formulas

$$f(x) = \sum_{k=0}^{\infty} a_k T_k(x), \quad a_k = \frac{2}{\pi} \int_{-1}^{1} \frac{f(x) T_k(x)}{\sqrt{1 - x^2}} \, dx, \tag{A.1}$$

where T_k is the degree k Chebyshev polynomial (for $k = 0$, the factor $2/\pi$ changes to $1/\pi$). If f is Lipschitz continuous, the series converges uniformly and absolutely, and the smoother f is, the faster the convergence.

For example, $f(x) = 50x \exp(-200x^2) - \tanh(e^x - 1)$ can be constructed and plotted like this:

```
f = chebfun(@(x) 50*x*exp(-200*x^2)-tanh(exp(x)-1));
```

```
plot(f), n = length(f)-1;
```

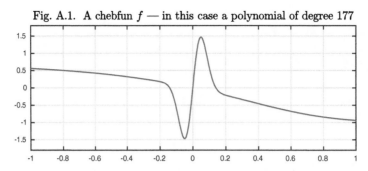

Fig. A.1. A chebfun f — in this case a polynomial of degree 177

The approximation f is called a chebfun, with a lowercase c. To compute quantities like the maximum, the integral, or the norm, Chebfun uses further Chebyshev-based algorithms, all invoked by overloads of familiar MATLAB commands.

```
max(f), sum(f), norm(f)
```

```
ans =  1.465550685258784
ans = -0.191484396292624
ans =  0.870958861441616
```

Algebraic and other operations are also overloaded in the expected manner:

```
min(exp(sin(1/(1+f^2))))
```

```
ans = 1.365723734142705
```

Zeros of functions are computed by the command `roots`:

```
roots(f)
```

```
ans =
  -0.141201098066150
  -0.000000000000000
   0.138729956795104
```

The relative accuracy of each computation is usually about 16 digits, and in principle the user need have no knowledge of the underlying algorithms. For example, this function f is approximated by a polynomial of degree in the hundreds. Here are the absolute values of its Chebyshev series coefficients, plotted on log scale. (As it happens, for this function the even coefficients decrease much faster than the odd ones, eventually reaching a plateau around 10^{-16} because of rounding errors.)

```
plotcoeffs(f)
```

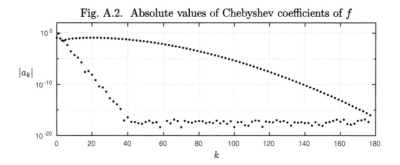

Fig. A.2. Absolute values of Chebyshev coefficients of f

To find this approximation, Chebfun samples f on Chebyshev grids $\{x_j^{(n)}\}$ with $n+1 = 17, 33, 65, \ldots$ points, defined by

$$x_j^{(n)} = -\cos(j\pi/n), \quad 0 \le j \le n. \tag{A.2}$$

On each grid, it determines the Chebyshev series coefficients of the degree n polynomial interpolant through the samples. When the coefficients hit a plateau of rounding errors at a relative magnitude of about 10^{-16}, the grid refinement stops and the series is trimmed [1]. For this function, the plateau is first detected on the grid of 257 points, and we can see what the Chebyshev series looks like before trimming by instructing Chebfun to sample in exactly 257 points:

```
f = chebfun(@(x) 50*x*exp(-200*x^2)-tanh(exp(x)-1),257);
plotcoeffs(f)
```

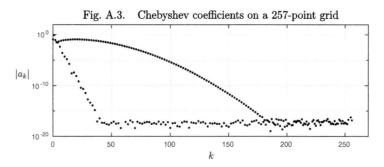

Fig. A.3. Chebyshev coefficients on a 257-point grid

The mathematics behind most Chebfun algorithms is presented in the book *Approximation Theory and Approximation Practice* [18], and user information can be found in the Chebfun *Guide* [10] and web site [6]. The collection of hundreds of examples posted at [6] may be particularly useful.

Two new team members joined the Chebfun project during 2006–07, Ricardo Pachón and Rodrigo Platte, and they introduced piecewise representations for problems with discontinuities [14], which were later incorporated in the BVP solution algorithms by Nick Hale and Toby Driscoll. Piecewise representations are exploited at many points in this book, starting with the problems (2.15) ("Sydney Opera House") and (2.16) ("Batman").

Linear BVPs. The same Chebyshev grids and expansions that work so well for approximating functions also have a distinguished history for solving differential equations, where they go by the name of *Chebyshev spectral methods* [17]. Beginning in 2008, following an initial proposal by Folkmar Bornemann, Toby Driscoll created the BVP side of Chebfun, initially for linear problems [8]. The principle is the same as before: solve the problem on grids of size 17, 33, 65 (actually, slightly different parameters are used), and in each case examine the Chebyshev series for convergence. When a grid is found for which convergence is achieved, the series is trimmed as usual, and the corresponding chebfun is returned as a solution to the BVP. Each solution on a given grid involves a discretization by so-called Chebyshev discretization matrices. Initially, Chebfun followed the traditional "square matrix" discretization strategy described in [17] (and many other places), but later, Driscoll and Hale found that a different "rectangular matrix" formulation offers greater reliability and robustness, especially for problems with nonstandard boundary conditions or multiple dependent variables [2,9,22].

For example, here is a "wavy Airy function" adapted from Chapter 7.

```
L = chebop(-50,20);              % domain
L.op = @(x,y) diff(y,2) - (2+sin(x/2))*x*y;   % diff'l operator
L.lbc = 0; L.rbc = 0;            % boundary conds
y = L\1;                         % solution
plot(y)                          % plot
```

Fig. A.4. A wavy Airy function

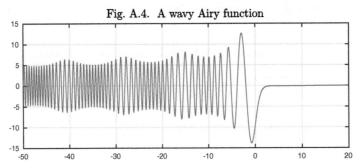

This polynomial representation is of degree over 500:

```
plotcoeffs(y)
```

Fig. A.5. Chebyshev coefficients of a wavy Airy function

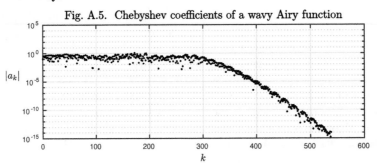

Since the problem domain is $[-50, 20]$ rather than $[-1, 1]$, the coefficients plotted correspond to Chebyshev polynomials appropriately transplanted.

In the code segment above, the command that invokes the solution of the BVP is y = L\1: MATLAB backslash. This is a continuous analogue of MATLAB's use of backslash to solve a matrix problem $\mathbf{Ax} = \mathbf{b}$ via x = A\b. In both cases, the purpose of the compact notation is to highlight the conceptually simple solve operation required while suppressing algorithmic details. Just as an advanced MATLAB user can call linsolve instead of \ to specify nondefault algorithmic parameters, an advanced Chebfun user can call solvebvp instead of \, though we have not found the need for that in this book.

An interesting conceptual step was involved in advancing Chebfun from functions to solutions of BVPs. To represent a function, one simply samples it at more and more points. For BVPs, however, the function being sampled is not known a priori. The "samples" at each particular point will vary from grid to grid until the spectral approximation converges, and moreover the work involved on each grid is proportional to the cube of the number of grid points. These new features of the problem have certain engineering consequences but in the end are not so significant.

Eigenvalue problems. Besides linear BVPs, in 2008 Driscoll also introduced Chebfun commands eigs for eigenvalue problems (Chapter 6), expm for exponentials of linear operators, and fred and volt for Fredholm and Volterra integral equations [7]. Like \, these operations are implemented via Chebyshev discretization matrices of adaptively determined dimensions. Here, to illustrate (compare Figure 6.8), are the first six eigenfunctions of the harmonic oscillator of quantum mechanics, the Schrödinger equation $-u'' + x^2 u = \lambda u$ on $[-5, 5]$ with $u(\pm 5) = 0$ (an approximation to the infinite real line):

```
L = chebop(-5,5); L.op = @(x,u) -diff(u,2) + x^2*u;
L.lbc = 0; L.rbc = 0; [V,D] = eigs(L,6); plot(V)
```

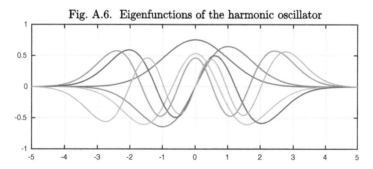

Fig. A.6. Eigenfunctions of the harmonic oscillator

In standard MATLAB, users of eigs can specify whether they want to compute eigenvalues of largest magnitude (the default), largest real part, largest imaginary part, etc. In Chebfun the same options are available, but the default is a different choice entirely: eigenvalues associated with *smoothest eigenfunctions.* In applications, like the one just illustrated, these are typically the eigenfunctions of interest, and this small point of eigenvalue calculations illustrates how new considerations may come into play when one takes the step from discrete to continuous.

Nonlinear BVPs. In 2009 two further Chebfun graduate students joined the project, Nick Hale and Ásgeir Birkisson. Birkisson began to work with Driscoll on the challenge of extending Chebfun's linear BVP algorithms to nonlinear problems. Nonlinearity requires a Newton iteration, as mentioned in Exercise 5.10 and Chapter 16, and in the Chebfun spirit, we wanted to realize this in "continuous mode" — or as it is often put in computational science, in the mode of *solve-then-discretize* rather than *discretize-then-solve*. The reader will be aware that Newton's method for finding a root of a nonlinear equation $f(y)$ requires evaluation of the derivative $f'(y)$ at various points. Similarly, for a system of equations $\mathbf{f}(\mathbf{y}) = \mathbf{0}$, one needs to evaluate a Jacobian matrix of partial derivatives, $J_{ij} = \partial f_i / \partial y_j$. In Chebfun's continuous setting, this matrix becomes an infinite-dimensional Fréchet derivative linear operator that must be discretized. Birkisson and Driscoll found a way to achieve this using automatic differentiation [5], and together with Nick Hale they became the primary developers of the ODE side of Chebfun for the next five years. The linear part of BVP solution is now contained in the Chebfun class `linop`, which the user normally does not call directly.

Even for nonlinear problems, Chebfun's basic BVP command is backslash. One can use `solvebvp`, however, to output additional information about the solution. For example, here we use `solvebvp` to solve the problem (16.8):

```
N = chebop(-1,1); N.lbc = 0; N.rbc = 0;
N.op = @(x,y) 0.2*diff(y,2) + y + y^2;
N.init = chebfun('sin(pi*x)');
[y,info] = solvebvp(N,1); plot(y)
```

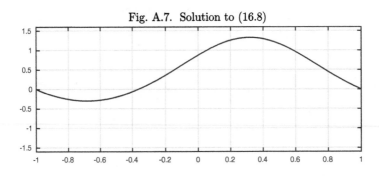

Fig. A.7. Solution to (16.8)

One of the fields of `info` then enables us to track the norms of the Newton updates during the iteration, showing 8 steps and quadratic convergence.

```
semilogy(info.normDelta,'.-')
```

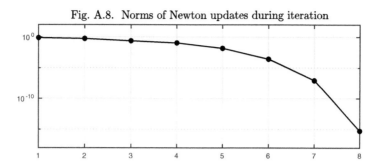

Fig. A.8. Norms of Newton updates during iteration

Initial-value problems. By 2013, Chebfun was a powerful and user-friendly tool for solving ODE BVPs and associated eigenvalue problems, and besides simplicity, three of its impressive features, though we have not emphasized them in this discussion, were its treatment of systems of equations, problems with discontinuities, and nonstandard "boundary" conditions such as integral conditions. Something big was still missing before this book could be written, however, and that was an equally effective treatment of IVPs following the same syntax.

Algorithmically, IVPs and BVPs differ greatly, for the best general methods for solving IVPs, whose roots go back to Adams, Bashforth, Runge, and Kutta more than a century ago, are based on *marching* in time, in contrast to the global spectral methods associated with Chebfun backslash. Global methods can be used for IVPs, and for linear problems this is typically quite effective, but for nonlinear problems the introduction of a Newton iteration is terribly wasteful and generally leads to nonconvergence or at best to great slowdown. Using backslash, Chebfun would have no chance of producing the solutions of the Lorenz and van der Pol equations shown at many points in this book, for example. (Conversely, using a shooting iteration based on marching as mentioned in Chapter 16, one would have trouble with many BVPs.)

In MATLAB, the disjunction between BVPs and IVPs is reflected in the provision of the separate codes bvp4c, bvp5c for the former and ode45, ode113, ode15s, etc. for the latter. These use different algorithms and different syntaxes. For Chebfun, Platte and Hale introduced Chebfun overloads of ode45 and ode113, among others, in 2008–09. The most important MATLAB ODE IVP solver for our purposes is ode113, because it is usually most efficient for the high-accuracy solutions aimed for in Chebfun (except for very stiff problems, where ode15s is superior; for an example see the Oregonator in Appendix B). This code is based on an Adams linear multistep method with variable order ranging from 1 to 13. Hale's algorithmic idea was to solve an IVP by calling MATLAB's ode113 with a tight tolerance specification, then convert the result to a chebfun by the usual process of sampling on finer and finer grids.

For many purposes, however, including a book like this, it would not do to confuse users with one syntax for BVPs and another for IVPs. We had to unify the disparate algorithms within the backslash framework, and here a seemingly small obstacle proved substantial: whereas Chebfun and its spectral methods readily discretize BVPs of any order, ode113 expects every IVP to be formulated as a first-order system. So a method was needed to convert higher-order ODE specifications automatically to first-order form, and in 2014 Birkisson achieved this by a method based on operator overloading and the generation of syntax trees of expressions as mathematical programs are evaluated [4].

For example, here is the solution of a van der Pol equation with a time-varying coefficient:

```
N = chebop(0,40); N.lbc = [3; 0];
N.op = @(t,y) diff(y,2) - 0.2*t*(1-y^2)*diff(y) + y;
y = N\0; plot(y)
```

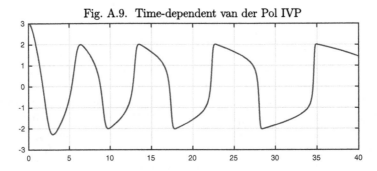

Fig. A.9. Time-dependent van der Pol IVP

The solution is a single long chebfun, a polynomial of high degree:

```
plotcoeffs(y)
```

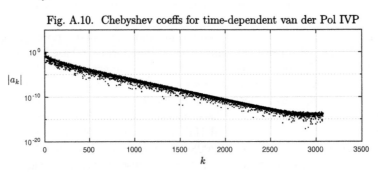

Fig. A.10. Chebyshev coeffs for time-dependent van der Pol IVP

Thus finally, beginning in 2014, a Chebfun user could specify a BVP or an IVP using the same backslash syntax and get a high-accuracy result quickly. The algorithms are completely different in the two cases, but the inputs have the same syntax and the outputs are always chebfuns. Advanced users can fine-tune the computation with **solvebvp** or **solveivp**, and an IVP can be solved by global spectral methods rather than marching, if desired, by calling **solvebvp**.

Periodic problems. Another new feature also appeared in 2014, introduced by new Chebfun contributor Grady Wright, who was visiting Oxford on sabbatical from Boise State University. From the beginning, Chebfun had been based on nonperiodic Chebyshev discretizations, even though one could specify a `'periodic'` flag as a boundary condition for a BVP. This was not really a satisfactory way to deal with periodic problems, however, since Chebyshev matrices have large condition numbers associated with the clustered grids, and derivatives of Chebyshev representations of periodic functions quickly develop discontinuities across the boundary. In 2014, Wright introduced Fourier-based "trigfun" representations to Chebfun and the corresponding Fourier discretizations for BVPs [21]. Together with Oxford graduate student Hadrien Montanelli, Wright adapted Chebfun's Chebyshev-based BVP capabilities to Fourier analogues for periodic functions, as presented in Chapter 19.

PDEs in space and time. As illustrated in Chapter 22, besides ODEs, Chebfun can also solve PDEs involving time t and one space variable x. The general tool for such solutions, `pde15s`, was developed by Nick Hale beginning in 2009, with further improvements later by Ásgeir Birkisson. This code uses spectral discretization in x combined with MATLAB's time-stepper `ode15s` in t, adapting grids and refining time steps adaptively to achieve chebfun outputs. Both nonperiodic (Chebyshev) and periodic (Fourier) discretizations are available. Unfortunately, there is no publication describing `pde15s`.

For time-dependent PDEs on a periodic 1D space domain, another more specialized option was added by Hadrien Montanelli in 2015 [12]: the code `spin`, which stands for *stiff PDE integrator*. This code uses exponential integrator formulas to solve equations of the form $u_t = Lu + N(u)$, where L is a linear differential operator and N is a nonlinear differential or algebraic operator of lower order. Equations of this type include the Burgers, Korteweg–de Vries, nonlinear Schrödinger, FitzHugh–Nagumo, Allen–Cahn, Cahn–Hilliard, Gray–Scott, Nikolaevskiy, and Kuramoto–Sivashinsky equations, and demos for the examples just listed are available with a syntax like `spin('kdv')`.

Chebgui. An easy way for users to explore all of these many sides of Chebfun's differential equations capabilities is with the graphical user interface `chebgui`, written by Birkisson and initially also Hale. In Chebfun, just type `chebgui` to get started, and note the many example problems available under the Demos tab. Chebfun code can be generated with the "Export to m-file" button, a good starting point for more finely tuned computations.

Additional capabilities and higher dimensions. This completes our outline of the solution of ODEs in Chebfun. We have given little attention to an aspect of the problem that in practice adds a great deal of complexity to the design: treatment of systems of equations, with its associated chebmatrix class in the software. We have also not mentioned various additional features of Chebfun that are numerically very interesting, though they have not played a role in this book, including first-kind as opposed to second-kind Chebyshev grids, ultraspherical discretizations, ODEs with unknown parameters, differential-algebraic equations (DAEs), and unbounded domains. Chebfun has capabilities in all of these areas.

There is also a big part of Chebfun that does not relate directly to this book: two- and three-dimensional spatial domains. Such capabilities began with Chebfun2, designed by graduate student Alex Townsend around 2011–12

[15], and a 3D extension Chebfun3 was released by postdoc Behnam Hashemi in 2016 [11]. Building on the periodic trigfun representations, a new Spherefun class for computing on spheres was introduced in 2015 by Townsend, Wright, and Heather Wilber, a student of Wright's at Boise State [16]. Later, at Cornell, Wilber went on to produce a related Diskfun class in 2016 for computing on a disk, again in collaboration with Townsend and Wright [20]. All four of these multidimensional parts of Chebfun — Chebfun2, Chebfun3, Spherefun, and Diskfun — come with PDE capabilities, including solution of reaction-diffusion and other stiff PDEs with `spin2`, `spin3`, and `spinsphere` [13].

Numerical limitations. Finally, we must emphasize that Chebfun has limitations. When the ODE side of Chebfun was developed, beginning in 2008, the expectation was not that it would compete with existing software, merely that it would be a convenient tool for exploring certain algorithms in a continuous setting. We were surprised to find how useful the tool was in practice and that in some cases it was competitive after all, especially for BVPs solved to high accuracy. Still, by pushing Chebfun too far, it is easy to make it slow down, break, or at least require expert handling, as we now outline following the paragraph at the end of Chapter 1. *Stiffness.* If an ODE features a wide range of time scales, Chebfun is likely to have trouble. For example, the computation will become very slow if the coefficient of the van der Pol equation (1.2) is changed from 0.3 to 0.01. For such problems one can switch from the default `ode113` to the stiff solver `ode15s`, as illustrated in examples 32 and 43 in Appendix B. *Scaling.* Some ODEs feature variables that differ by many orders of magnitude from 1, from other variables, or from values taken by the same variable at other times. Taking advantage of floating point arithmetic, some numerical ODE software can cope with such problems, but Chebfun will have difficulty in its default mode. For a simple problem like $y' = -y$ on $[0, 1]$ with initial condition $y(0) = 10^{-20}$, one can get a successful result by overriding the default absolute tolerance. For a more difficult case like the same equation on $[0, 50]$, Chebfun will be sure to fail because its function representations are global. *Discontinuities in y.* Chebfun can treat coefficients with discontinuities in the independent variable, as a number of our examples beginning with Figure 2.3 have shown, but it cannot handle discontinuities in the dependent variable. Calculating the "bounce pass" trajectories of Exercise 16.2, for example, is beyond Chebfun. *Singularities.* Many ODEs have singular coefficients or leading-order coefficients that pass through zero, starting with the Bessel equation with its zero coefficients at $x = 0$, and this is a familiar chapter of the classical theory of ODEs. Sometimes Chebfun can handle such problems, but not always, and if the solution itself has singularities, there will almost certainly be difficulty. *Side conditions.* Some ODE software can impose side conditions such as a nonnegativity constraint on a dependent variable, but Chebfun cannot. For example, it has no very satisfactory way of treating the "leaky bucket" problem $y' = y^{1/2}$ (see example 53 of Appendix B). This limitation is related to the previous two. *Large systems.* Chebfun can solve a system of ODEs involving explicitly named variables such as u, v, w, and there is also an option involving "chebmatrices" to use indexed variables such as u{1}, u{2}, u{3}, illustrated in example 42 of Appendix B. However, its capabilities for working with systems are not very developed. This has constrained our choice of illustrations in this book, where no systems of more than three variables are to be found, and it would make Chebfun an unattractive choice for many larger scale problems of computational science.

It would hardly do to end on a negative note, however. The fact is that Chebfun's efficiency is often very good, and despite the limitations just outlined, it is probably unrivaled in convenience. For more examples, turn the page to Appendix B.

References

[1] J. L. Aurentz and L. N. Trefethen, Chopping a Chebyshev series, *ACM Trans. Math. Softw.* 43 (2017), 33.

[2] J. L. Aurentz and L. N. Trefethen, Block operators and spectral discretizations, *SIAM Rev.* 59 (2017), pp. 423–446.

[3] Z. Battles and L. N. Trefethen, An extension of MATLAB to continuous functions and operators, *SIAM J. Sci. Comp.* 25 (2004), pp. 1743–1770.

[4] A. Birkisson, Automatic reformulation of ODEs to systems of first order equations, *ACM Trans. Math. Softw.*, to appear.

[5] A. Birkisson and T. A. Driscoll, Automatic Fréchet differentiation for the numerical solution of boundary-value problems, *ACM Trans. Math. Softw.* 38 (2012), 26.

[6] Chebfun web site, www.chebfun.org.

[7] T. A. Driscoll, Automatic spectral collocation for integral, integro-differential, and integrally reformulated differential equations, *J. Comp. Phys.* 229 (2010), pp. 5980–5998.

[8] T. A. Driscoll, F. Bornemann, and L. N. Trefethen, The chebop system for automatic solution of differential equations, *BIT Numer. Math.* 48 (2008), pp. 701–723.

[9] T. A. Driscoll and N. Hale, Rectangular spectral collocation, *IMA J. Numer. Anal.* 36 (2016), pp. 108–132.

[10] T. A. Driscoll, N. Hale, and L. N. Trefethen, eds., *Chebfun Guide*, Pafnuty Publications, Oxford, 2014; freely available at [6].

[11] B. Hashemi and L. N. Trefethen, Chebfun in three dimensions, *SIAM J. Sci. Comp.* 39 (2017), pp. C341–C363.

[12] H. Montanelli and N. Bootland, Solving periodic semilinear stiff PDEs in 1D, 2D and 3D with exponential integrators, arXiv:1604.08900, 2016.

[13] H. Montanelli and Y. Nakatsukasa, Fourth-order time-stepping for stiff PDEs on the sphere, *SIAM J. Sci. Comp.*, to appear.

[14] R. Pachón, R. B. Platte, and L. N. Trefethen, Piecewise-smooth chebfuns, *IMA J. Numer. Anal.* 30 (2010), pp. 898–916.

[15] A. Townsend and L. N. Trefethen, An extension of Chebfun to two dimensions, *SIAM J. Sci. Comp.* 35 (2013), pp. C495–C518.

[16] A. Townsend, H. Wilber, and G. B. Wright, Computing with functions in spherical and polar geometries I. The sphere, *SIAM J. Sci. Comp.* 38 (2016), pp. C403–C425.

[17] L. N. Trefethen, *Spectral Methods in MATLAB*, SIAM, 2000.

[18] L. N. Trefethen, *Approximation Theory and Approximation Practice,* SIAM, 2013.

[19] L. N. Trefethen, Computing numerically with functions instead of numbers, *Math. Comput. Sci.* 1 (2007), 9–19; expanded version in *Commun. ACM* 10 (2015), pp. 91–97.

[20] H. Wilber, A. Townsend, and G. B. Wright, Computing with functions in spherical and polar geometries II. The disk, *SIAM J. Sci. Comp.* 39 (2017), pp. C238–C262.

[21] G. B. Wright, M. Javed, H. Montanelli, and L. N. Trefethen, Extension of Chebfun to periodic functions, *SIAM J. Sci. Comp.* 37 (2015), pp. C554–C573.

[22] K. Xu and N. Hale, Explicit construction of rectangular differentiation matrices, *IMA J. Numer. Anal.* 36 (2016), pp. 618–632.

Appendix B. 100 more examples

References, which are just representative, are listed at the end. As usual, formatting commands have been removed and can be obtained by downloading the m-file from www.chebfun.org.

1. Van der Pol equation [Chap. 1]

```
N = chebop(0,5);
N.op = @(y) 0.05*diff(y,2)-(1-y^2)*diff(y)+y;
N.lbc = [1;0];
y = N\0; plot(y)
```

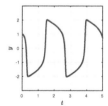

2. Chirp [Chap. 2]

```
L = chebop(0,10); L.lbc = 1;
L.op = @(t,y) diff(y)-cos(t^2)*y;
y = L\0; plot(y)
```

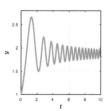

3. Growth with diminishing rate [Chap. 2]

```
L = chebop(0,40); L.lbc = 1;
L.op = @(t,y) diff(y)-exp(-t/4)*y;
y = L\0; plot(y)
```

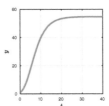

4. Riccati equation [Chap. 3]

```
N = chebop(0,6); N.lbc = 0;
N.op = @(t,y) diff(y)-y+t*y^2-t;
y = N\0; plot(y)
```

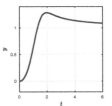

5. Bunching oscillations (B&O, p. 198) [Chap. 3]

```
N = chebop(@(t,y) diff(y)-cos(pi*t*y),[0 5]);
for a = 0:.2:2.8
  N.lbc = a; y = N\0; plot(y), hold on
end
```

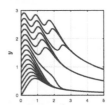

6. Logistic equation [Chap. 3]

```
N = chebop(@(y) diff(y)-(1-y)*y,[0 5]);
for a = .25:.25:2
  N.lbc = a; y = N\0; plot(y), hold on
end
```

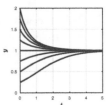

7. Surprising complexity [Chap. 3]

```
N = chebop(0,15);
N.op = @(t,y) diff(y)-cos(t*y)*y-cos(t);
N.lbc = 0;
y = N\0; plot(diff(y))
```

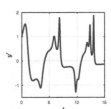

8. Equation with two steady states (Davis) [Chap. 3]

```
d = [0 2.7]; t = chebfun('t',d);
N = chebop(@(t,y) diff(y)-t*y*(y-2),d);
for a = -2.5:.25:2
  N.lbc = a; y = N\0; arrowplot(t,y+1e-10)
  hold on, plot(-flipud(t),flipud(y))
end
```

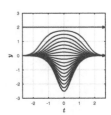

9. Equation with three steady states [Chap. 3]

```
N = chebop(0,4); N.maxnorm = 4;
N.op = @(t,y) diff(y)-y*abs(y)+t*y;
for y0 = -4:.1:4
  N.lbc = y0; y = N\0; plot(y), hold on
end
```

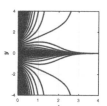

10. Chase around the circle at 3/4 speed [Chap. 3]

```
d = [0 1.95*pi]; a = chebfun('exp(1i*t)',d);
N = chebop(d);
N.op = @(t,z) diff(z)-.75*(a(t)-z)/abs(a(t)-z);
N.lbc = 0; arrowplot(a), hold on, arrowplot(N\0)
```

11. Oscillation in a Lennard–Jones potential [Chap. 4]

```
N = chebop(0,70); N.lbc = [25;0];
N.op = @(r) 0.1*diff(r,2)-(r/12)^(-12)+(r/12)^(-6);
r = N\0; plot(r)
```

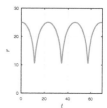

12. Alternating growth and decay [Chap. 4]

```
L = chebop(0,200); L.lbc = [1;0];
L.op = @(t,y) diff(y,2)+.06*sin(t/10)*diff(y)+y;
y = L\0; plot(y)
```

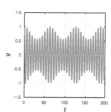

13. Transient damping [Chap. 4]

```
L = chebop(0,100); L.lbc = [1;0];
L.op = @(t,y) diff(y,2) + ...
       0.2*exp(-(t-50)^2/16)*diff(y)+y;
y = L\0; plot(y)
```

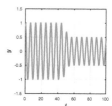

14. Washing hanging on the line [Chap. 5]

```
L = chebop(@(y) diff(y,2),[0 3],1,1);
x = chebfun('x',[0 3]);
rhs = .1+0*x+(abs(x-2)<.1);
y = L\rhs; plot(y)
```

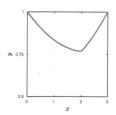

15. *Third-order problem* [Chap. 5]

```
L = chebop(-1,1);
L.op = @(y) 0.5*diff(y,3)+diff(y,2)+diff(y)+y;
L.lbc = [0;0]; L.rbc = 1;
y = L\0; plot(y)
```

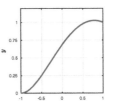

16. *Gaussian* [Chap. 5]

```
L = chebop(-2,2);
L.lbc = 0; L.rbc = 1;
L.op = @(x,y) diff(y,2)+x*diff(y)+y;
y = L\0; plot(y)
```

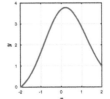

17. *Beam with 4 interpolation pts (= spline)* [Chap. 5]

```
L = chebop(@(y) diff(y,4),[0 3]);
L.bc = @(x,y) [y(0); y(1); y(2)-1; y(3)-1];
y = L\0; plot(y)
hold on, plot(0:3,[0 0 1 1],'.')
```

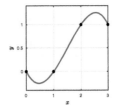

18. *Troesch equation* [Chap. 5]

```
N = chebop(0,1);
N.op = @(y) diff(y,2)-6*sinh(6*y);
N.lbc = 0; N.rbc = 1;
y = N\0; plot(y)
```

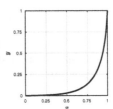

19. *Schrödinger harmonic oscillator* [Chap. 6]

```
x = chebfun('x',[-3 3]); V = x^2; h = 0.1; plot(V)
L = chebop(@(y) -h^2*diff(y,2)+V*y,[-3 3]);
L.lbc = 0; L.rbc = 0; [W,D] = eigs(L,10); hold on
for k = 1:10, plot(D(k,k)+0.06*W{k}), end
```

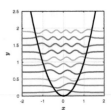

20. *V-shaped oscillator via* quantumstates [Chap. 6]

```
x = chebfun('x',[-3 3]);
V = abs(x);
quantumstates(V);
```

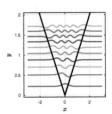

21. Lennard–Jones eigenstates [Chap. 6]

```
r = chebfun('r',[10 32]);
V = (r/12)^(-12)-(r/12)^(-6);
quantumstates(V);
```

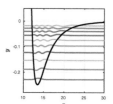

22. Orr–Sommerfeld eigenvalues [Chap. 6]

```
B = chebop(-1,1); B.op = @(x,u) diff(u,2)-u;
A = chebop(-1,1);
A.op = @(x,u) (diff(u,4)-2*diff(u,2)+u)/5772 ...
       -1i*(2*u+(1-x^2)*(diff(u,2)-u));
A.lbc = [0;0]; A.rbc = [0;0];
lam = eigs(A,B,47); plot(lam,'.')
```

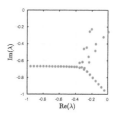

23. Bessel equation [Chap. 7]

```
L = chebop(0,150); L.lbc = 0; L.rbc = 1; nu = 50;
L.op = @(x,y) x^2*diff(y,2)+x*diff(y)+(x^2-nu^2)*y;
y = L\0; plot(y)
```

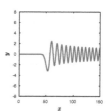

24. Airy-like equation (L&G) [Chap. 7]

```
L = chebop(-1,1); L.lbc = 1; L.rbc = 2;
L.op = @(x,y) 1e-4*diff(y,2)+(x^2-0.25)*y;
y = L\0; plot(y)
```

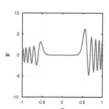

25. Nearly ill-posed problem [Chap. 7]

```
L = chebop(-1,1); x = chebfun('x');
L.op = @(x,y) -.05*diff(y,2)+x*diff(y)-y;
L.lbc = 0; L.rbc = 0;
y = L\exp(x); plot(y)
```

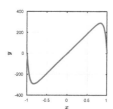

26. Forcing at the resonant frequency [Chap. 8]

```
d = [0 80]; t = chebfun('t',d);
L = chebop(d); L.lbc = [0;0];
L.op = @(y) diff(y,2)+y;
y = L\sin(t); plot(y)
```

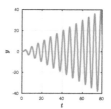

27. *The same with damping* [Chap. 8]

```
d = [0 80]; t = chebfun('t',d);
L = chebop(d); L.lbc = [0;0];
L.op = @(y) diff(y,2)+.08*diff(y)+y;
y = L\sin(t); plot(y)
```

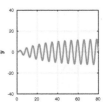

28. *Duffing equation (Davis, p. 399)* [Chap. 8]

```
d = [0 30]; t = chebfun('t',d);
N = chebop(d); N.lbc = [-1;0];
N.op = @(y) diff(y,2)+y-.088*y^3;
y = N\sin(0.05*t); arrowplot(y,diff(y))
```

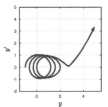

29. *Forcing at the resonant frequency* [Chap. 9]

```
d = [0 80]; t = chebfun('t',d);
L = chebop(d); L.lbc = [0;0];
L.op = @(y) diff(y,2)+y;
y = L\sin(t); plot(y,diff(y))
```

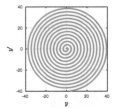

30. *The same with damping* [Chap. 9]

```
d = [0 80]; t = chebfun('t',d);
L = chebop(d); L.lbc = [0;0];
L.op = @(y) diff(y,2)+.08*diff(y)+y;
y = L\sin(t); plot(y,diff(y))
```

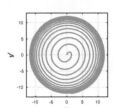

31. *Van der Pol equation limit cycle* [Chap. 9]

```
T = 16; N = chebop(0,T); N.lbc = [1;1];
N.op = @(y) diff(y,2)-4*(1-y^2)*diff(y)+y;
y = N\0; y = y{4,T}; plot(y,diff(y))
hold on, plot(0,0,'.')
```

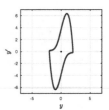

32. *Van der Pol equation in the stiff regime* [Chap. 9]

```
N = chebop(0,4); N.lbc = [2;0];
N.op = @(y) .001*diff(y,2)-(1-y^2)*diff(y)+y;
pref = cheboppref; pref.ivpSolver = 'ode15s';
y = solveivp(N,0,pref); plot(y)
```

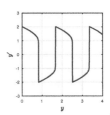

33. Rayleigh equation limit cycle [Chap. 9]

```
N = chebop(0,20); N.lbc = [3;1]; N.maxnorm = 20;
N.op = @(y) diff(y,2)+6*(diff(y)^3-diff(y))+y;
y = N\0; y = y{4,18}; plot(y,diff(y))
hold on, plot(0,0,'.')
```

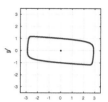

34. Nonlinear pendulum heteroclinic paths [Chap. 9]

```
N = chebop(@(y) diff(y,2)+sin(y),[0 21]);
N.lbc = [-3.1;0];
y = N\0; arrowplot(y,diff(y))
hold on, plot(0,0,'.')
```

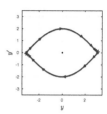

35. Unforced Duffing equation [Chap. 9]

```
N = chebop(@(y) diff(y,2)+y-.088*y^3,[0 20]);
plot(0,0,'.'), hold on
for a = 0.28:.3:2.6
  N.lbc = [0; a]; y = N\0; arrowplot(y,diff(y))
end
```

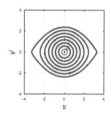

36. Cubic oscillator [Chap. 9]

```
N = chebop(@(t,y) diff(y,2)+y^3,[0 20]);
plot(0,0,'.'), hold on
for a = 0.1:.2:1.5
  N.lbc = [0;a]; y = N\0; arrowplot(y,diff(y))
end
```

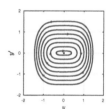

37. Close to a saddle point (Seydel, p. 82) [Chap. 9]

```
N = chebop(0,14.5); N.lbc = [0;.3];
N.op = @(y) diff(y,2)-y+y^2 + ...
       0.45*diff(y)-0.5*y*diff(y);
N.lbc = [0;.3]; y = N\0; arrowplot(y,diff(y))
hold on, plot(0,0,'.')
```

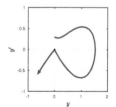

38. Stable spiral point (scalar second-order) [Chap. 9]

```
L = chebop(0,29); L.lbc = [0;1];
L.op = @(y) diff(y,2)+.1*diff(y,1)+y;
y = L\0; arrowplot(y,diff(y))
hold on, plot(0,0,'.')
```

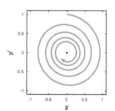

39. Walk on the sphere [Chap. 10]

```
d = [0 60]; t = chebfun('t',d); L = chebop(d);
L.lbc = [1;0;0]; f = 1; g = 0; h = 2*sin(t);
L.op = @(t,x,y,z) [diff(x)-f*y-g*z;
  diff(y)+f*x-h*z; diff(z)+g*x+h*y];
[x,y,z] = L\0; plot3(x,y,z), hold on
plot3(x([0 end]),y([0 end]),z([0 end]),'.')
```

40. Stable spiral point (first-order system) [Chap. 10]

```
L = chebop(0,29); L.lbc = [0;1];
L.op = @(t,u,v) [diff(u)-v; diff(v)+u+.1*v];
[u,v] = L\0; arrowplot(u,v)
hold on, plot(0,0,'.')
```

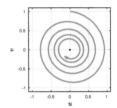

41. Brusselator chemical reaction [Chap. 10]

```
N = chebop(0,15.3); N.lbc = [1;3.07]; a = 1; b = 3;
N.op = @(t,u,v) [diff(u)-a+(b+1)*u-u^2*v
                 diff(v)-b*u+u^2*v];
[u,v] = N\0; arrowplot(u,v)
hold on, plot([0 1],[0 3],'.')
```

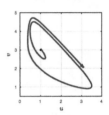

42. Full Brusselator (HNW) [Chap. 10]

```
N = chebop(0,60); N.lbc = [1;2;2];
N.op = @(t,u) [
       diff(u{1})-1-u{1}^2*u{2}+(u{3}+1)*u{1}
       diff(u{2})-u{1}*u{3}+u{1}^2*u{2}
       diff(u{3})-1.2+u{3}*u{1}];
u = N\0; plot3(u{1},u{2},u{3})
```

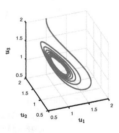

43. Field–Noyes Oregonator (stiff) (Danby) [Chap. 10]

```
s = 20; r = 0.1610; q = 8.375e-6;
N = chebop(0,250); N.lbc = [0;800;16];
N.op = @(t,u,v,w) [diff(u)-s*(v-u*v+u-q*u^2);
   diff(v)-(-v-u*v+w)/s; diff(w)-r*(u-w)];
pref = cheboppref; pref.ivpSolver = 'ode15s';
[u,v,w] = solveivp(N,0,pref); semilogy([u v w])
```

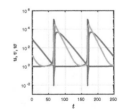

44. Phase plane, nonautonomous first-order [Chap. 10]

```
L = chebop(@(s,t,y) ...
    [diff(t)-1; diff(y)-exp(-t)+2*y],[0 3]);
quiver(L,[-1.5 2.5 -.5 1]), hold on
L.lbc = [-1;0];
[t,y] = L\0; arrowplot(t,y)
```

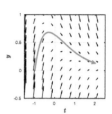

45. Homoclinic orbit [Chap. 10]

```
N = chebop(0,35); N.lbc = [0.16;0.01];
N.op = @(t,u,v) [diff(u)-u.^3+2.*u.*v.^2
                 diff(v)-2.*u.^2.*v+v.^3];
[u,v] = N\0; arrowplot(v,u)
hold on, plot(0,0,'.')
```

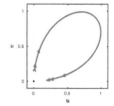

46. Cubic damping (Duan, p. 6) [Chap. 10]

```
L = chebop(0,40);
L.op = @(t,u,v) [diff(u)-v; diff(v)+u+v^3];
L.lbc = [0;1];
[u,v] = L\0; arrowplot(u,v)
hold on, plot(0,0,'.')
```

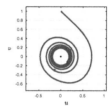

47. Oscillatory system (HSD, p. 229) [Chap. 10]

```
a = 10; b = 1; N = chebop(0,11.8); N.lbc = [2.2;5];
N.op = @(t,u,v) [diff(u)-a+u+4*u*v/(1+u^2)
                 diff(v)-b*u*(1-v/(1+u^2))];
[u,v] = N\0; arrowplot(u,v)
hold on, plot(2,5,'.')
```

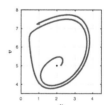

48. Square limit cycle (HSD, p. 215) [Chap. 10]

```
N = chebop(0,60); N.lbc = [1.5;1.5];
N.op = @(t,u,v) [diff(u)+sin(u)*(.1*cos(u)+cos(v))
                 diff(v)+sin(v)*(.1*cos(v)-cos(u))];
[u,v] = N\0; arrowplot(u,v)
hold on, plot(pi/2,pi/2,'.')
```

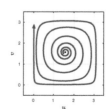

49. Four fixed points (Davis, p. 345) [Chap. 10]

```
N = chebop(0,5); N.maxnorm = [1.7 3];
N.op = @(t,u,v) [diff(u)+v-u^2-v^2
                 diff(v)-u+2*u*v];
plot([0 0 .5 -.5],[0 1 .5 .5],'.'), hold on
for v0 = .5+.147*(-10:10)
  N.lbc = [0;v0]; [u,v] = N\0; plot([u -u],v), end
```

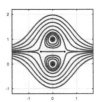

50. Synchronizing three fireflies (Danby) [Chap. 10]

```
N = chebop(0,40); N.lbc = [0;2;4]; c = .2;
N.op = @(t,u,v,w) [
       diff(u)-0.97-c*sin(v-u)-c*sin(w-u)
       diff(v)-1.00-c*sin(u-v)-c*sin(w-v)
       diff(w)-1.03-c*sin(u-w)-c*sin(v-w)];
[u,v,w] = N\0; plot(sin([u v w]))
```

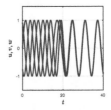

51. Hamiltonian system (J&S, p. 79) [Chap. 10]

```
N = chebop(0,2); plot([-4 1 3],[0 0 0],'.'), hold on
N.op = @(t,u,v) [diff(u)-v*(13-u^2-v^2)
                 diff(v)-12+u*(13-u^2-v^2)];
for a = -4.5:5.5
  N.lbc = [a;.2]; [u,v] = N\0; plot(u,v)
end
```

52. A center and a saddle point [Chap. 10]

```
N = chebop(0,10); N.maxnorm = [3;3];
plot([-1 0],[-1 0],'.'), hold on
N.op = @(t,u,v) [diff(u)+u+v^2,diff(v)-v-u^2];
for a = -2:.15:0
  N.lbc = [2;a]; [u,v] = N\0; plot(u,v)
  arrowplot(u{0,.5},v{0,.5}), end
for a = -.81:.15:-.3
  N.lbc = [-1;a]; [u,v] = N\0; plot(u,v)
  arrowplot(u{0,.5},v{0,.5}), end
```

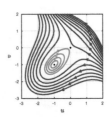

53. Leaky bucket [Chap. 11]

```
N = chebop(0,4); N.lbc = 1;
N.op = @(y) diff(y)+y/sqrt(abs(y));
y = N\0; plot(y)
```

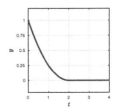

54. Nonuniqueness and extinction [Chap. 11]

```
S = chebfun('cos(pi*x/2)^2',[0 1]);
for h = 0:.125:1
  plot([h*S 1-h*(1-S)]), hold on
end
```

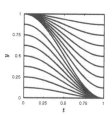

55. Smooth random walk on the sphere [Chap. 12]

```
d = [0 2]; rng(6), u0 = randn(3,1); u0 = u0/norm(u0);
L = chebop(d); L.lbc = u0;
R = randnfun(0.05,3,d,'big');
f = R(:,1); g = R(:,2); h = R(:,3);
L.op = @(t,x,y,z) [diff(x)-f*y-g*z;
  diff(y)+f*x-h*z; diff(z)+g*x+h*y];
[x,y,z] = L\0; plot3(x,y,z), hold on
plot3(x([0 2]),y([0 2]),z([0 2]),'.')
```

56. Less smooth random walk on the sphere [Chap. 12]

```
d = [0 2]; rng(6), u0 = randn(3,1); u0 = u0/norm(u0);
L = chebop(d); L.lbc = u0;
R = randnfun(0.005,3,d,'big');
f = R(:,1); g = R(:,2); h = R(:,3);
L.op = @(t,x,y,z) [diff(x)-f*y-g*z;
  diff(y)+f*x-h*z; diff(z)+g*x+h*y];
[x,y,z] = L\0; plot3(x,y,z), hold on
plot3(x([0 2]),y([0 2]),z([0 2]),'.')
```

57. Smooth Brownian motion to the circle [Chap. 12]

```
d = [0 2]; lam = 1e-3;
rng(0), f = randnfun(lam,d,'complex','big');
L = chebop(@(y) diff(y),d); L.lbc = 0; L.maxnorm = 1;
plot(chebfun('exp(1i*pi*x)')), hold on
y = L\f; plot(y)
```

58. BVP with smooth random coefficient [Chap. 12]

```
rng(0), d = [0 10]; f = randnfun(1,d);
L = chebop(@(y) .005*diff(y,2)+f*y,d,0,0);
y = L\1; plot(y)
```

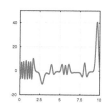

59. *Decay with sideways randomness* [Chap. 12]

```
d = [0 40]; rng(1), f = randnfun(0.1,d,'big');
L = chebop(@(y) diff(y)+(.3+1i*f)*y,d,1,[]);
plot(chebfun('exp(1i*pi*x)')), hold on
y = L\0; plot(y)
```

60. *Conveyor belt* [Chap. 12]

```
d = [0 1]; l = 0.005; rng(0)
f = randnfun(l,d,'big'); g = randnfun(l,d,'big');
N = chebop(@(t,u,v) ...
    [diff(u)-60*exp(-40*v^2); diff(v)],d);
N.lbc = [0;0]; [u,v] = N\[f;g]; plot(u,v)
```

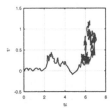

61. *Equation with random ±1 forcing* [Chap. 12]

```
rng(0), f = sign(randnfun(.5,[0,8]));
L = chebop(0,8); L.lbc = 1;
L.op = @(t,y) diff(y)-f*y;
y = L\0; plot(y)
```

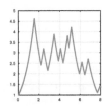

62. *Equation with intermittent kicks* [Chap. 12]

```
d = [0 10]; t = chebfun('t',d); rng(2)
f = randnfun(.1,d,'big')/(1.1-cos(2*pi*t));
L = chebop(@(t,y) diff(y)-f,d,0,[]);
y = L\0; plot(y)
```

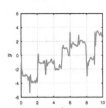

63. *Smooth geometric Brownian motion* [Chap. 12]

```
d = [0 10]; lam = 0.05;
rng(2), f = randnfun(lam,d,'big');
L = chebop(@(y) diff(y)-f*y,d,1,[]);
y = L\0; plot(y)
```

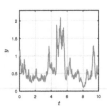

64. *Scalar chaotic equation* (ESK) [Chap. 13]

```
N = chebop(0,200); N.lbc = [2;0;0];
N.op = @(t,y) 1.5*diff(y,3) + ...
    diff(y,2)+diff(y)+y-tanh(8*y);
y = N\0; plot(y)
```

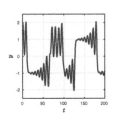

65. Forced nonlinear pendulum (Danby) [Chap. 13]

```
N = chebop(0,200); N.lbc = [0;.74];
N.op = @(t,y) diff(y,2)+.1*diff(y)+sin(y)-sin(t);
y = N\0; plot(y)
```

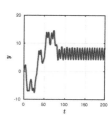

66. Rössler equations period doubling [Chap. 13]

```
N = chebop(0,250); N.lbc = [2;0;0];
N.op = @(t,u,v,w) [diff(u)+v+w;
    diff(v)-u-.2*v; diff(w)-.2-w*(u-3.5)];
[u,v,w] = N\0; plot(u{200,250})
```

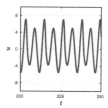

67. 3-body problem [Chap. 13]

```
N = chebop(0,4);
N.op = @(t,u,v,w) [
    diff(u,2)+(u-v)/abs(u-v)^3+(u-w)/abs(u-w)^3
    diff(v,2)+(v-u)/abs(v-u)^3+(v-w)/abs(v-w)^3
    diff(w,2)+(w-u)/abs(w-u)^3+(w-v)/abs(w-v)^3];
N.lbc = @(u,v,w) [u-1; v+1; w-(0.1+1.5i);
                  diff(u); diff(v); diff(w)];
[u,v,w] = N\0; plot([u;v;w])
```

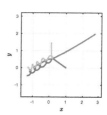

68. 3-body problem, slightly different data [Chap. 13]

```
N = chebop(0,6);
N.op = @(t,u,v,w) [
    diff(u,2)+(u-v)/abs(u-v)^3+(u-w)/abs(u-w)^3
    diff(v,2)+(v-u)/abs(v-u)^3+(v-w)/abs(v-w)^3
    diff(w,2)+(w-u)/abs(w-u)^3+(w-v)/abs(w-v)^3];
N.lbc = @(u,v,w) [u-1; v+1; w-(0.1+1i);
                  diff(u); diff(v); diff(w)];
[u,v,w] = N\0; plot([u;v;w])
```

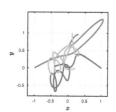

69. *Double pendulum* (Danby) [Chap. 13]

```
N = chebop(0,150);
c = @(u) cos(u); s = @(u) sin(u);
cs = @(u) cos(u).*sin(u); d = @(u) diff(u);
N.op = @(t,u,v) [
    diff(u,2)+(d(u)^2*cs(u-v)+d(v)^2*s(u-v)+ ...
        2*s(u)-c(u-v)*s(v))/(2-c(u-v)^2)
    diff(v,2)+(-2*d(u)^2*s(u-v)-d(v)^2*cs(u-v)- ...
        2*c(u-v)*s(u)+2*s(v))/(2-c(u-v)^2)];
N.lbc = @(u,v) [u-3.14159; v; diff(u); diff(v)];
[u,v] = N\0; plot([u v])
```

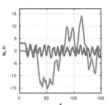

70. *Hénon–Heiles equations* [Chap. 13]

```
N = chebop(0,100);
N.op = @(t,u,v) [diff(u,2)+u+2*u*v
                 diff(v,2)+v+u^2-v^2];
N.lbc = @(u,v) [u-.32; v-.35; diff(u); diff(v)];
[u,v] = N\0; plot(u,v)
```

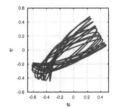

71. *Spiral sink* [Chap. 15]

```
L = chebop(0,30); L.lbc = [0;1];
L.op = @(t,u,v) [diff(u)+u/2-v; diff(v)+u-v/3];
[u,v] = L\0; arrowplot(u,v)
hold on, plot(0,0,'.')
```

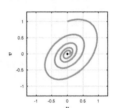

72. *Spiral source* [Chap. 15]

```
L = chebop(0,30); L.lbc = [0;1];
L.op = @(t,u,v) [diff(u)-.4*u+v; diff(v)-u+.2*v];
[u,v] = L\0; arrowplot(u,v)
hold on, plot(0,0,'.')
```

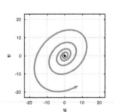

73. *Linear transient growth* [Chap. 15]

```
L = chebop(0,3); L.lbc = [0;1];
L.op = @(t,u,v) [diff(u)+u-20*v; diff(v)+2*v];
[u,v] = L\0; arrowplot(u,v)
hold on, plot(0,0,'.')
```

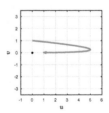

74. From slightly unstable to slightly stable [Chap. 15]

```
N = chebop(0,70); N.lbc = [-pi;1];
N.op = @(t,y) diff(y,2)+.05*tanh(y)*diff(y)-sin(y);
y = N\0; arrowplot(y,diff(y))
hold on, plot(pi*(-1:1),0*(-1:1),'.')
```

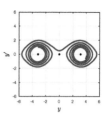

75. Euler buckling [Chap. 16]

```
N = chebop(@(x,y) diff(y,2)+3*sin(y),[-1 1],0,0);
for k = 1:-1:-1
  N.init = chebfun(@(x) k*cos(pi*x/2));
  plot(N\0), hold on
end
```

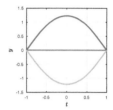

76. Carrier equation [Chap. 16]

```
N = chebop(-1,1);
N.op = @(x,y) 0.001*diff(y,2)+2*(1-x^2)*y+y^2;
N.lbc = 0; N.rbc = 0;
y = N\1; plot(y)
```

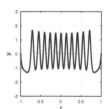

77. Orbit around two fixed suns [Chap. 16]

```
N = chebop(0,12); c = 1.5;
N.op = @(t,x,y) [
    diff(x,2)+x/(x^2+y^2)^c+x/(x^2+(y-1)^2)^c;
    diff(y,2)+y/(x^2+y^2)^c+(y-1)/(x^2+(y-1)^2)^c];
N.lbc = @(x,y) [x+2; y-1; diff(x)-.8; diff(y)-.454];
[x,y] = N\0; plot([0 0],[0 1],'.')
hold on, arrowplot(x,y)
```

78. Linear Hopf bifurcation [Chap. 17]

```
T = 100; d = [-T,T];
L = chebop(@(t,y) diff(y,2)-.15*(t/T)*diff(y)+y,d);
L.lbc = [0;0]; rng(0), f = 0.1*randnfun(d,'big');
y = L\f; plot(y)
```

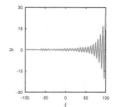

79. Nonlinear Hopf bifurcation (Seydel, p. 76) [Chap. 17]

```
T = 100; d = [-T/5,T]; N = chebop(d);
N.op = @(t,u,v) [diff(u)+v-u*(t/T-u^2-v^2)
                 diff(v)-u-v*(t/T-u^2-v^2)];
N.lbc = [0;0];
rng(0), f = 0.01*randnfun(1,d,'big');
[u,v] = N\[f;0]; t = chebfun('t',d);
plot3(t,u,v)
```

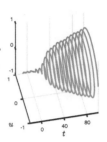

80. Van der Pol Hopf bifurcation [Chap. 17]

```
T = 60; d = [-T,T]; N = chebop(d);
N.op = @(t,y) diff(y,2)-2*(t/T)*(1-y^2)*diff(y)+y;
N.lbc = [0;0];
rng(0), f = 0.05*randnfun(d,'big');
y = N\f; plot(y)
```

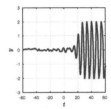

81. Stirred tank reactor (Seydel, p. 157) [Chap. 17]

```
T = 50; N = chebop(0,T); N.lbc = [.2;.6];
N.op = @(t,u,v) [diff(u)+u-(0.1+.2*t/T)*(1-u)*exp(v)
    diff(v)+v-16.2*(0.1+.2*t/T)*(1-u)*exp(v)+3*v];
[u,v] = N\0; plot(u)
```

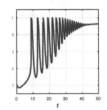

82. Periodic variant of Figure 7.5 [Chap. 19]

```
L = chebop(-2*pi,2*pi);
L.op = @(x,y) 0.005*diff(y,2)-sin(x)*y;
L.bc = 'periodic';
y = L\1; plot(y)
```

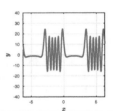

83. Periodic ODE in polar coordinates [Chap. 19]

```
L = chebop(0,2*pi);
L.op = @(t,r) diff(r,2)+(r+.35)/(1.1+sin(6*t));
t = chebfun('t',[0 2*pi]);
L.bc = 'periodic'; r = L\1; plot(exp(1i*t)*r)
```

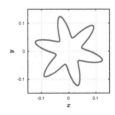

84. *Stable Hill equation* [Chap. 19]

```
L = chebop(0,100); L.lbc = [1;0];
L.op = @(t,y) diff(y,2)+exp(2.40*sin(t))*y;
y = L\0; plot(y)
```

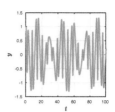

85. *Unstable Hill equation* [Chap. 19]

```
L = chebop(0,100); L.lbc = [1;0];
L.op = @(t,y) diff(y,2)+exp(2.45*sin(t))*y;
y = L\0; plot(y)
```

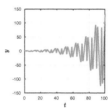

86. *Periodic discontinuous coefficient* [Chap. 19]

```
L = chebop(@(x,y) diff(y)+(abs(x-3)<1)*y,[0 2*pi]);
L.bc = 'periodic';
y = L\1; plot(y)
```

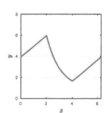

87. *Periodic Carrier equation* [Chap. 19]

```
N = chebop(-pi,pi); N.bc = 'periodic';
N.op = @(x,y) diff(y,2)+2*(2-cos(x))*y+y^2;
N.init = chebfun('-cos(2*x)',[-pi pi],'trig');
y = N\1; plot(y)
```

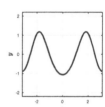

88. *Periodic Carrier equation, 2nd soln.* [Chap. 19]

```
N = chebop(-pi,pi); N.bc = 'periodic';
N.op = @(x,y) diff(y,2)+2*(2-cos(x))*y+y^2;
N.init = chebfun('1.5*cos(2*x)',[-pi pi],'trig');
y = N\1; plot(y)
```

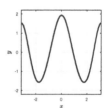

89. *Periodic Carrier equation, 3rd soln.* [Chap. 19]

```
N = chebop(-pi,pi); N.bc = 'periodic';
N.op = @(x,y) diff(y,2)+2*(2-cos(x))*y+y^2;
N.init = chebfun('cos(x)^2',[-pi pi],'trig');
y = N\1; plot(y)
```

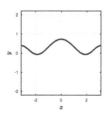

90. Boundary layer at left (Hemker) [Chap. 20]

```
ep = 0.05;
L = chebop(@(x,y) ep*diff(y,2)+diff(y)-(1+ep)*y);
L.lbc = 1+exp(-2); L.rbc = 1+exp(-2*(1+ep)/ep);
y = L\0; plot(y)
```

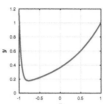

91. Linear shock (L&G) [Chap. 20]

```
ep = 1e-4;
L = chebop([-1 0 1]);
L.op = @(x,y) ep*diff(y,2)+2*x*diff(y);
L.lbc = -1; L.rbc = 1;
y = L\0; plot(y)
```

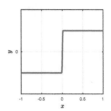

92. Linear corner layer (Hemker) [Chap. 20]

```
ep = 0.001;
L = chebop(@(x,y) ep*diff(y,2)+x*diff(y)-y);
L.lbc = .8; L.rbc = 1.2;
y = L\0; plot(y)
```

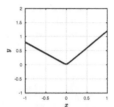

93. Nonlinear corner layer (Hemker) [Chap. 20]

```
N = chebop(@(y) 0.05*diff(y,2)+diff(y)^2-1);
N.lbc = .8; N.rbc = 1.2;
y = N\1; plot(y)
```

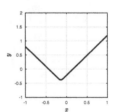

94. Cusp (Hemker, L&G) [Chap. 20]

```
L = chebop([-1 0 1]);
L.op = @(x,y) 1e-6*diff(y,2)+x*diff(y)-.5*y;
L.lbc = 1; L.rbc = 2;
y = L\0; plot(y)
```

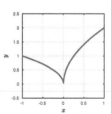

95. Ill-conditioned equation (L&G) [Chap. 20]

```
L = chebop(-1,1);
L.op = @(x,y) 0.02*diff(y,2)-x*diff(y)+y;
L.lbc = 1; L.rbc = 2;
y = L\0; plot(y)
```

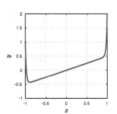

96. Shock layer (Hemker) [Chap. 20]

```
ep = 1e-6;
L = chebop([-1 0 1]);
L.op = @(x,y) ep*diff(y,2)+x*diff(y);
L.lbc = -2; L.rbc = 0;
f = chebfun(@(x) -ep*pi^2*cos(pi*x)-pi*x*sin(pi*x));
y = L\f; plot(y)
```

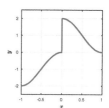

97. Blowup eq., complex perturbation (H&M) [Chap. 21]

```
d = [0 1.03]; N = chebop(@(y) diff(y)-y^2,d);
N.lbc = 1; rng(0)
f = 0.01*randnfun(d,'big','complex');
y = N\f; arrowplot(y)
```

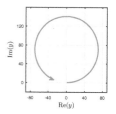

98. KdV train of solitons [Chap. 22]

```
d = [-5,5]; x = chebfun('x',d); S = spinop(d,[0 2]);
S.lin = @(u) -0.01*diff(u,3);
S.nonlin = @(u) -0.03*diff(u.^2);
c = 1; soliton = 50*c*sech(sqrt(100*c)*x/2)^2;
S.init = .25*soliton;
u = spin(S,160,.005,'plot','off'); plot([S.init u])
```

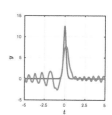

99. Kuramoto–Sivashinsky chaotic state [Chap. 22]

```
d = [-50,50]; x = chebfun('x',d);
S = spinop(d,[0 100]);
S.lin = @(u) -diff(u,2)-diff(u,4);
S.nonlin = @(u) -0.5*diff(u.^2);
S.init = exp(-(x/5)^2);
u = spin(S,200,.1,'plot','off'); plot(u)
```

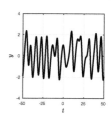

100. Ginzburg–Landau PDE [Chap. 22]

```
u = spin2('gl','plot','off');
plot(real(u)), view(0,90)
```

B&O = C. M. Bender and S. A. Orszag, *Advanced Mathematical Methods for Scientists and Engineers,* Springer Science and Business Media, 2013.

Danby = J. M. A. Danby, *Computer Modeling: From Sports to Spaceflight... from Order to Chaos,* Willmann-Bell, Richmond, VA, 1997.

Davis = H. T. Davis, *Introduction to Nonlinear Differential and Integral Equations,* Courier Corp., 1962.

Duan = J. Duan, *An Introduction to Stochastic Dynamics,* Cambridge U. Press, 2015.

ESK = A. S. Elwakil, K. N. Salama, and M. P. Kennedy, An equation for generating chaos and its monolithic implementation, *Int. J. Bifurc. Chaos* 12 (2002), pp. 2885–2895.

HNW = E. Hairer, S. P. Nørsett, and G. Wanner, *Solving Ordinary Differential Equations I, Nonstiff Problems,* 2nd revised ed., Springer-Verlag, 1993.

Hemker = P. W. Hemker, *A Numerical Study of Stiff Two-Point Boundary Problems,* Mathematisch Centrum, Amsterdam, 1977.

H&M = D. Herzog and J. Mattingly, Noise-induced stabilization of planar flows I, *Electr. J. Prob.* 20 (2015).

HSD = M. W. Hirsch, S. Smale, and R. L. Devaney, *Differential Equations, Dynamical Systems, and an Introduction to Chaos,* 3rd ed., Elsevier, 2013.

J&S = D. W. Jordan and P. Smith, *Nonlinear Ordinary Differential Equations: An Introduction to Dynamical Systems,* Oxford U. Press, 1999.

L&G = J.-Y. Lee and L. Greengard, A fast adaptive numerical method for stiff two-point boundary value problems, *SIAM J. Sci. Comp.* 18 (1997), pp. 403–429.

Seydel = R. Seydel, *Practical Bifurcation and Stability Analysis,* Springer Science & Business Media, 2009.

Index